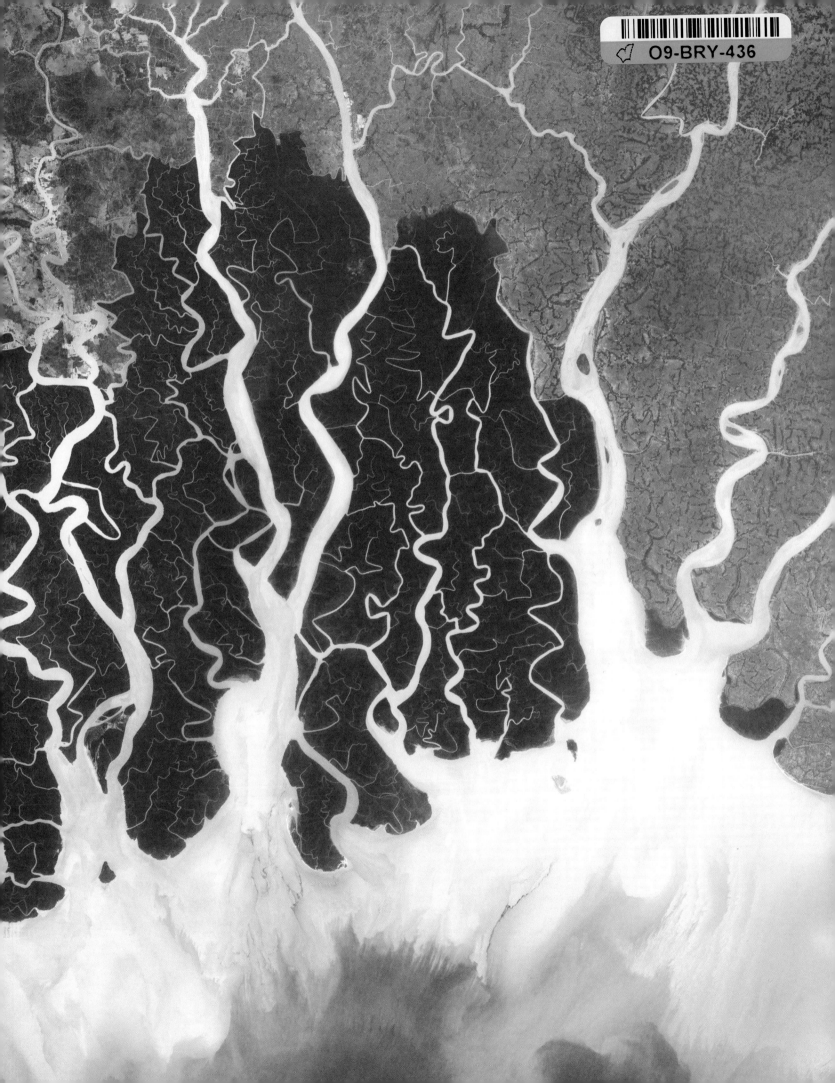

EXTREME
EARTH

WILDLIFE · WILD PLACES · WILD WEATHER

EXTREME EARTH

WILDLIFE · WILD PLACES · WILD WEATHER

FOREWORD

Extreme Earth is a masterpiece – the perfect Reader's Digest guide to our planet's most astonishing extremes, which have been brought together for the first time in one exceptional volume.

WITH EVERY TURN of the page, *Extreme Earth* inspires us, its audience, with the finest and most amazing nature photography ever captured – more than 300 images in total, assembled from the libraries of many of the world's best photographers. These captivating visuals, together with their illuminating captions and the book's engaging text, highlight the remarkable nature of Earth and allow us to effortlessly absorb and wonder at the most incredible extremes that our planet has to offer.

At the same time, *Extreme Earth* leads us to contemplate some of the bigger questions of life, such as where do we come from? What is our humble place in Earth's complex and extreme web of life? Where are we ultimately heading?

Extreme Earth is divided into five intriguing and informative sections, covering every aspect of the planet and its geological history. Portrait of our Planet paints the big picture of Earth's extremes, our position in the Universe and the mystery of life – it's a breathtaking tale that spans billions of years.

Extreme Fire and Movement is a unique expedition into the inner workings of our planet, its volcanic eruptions, earthquakes and ever-moving continents. Extreme Land takes a look at Earth's remote islands, soaring mountains, crystal-packed caves, driest deserts, wettest forests and more, and describes in stunning detail the most extreme living things found on land. Extreme Water plunges into the watery world of Earth's mightiest oceans, rivers, lakes and waterfalls, encountering some terrifying tsunamis along the way. Extreme Air and Weather is a fantastic flight into the world's worst blizzards, thunderstorms, cyclones, tornadoes, floods and droughts, with a spectacular side trip to see rainbows, auroras and other beautiful visual phenomena.

Prepare to be excited, surprised and even challenged by what you are about to read on the coming pages – *Extreme Earth* is a sensational journey of discovery that will leave you spellbound.

Dr Robert R Coenraads
BA(Hons), MSc, PhD, FGAA, FAusIMM

FROZEN EXPANSE
Russia's Lake Baikal is the world's oldest and deepest lake. During winter, the ice is so thick that it can support the weight of people, horses and snowmobiles.

CONTRIBUTORS

Consultant

Dr Robert R Coenraads BA(Hons), MSc, PhD, FGAA, FAusIMM

Dr Robert Coenraads is a geoscientist, and author of four books and over 30 scientific publications. He has led archaeology, natural history and geology field trips to various corners of the globe – including the magnificent Olmec, Maya and Aztec sites of Mexico, active volcanoes of the Pacific region, and a number of gem mines. During his 35-year exploration career, travel to some of the world's poorest regions has sparked a strong humanitarian interest. Dr Coenraads is currently President of FreeSchools World Literacy – Australia, and has established a support network to provide free education for underprivileged children in India, Thailand and Africa.

Authors

David Burnie worked as a biologist and nature reserve ranger, before becoming a writer specialising in wildlife and the environment. He has written or contributed to more than 100 books, ranging from field guides to wild plants to major encyclopaedias on geology, birds, mammals, ocean life and dinosaurs. A Fellow of the Zoological Society of London, he lives and works in France.

Jack Challoner has written more than 30 books on science and technology, and also acts as a science consultant on books, magazines and television programs. He worked on the London Science Museum's flagship interactive gallery, LaunchPad, and has also developed television programs for BBC Scotland.

Celia Coyne is trained in Earth sciences, and has written and edited science and natural history books and articles for publishers in the United Kingdom, Australia and New Zealand. She is the author of *Earth's Riches* and *The Power of Plants* (both published by Reader's Digest).

Sari Harrar is a freelance health and science journalist who writes for a wide range of US magazines, books, websites and newspapers. As a recipient of a Council for Advancement of Science Education fellowship, she learned about targeted cancer therapies at Harvard Medical School.

Karen McGhee has a background in marine biology and zoology, and as an Australian journalist has focused on natural history, health and the environment. Her writing has been published in books, newspapers and magazines worldwide, and she has worked on television documentaries and museum exhibits.

CONTENTS

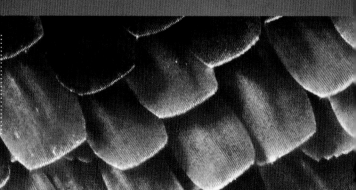

FRONT COVER CAPTIONS *Japanese macaques at Jigokudani onsen; Australia's Uluru (Ayers Rock); great grey owl; snow-covered tree.*
BACK COVER CAPTIONS *Brown bear at Alaska's Brooks Falls; aurora borealis over Alaska's Talkeetna Mountains; ringed seal in its breathing hole; Samburu warrior at the East African Rift in Kenya; Antelope Canyon in Arizona.*
ENDPAPER CAPTION *Satellite image of the Sundarbans delta in India/Bangladesh.*
TITLE PAGE CAPTION *The giraffe is the world's tallest living land animal.*

1

INTRODUCTION Earth's thrilling extremes 10

Portrait of our planet 14

Earth in space **16** Earth from the inside **22**
Earth through time **30**

2

Extreme fire and movement 36

Faults and rifts **38** Earthquakes and tremors **46**
Volcanoes and craters **54** Geysers and mud pools **66**
Sinkholes and landslides **78**

3

Extreme land 86

Mountains and cliffs **88** Canyons and gorges **100**
Caves and caverns **108** Deserts and dunes **118**
Trees and forests **128** North and South Poles **140**
Islands and archipelagos **148**

4

Extreme water 158

Oceans and seas **160** Tsunamis and 'king' tides **172**
Coastlines and seashores **180** Rivers and deltas **190**
Waterfalls and cascades **200** Lakes and reservoirs **212**
Swamps and other wetlands **220** Glaciers and sea ice **230**

5

Extreme air and weather 238

Lightning and thunder **240** Rainbows and auroras **250**
Cyclones and tornadoes **258** Storms and floods **268**
Snow and blizzards **278** Droughts and dust storms **290**
Wildfires and fire whirls **298**

6

Reference 306

Extreme 100 world map – Earth's record holders **308**
Glossary **310** Index **312** Acknowledgements **320**
Photo credits **320**

Earth's thrilling extremes

On 12 April 1961, a history-making rocket launch changed forever the way we see our planet. Inside the cramped cockpit of the *Vostok 1* spacecraft, Soviet cosmonaut Yuri Gagarin zoomed skyward at 28,200 km/h (17,500 mph) – the first human to escape Earth's gravity and circle the globe. Gagarin's 108-minute flight was long enough for just one orbit around our planet. But the extraordinary view was timeless.

A S GAGARIN noted later, 'When I orbited Earth in a spaceship, I saw for the first time how beautiful our planet is. I saw clouds and their light shadows on the distant, dear earth. The water looked like darkish, slightly gleaming spots … I enjoyed the rich colour spectrum of Earth. It is surrounded by a light blue aureole that gradually darkens, becoming turquoise, dark blue, violet and finally coal black.'

Most of us will never soar to the fringes of outer space to drink in our home planet's extreme beauty. Well, a few may – by the early months of 2014, about 600 people had signed up to become the world's first space tourists aboard airline mogul Sir Richard Branson's planned fleet of Virgin Galactic spaceships. But why wait? Now, you can relax in your favourite armchair and experience Earth as never before – in the pages of *Extreme Earth*. At last, the most amazing facts, brilliant behind-the-scenes stories and breathtaking photographs depicting our planet's many extremes have been gathered in one astonishing, exciting and authoritative book.

EXPLORE STAGGERING EXTREMES

Fasten your seatbelt! You're about to be transported to the summit of Earth's tallest mountain, plunged into the deepest seas and taken back billions of years in time to witness our planet's cataclysmic birth. You'll discover the secret lives of the tenacious, adaptable animals and plants that call Earth's most extreme environments home – from single-celled creatures living beneath polar ice caps and around superhot sea vents to waterfall-climbing fish and beautiful birds by the tens of thousands. You'll find yourself in the midst of the powerful natural forces that drive our planet's loveliest, strangest and most destructive phenomena – from vibrant rainbows, crystal-packed caves and fountain-like geysers to super typhoons, megathrust earthquakes and the world's most dangerous volcanoes.

EXTREME FACT
Yuri Gagarin, the first person to make the journey to space, tragically died just seven years after his monumental trip when the jet fighter he was piloting crashed to the ground.

You'll learn about snow that never touches the ground, giant waterfalls beneath the sea and souvenirs from the Big Bang that float in your cereal bowl. And that's just the beginning of your incredible journey.

Extreme Earth reveals our planet from every angle, with extraordinary inside information and gripping tales alongside sensational statistics – including the longest, shortest, tallest, deepest, fastest, slowest, hottest, coldest, biggest, smallest, driest and wettest. Find out how our planet, Solar System, Milky Way galaxy and Universe came into being – and how those early events still fuel Earth's fiery volcanoes, massive earthquakes and growing mountain ranges today. Experience the extreme cold of the North and South Poles, meet the tallest and oldest trees in the planet's forests, discover why more sinkholes than ever are swallowing buildings, pay a visit to the most remote island on Earth and see first-hand how a deadly wildfire (ignited by sparks from a steam locomotive) created its own destructive weather pattern.

Love water? You'll find plenty to splash in with the colourful images and cool facts about our blue planet's oceans, rivers, coastlines, lakes, waterfalls, glaciers and wetlands. Rivers that run backwards, lakes tinted pink, prehistoric humans and animals preserved in bogs and tar pits, deadly rapids and the world's most dangerous tides are among the fascinating subjects in which you can immerse yourself.

EARTH FROM SPACE
Space Shuttle Endeavour astronauts servicing the Hubble Space Telescope enjoy a stunning view of our planet. Clear skies reveal a brownish continent bordered by a cerulean ocean.

Want to know more about the extreme weather that hits the headlines so often these days? *Extreme Earth* delves into hurricanes, cyclones, tornadoes, droughts, wildfires, floods, blizzards and more. Wonder at the crystal 'art' that makes every snowflake a unique creation, visit a region of India that receives an average of 12,000 mm (470 in) of rain every year and discover what to do if a tornado is heading towards you.

BEYOND CONVENTIONAL WISDOM

Drawing on current science, this book also overturns long-held, popular beliefs about Earth (hint: by some reckonings, Mount Everest *isn't* the planet's tallest peak!). Among the surprises ahead:

✦ **What is hotter than the surface of the Sun?**
At 30,000ºC (54,000ºF), it's lightning. Although a bolt can be almost six times hotter than the solar surface, you'll meet a person who's been struck seven times and lived to tell the tale.

✦ **Where is the world's tallest mountain?**
Hawaii! Measured from base to summit, Mauna Kea volcano is over 1300 m (4300 ft) higher than Mount Everest – though most of it is under water. Even more remarkable: Mauna Kea has been erupting for most of the last million years.

✦ **When did it rain the hardest?**
In recent memory, it was on 22 June 1947, when 305 mm (12 in) of precipitation hammered the town of Holt in Missouri over the course of one hour. But did you know that 3.8 billion years ago, it rained continuously over most, if not all, of Earth for many thousands or perhaps even a million years?

✦ **Who loves a hot bath on a cold winter's day?**
(Besides you.) The Japanese macaque or snow monkey takes daily baths in mountain hot springs – but has only been warming up this way since 1963.

✦ **Is there 'stardust' in your kitchen?**
Chemical elements that formed during the birth of the Universe include silicon, aluminium, calcium, sodium and magnesium. You'll find silicon in the computer chip that runs your microwave oven, sodium in your salt shaker and calcium in your milk.

✦ **Can sand dunes sing?**
Sand dunes the world over have unusual habits – some march across Earth at 100 m (330 ft) per year, gobbling up any vegetation and buildings in their path. But one group deep in northern China's Badain Jaran Desert makes loud throbbing sounds when the wind blows fiercely. The source: sand slipping across the surface of the enormous dunes.

SURVIVING EARTH'S EXTREME WEATHER

In the 1920s, American palaeontologist Roy Chapman Andrews explored Asia's inhospitable Gobi Desert. He later described the moment that his camp was hit by a vicious sandstorm: 'A thousand shrieking demons seemed to be pelting my face … We could not see twenty feet [6 m], but we heard the clatter of tins, the sharp rip of canvas, and then a tumbling mass of camp beds, tables, chairs, bags, and pails swept down the hill.' Without dust-proof headgear, Andrews and his team had to lie face down on the ground, breathing through makeshift filters of wet clothes.

A FRONT-ROW SEAT

Earth's extremes have long captivated humankind. This fascination is shared across borders and through time: we never tire of getting up close and personal with Nature at its most exciting. It's always been this way.

Six thousand years ago, Native Americans in the south-eastern section of the current-day United States created celestial rock paintings high on mountains and hills, to be closer to the Moon and stars. We're not too different today. Nearly 6 million people around the world follow Twitter feeds from the US National Aeronautics and Space Administration (NASA). And when a total solar eclipse plunged northern Australia into darkness on 14 November 2012, tens of thousands watched the rare show from hot-air balloons, boats, hilltops and beaches.

We're equally riveted by events on the ground – and always have been. Archaeologists recently unearthed a mural in a 9000-year-old Turkish home that depicts the eruption of nearby Mount Hasan. Today, 2.6 million tourists a year visit Hawaii's Kilauea volcano – and a three-minute video of its glowing lava has been viewed more than 3.3 million times on YouTube!

We all share the need to be awed by Earth's most thrilling extremes – and to understand her mysterious capacity for destruction. So keep reading. Share what you find in these pages with loved ones. Return again and again to reconnect with the natural world, deepen your understanding of current events, expand your knowledge or simply to gaze at Earth's marvels. You'll come away feeling renewed and enriched. As American biologist and environmental advocate Rachel Carson noted in her book *The Sense of Wonder*, 'Those who dwell, as scientists or laymen, among the beauties and mysteries of the earth are never alone or weary of life … Those who contemplate the beauty of Earth find reserves of strength that will endure as long as life lasts.'

PORTRAIT OF OUR PLANET

As scientists train ever-more sophisticated telescopes on Deep Space, one fact hasn't changed: we occupy a unique place in the Universe. Endowed with just-right conditions, Earth teems with an astonishing diversity of life, from microscopic algae to towering redwoods, from tiny hog-nosed bats to giant whales ... and us, of course. Equipped with insatiable curiosity, sharp intelligence and unending resourcefulness, humans are slowly unravelling the mystery of life on Earth. This exciting tale of extremes spans billions of years and is fuelled by numerous cataclysmic events, from the Big Bang and massive asteroid crashes to the most recent ice age.

THE SAHARA
In this true-colour satellite image, the Sahara's sands have an orange hue, while large, barren massifs appear in shades of brown.

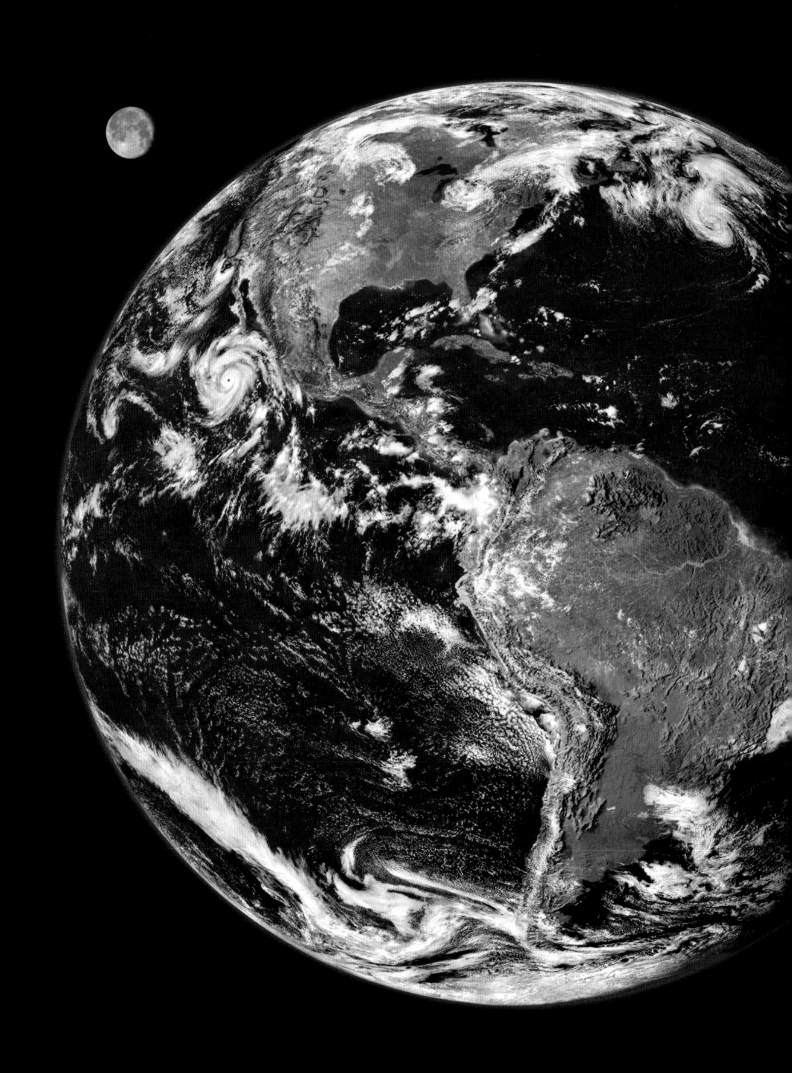

Earth in space

It's a story wilder than most science-fiction
movies. Around 13.8 billion years ago, the
building blocks of our Universe scrunched
themselves into an unbelievably hot, dense
blob – a singularity in space. A teaspoonful
of this material, astronomy experts guess,
weighed some 50,000 trillion trillion
trillion tonnes – mind-boggling!

BUT THE BIG BANG – science's most widely
accepted theory of how time, space and all
things astronomical began – was about to
become even more extraordinary. Just a fraction of
a second after compressing itself, the blob expanded
with phenomenal force. The cataclysm hurled a
superheated wave of neutrons, protons, electrons and
other atomic particles across 530 trillion km (330 trillion
miles) of space. Within three minutes, all of the hydrogen
molecules in existence today – including those in your
own body – came into being. The infant Universe spent
the next billion years cooling into clumps that would
become the twinkling stars, shining planets and
dazzling comets we now admire in the night sky.

WONDERS ALL AROUND

Amazingly, the 'fingerprints' of this rapid expansion
can still be detected today. For example, the Universe is
still rippling outwards at enormous speed. Astronomers
first noticed in 1929 that galaxies are, in general, moving
away from each other – with those furthest from Earth
accelerating the fastest. In addition, the 'afterglow' of
the Big Bang still saturates space as cosmic radiation.
Before the digital age, you could experience this form
of leftover energy by tuning your television to the
white noise between channels; about 1 per cent of
the static hiss was caused by Big-Bang microwave
radiation. Finally, there is an abundance of helium
and deuterium in the Universe, atoms that can only
be produced by nuclear fusion such as the superhot
conditions right after the Big Bang.

You don't have to be an astrophysicist, however,
to savour the wonders of the Universe – including

EXTREME FACT
Every planet in the Solar System is
named after a Classical deity, except
Earth – its name derives from the Old
English word *eorthe*, meaning ground.

PLANETARY PORTRAITS

In addition to Earth and the Moon, our Solar System is home to seven other major planets, five dwarf planets and an estimated 173 moons, 620,661 asteroids and 3224 comets. From your own backyard on a clear, moonless night, the five major planets closest to Earth – Mercury, Venus, Mars, Jupiter and Saturn – may be visible at various times of the year because their surfaces reflect sunlight and shine with a steadier, brighter light than fainter, distant stars. The two furthest planets, Uranus and Neptune, can only be seen with a telescope. Each planet boasts notable features and shocking extremes.

All distances quoted are from the Sun. M = million. The relative size of planets is not to scale.

MERCURY
58M km (36M miles)

Mercury, the Solar System's smallest planet and the one nearest to the Sun, has an egg-shaped orbit that brings it close to the Sun every 88 days – raising its surface temperature to 427°C (801°F) by day, and dropping it to -179°C (-197°F) by night. It is the second-densest planet (only Earth is denser).

VENUS
108M km (67M miles)

Shrouded in clouds caused by volcanic activity, Venus is seared by temperatures that are hot enough to melt lead. It rotates so slowly that one day on Venus is as long as 117 days on Earth. As our nearest planetary neighbour, Venus is the second-brightest object in the night sky after the Moon.

EARTH
150M km (93M miles)

Often referred to as 'the ocean planet' or 'the blue planet' because 70 per cent of its surface is covered by seas and oceans, Earth is the only planet that is currently known to support life. There is enough gold in Earth's superhot core to coat the planet in a 46-cm (18-in) layer of the precious metal.

---

swirling spiral galaxies, menacing black holes and the massive, spangled clouds in which stars are born. The need to look up and enjoy the view seems to be hard-wired into the human psyche, from prehistoric stargazers gathered around primitive camp fires and the ancient Chinese astronomers who drew the world's first star map 2800 years ago to backyard star-peepers today. And perhaps the most exciting space story for us is that of our own Earth and its two major companions, the Sun and Moon.

EARTH, SUN AND MOON

How does our quiet little planet fit into the big drama of the Universe? True, Earth is a mere speck in a Universe estimated to measure at least 28 billion light years across. (A staggering vastness, considering that one light year is equivalent to nearly 9.5 trillion km, or 5.9 trillion miles.) Our world may not even be alone in its ability to support life. In 2013, researchers from The University of Chicago announced that 60 billion of our sister planets in the Milky Way galaxy might also be habitable. But take a closer look – Earth has both a dynamic past and a unique prominence in present-day space.

The planet – and the rest of our Solar System – got its start 5 billion years ago in a cloud of gas and dust. Researchers believe that an outside force (perhaps a nearby supernova, a giant exploding star) heated up this interstellar fog so much that it collapsed on itself. The hot centre became our fiery Sun. The rest of the

MILKY WAY
Up to 15 per cent of the Milky Way's visible matter is made up of dust and interstellar gas, giving the galaxy its well-known hazy appearance.

MARS
228M km (142M miles)

Mars, the fourth planet from the Sun, is a chilly desert painted red by the iron in its rocks and dust. It has polar ice caps as well as intriguing signs of massive floods 3.5 billion years ago. Mars is home to the Solar System's largest-known volcano, 25-km (16-mile) high Olympus Mons.

JUPITER
778M km (484M miles)

Massive Jupiter is a 'gas giant' robed in striped clouds of ammonia vapour. Circling the planet are four moons – Io, Europa, Ganymede and Callisto – as well as three rings. Ganymede is the Solar System's largest moon. If it broke free from Jupiter's orbit, it would be classified as a planet in its own right!

SATURN
1427M km (887M miles)

Winds in Saturn's upper atmosphere are five times stronger than hurricane-force winds on Earth. Saturn's famous rings extend into space for hundreds of thousands of kilometres, yet are just 10 m (30 ft) thick in most places. Some of Saturn's 67 known moons act as 'shepherds', herding the rings along.

URANUS
2872M km (1785M miles)

Beneath its gassy atmosphere, Uranus has a core of icy water, ammonia and methane; around this planet spin nine rings and 27 moons. The innermost moon, Miranda – named after a Shakespearean character – has canyons that are 12 times deeper than the Grand Canyon in the United States.

NEPTUNE
4495M km (2793M miles)

Buffeted by high-speed winds, Neptune is 30 times further from the Sun than Earth. Its brilliant blue colour is the result of atmospheric methane mixed with a mysterious compound astronomers have yet to identify. Neptune's largest moon, Triton, has geyser-like eruptions of liquid nitrogen.

IT'S ABOUT TIME

Right now, our Sun is a healthy yellow dwarf star. But it is slowly heating up. Astronomers predict that in around 7 billion years it will morph into a planet-gobbling red giant that could annihilate Mercury, Venus and even Earth. Ultimately, it will shrink back to the size of Earth, becoming a superhot white dwarf star.

rubble circled it for millions of years, colliding and crashing. Some of the debris formed the core of planets. Still more became moons, dwarf planets, asteroid belts and comets.

The Sun flings ultraviolet radiation, solar flares and solar winds out to the far reaches of the Solar System. It's huge – a million Earths could fit inside it – and beyond hot. This orb of glowing gases burns hydrogen, creating internal temperatures that exceed 15 million°C (27 million°F). Its heat and radiation have scorched Mercury, the closest planet to the Sun, and turned Venus, the second closest planet, into a suffocating hothouse with an average temperature of 460°C (860°F).

But on the third planet from the Sun, conditions were right for life. A perfect distance from the Sun, its rays warm us up but aren't hot enough to vaporise the oceans where early life incubated. (Earth is the only planet where liquid water is known to exist.) Our atmosphere – a mixture of nitrogen, oxygen and a smidgin of other ingredients – shields us from the Sun's harmful radiation and incinerates many meteors before they can do damage. And the tilt of Earth's rotational axis adds charming variety – the seasons – as the Northern and Southern Hemispheres in turn lean a little closer to the Sun in summer, and a little further away in winter.

Our Moon keeps us company, waxing and waning as it orbits Earth. Astronomers suspect that a large object the size of Mars rammed into Earth around 4.5 billion years ago; the impact ejected molten debris and other matter that ultimately coalesced to become the Moon we see in the sky today. Pocked with craters created by constant pounding from comets, asteroids and meteors, the Moon's surface is a jumble of boulders, rocks and pulverised dust. Its gravity tugs on our oceans, raising and lowering tides.

DWARF PLANETS, COMETS AND ASTEROIDS

PLUTO

Poor Pluto. Long considered our ninth major planet, it was downgraded to dwarf planet status in 2006. Astronomers now say this mini-planet is one of a handful of intriguing, icy worlds known as 'transneptunian objects' that are orbiting the Sun in a zone beyond Neptune called the Kuiper Belt. A NASA satellite called *New Horizons*, launched in 2006, is scheduled to reach this region in 2015. It is expected to beam home fascinating images and information about these space rocks that formed early in the history of our Solar System.

Even further out, billions of kilometres from the Sun, lies the Oort Cloud – a strange realm containing trillions of orbiting space rocks. It may be one source of the Solar System's comets, enormous balls of ice, gas, rock and dust that heat up as they approach the Sun; their glowing heads and long, bright tails may be seen from Earth. This is the case with the renowned Halley's Comet, which appears in the sky every 76 years. Other famous, recent comets include Hale-Bopp, viewed from Earth in 1997 and, before that, in 2215 BC (during the Bronze Age); Hyakutake, which gave a spectacular show in 1996; and Shoemaker Levy-9, which shattered near Jupiter in 1994 and slammed into the planet – creating an explosion equivalent to 6 million megatonnes of TNT.

While comets tend to fly in from the cold reaches of the outer Solar System, asteroids hail from a doughnut-shaped belt of small, airless minor planets between Mars and Jupiter. Leftovers from the formation of planets closest to the Sun, most asteroids stay put – but some venture towards the Sun as meteors and meteorites. Small space rocks that burn up in Earth's atmosphere are the shooting stars called meteors. Those that survive and hit the ground are known as meteorites.

GALAXIES AND STARS

The Solar System is situated about halfway along the Orion Arm of the Milky Way galaxy, which was so named because of the misty appearance of its 200 billion stars. Slowly wheeling through space, the Milky Way's four spiral arms move at about 830,000 km/h (515,000 mph), yet it takes our galaxy 280 million years to make one complete rotation.

Look up into a clear night sky, in an area without light pollution, and you may see a branched band of crowded stars. That's a view of the centre of the Milky Way. However, this dense cloud of stars, dust and gas hides a strange secret: an enormous black hole with a massive gravitational force that pulls in hapless stars. Over 90 per cent of our galaxy is made up of dark matter that scientists are still trying to explore and measure.

TAKING AIM AT EARTH

Made famous in YouTube videos that were
watched around the world, the Chelyabinsk
meteor weighed a massive 10,000 tonnes
(11,000 tons) when it slammed into Earth's
atmosphere on 15 February 2013. It exploded

with a force greater than 30 atomic bombs,
releasing a shockwave that set off car alarms
and shattered windows in southern Russia,
injuring more than 1000 people. While many
fragments fell to Earth (and were later sold for
hundreds of dollars), the meteor also released
hundreds of tonnes of dust into the atmosphere.
The thin, high plume circled Earth within
four days and lingered for several months.

The Milky Way is just one of more than 50 galaxies
in the Local Group. Other residents of the Local Group
include the Andromeda galaxy – with 1 trillion stars –
and two smaller galaxies called the Magellanic Clouds
that are visible from the Southern Hemisphere.

Yet the brightest stars that are visible in the night
sky don't necessarily dwell in our Local Group. Some
are so large and so brilliant that their light outshines
closer luminaries. Among the best known stars is
Sirius, a double star just 8.6 light years away from
Earth; Canopus, a yellow-white supergiant 313 light
years away from Earth; Arcturus, a red-orange giant
that is 26 times larger than our Sun; Vega, a brilliant
blue-white star found in the constellation Lyra; and
Alpha Centauri, the star system that is our Sun's
closest stellar neighbour.

TECTONIC PLATES
At Silfra rift located in Iceland's Lake Pingvallavatn, divers can explore the ever-widening gap between the North American and Eurasian Plates. The plates are moving apart at a rate of 2 cm (⅘ in) per year.

Earth from the inside

If you could slice Earth open, you'd see a structure that resembles an elaborate confection – but this geological bonbon is made from rocks and minerals rather than sugar. At the centre is an iron ball 2400 km (1500 miles) in diameter. Nearly as hot as the Sun, our planet's inner core remains solid because it's under tremendous pressure.

THE INNER CORE is wrapped in three 'shells', and actually rotates slightly faster than the surrounding layers. The first 'shell' is the outer core, an ocean of liquid iron 2300 km (1400 miles) thick. Surrounding this is our planet's 2900-km (1800-mile) thick mantle, a layer of hot, pressurised rock that contains 84 per cent of Earth's weight and mass. Covering the mantle is a thin, brittle crust – the mountains, valleys, fields, riverbeds and seabeds that we know so well.

SPINNING AND CRACKING

Earth's layered look developed about 3.6 billion years ago – 1 billion years into Earth's existence – during a planetary meltdown triggered by meteor bombardments, by energy from radioactive materials and by friction from gravity. As the molten planet whirled through space, denser materials such as iron and nickel settled in the centre, while less-dense materials were spun to the edges, forming Earth's outer layers.

But something else happened back then that's still making headlines – and changing lives – today. As the planet cooled, the crust and uppermost mantle cracked into vast slabs like mud in a dried-up puddle. Today, these tectonic plates form Earth's continents and seabeds. Because they 'float' on a cushion of hot, oozing rock deeper in the mantle, the plates move. Over billions of years, tectonic plates have gradually pushed together, separated and moved past each other – setting off earthquakes, tsunamis and volcanic eruptions as they remake the planet's surface.

CONTINENTAL DRIFT

Glance at a globe or world map, and Earth's surface appears fixed. But a closer look reveals clues – in mountain ranges, volcanic island chains and deep-sea trenches – that our restless planet is, in fact, always in motion. The process is called plate tectonics, or continental drift.

Science divides Earth's surface into eight major plates, including the North American, Indo-Australian and Eurasian plates. The world's largest, the Pacific Plate, measures over 103 million sq km (40 million

?

EXTREME FACT

Earth's mantle is not made from liquefied rock. This vast layer of hot yet solid rock is under such immense pressure that it flows slowly like road tar.

sq miles). There are also seven minor plates – the smallest of which is the Juan de Fuca Plate, located off the north-western coast of the United States and south-western coast of Canada, at 252,000 sq km (97,000 sq miles).

These plates move slowly as the mantle below heats and cools. The motion is imperceptible (as little as 1 cm [²⁄₅ in] per year), yet has reshuffled Earth's seas and continents many times over hundreds of millions of years. At one geologically dramatic moment some 600 million years ago, major plates collided to form a supercontinent that scientists now call Gondwana. It was a mash-up of the plates that today form South America, Africa, Arabia, Madagascar, India, Australia and Antarctica. Then Gondwana grew even larger, by meeting up with the plates that form present-day North America, Europe and Siberia. The unification

EARTH'S INTERNAL STRUCTURE

Forces deep within Earth's interior power the movement of the planet's numerous tectonic plates, while currents in the liquid outer core drive Earth's magnetic field.

CRUST
Thickness ranges from 6 to 70 km (4 to 43 miles).

MANTLE
The upper part is relatively rigid, but the lower part flows plastically.

OUTER CORE
Comprises a liquid formed from iron and iron sulfide.

INNER CORE
Temperatures can reach 6000°C (10,800°F).

created the supercontinent called Pangaea. Once formed, this enormous landmass began pulling apart around 200 million years ago.

DISCOVERING THE SECRET

Dutch mapmakers had the first inkling about the nature of plate tectonics in 1596 while pondering the shape of the western African and eastern South American coastlines – they noticed that the edges of these two distant continents fit together like pieces of a puzzle. In 1915, German geologist Alfred Wegener proposed the theory of continental drift, based on evidence including the discovery of similar types of rock (such as 290-million-year-old glacial deposits) and similar plants and fossils on divergent continents. Wegener's revolutionary notion – that huge, rock-solid continents could travel – was met with hostility, and ridiculed by one leading scientist of the day as a 'footloose' theory that 'took considerable liberty with our globe'.

Today, continental drift is an established fact. But surprisingly, it only reached wide acceptance in the late 1960s. The turning point came as researchers learned more about the odd behaviour of the mantle by studying places on the seabed where molten rock wells up from deep beneath Earth's crust. The discovery proved that continents actually 'float' on a viscous mantle, rather than plough across the seabed as Wegener supposed. With a mechanism to explain the motion of plates, continental drift at last made sense.

PLATES ON THE MOVE

What happens when continents 'wander'? Like bumper cars jostling at an amusement park, tectonic plates travel at different speeds, in different directions.

They can interact with each other in one of three ways: move apart, crash together or slide past each other.

Where plates move apart – which often occurs on the seabed – new crust forms. One dramatic example is the Mid-Atlantic Ridge – a 10,000-km (6200-mile) long mountain range that runs down the middle of the Atlantic Ocean. On maps and globes that show the contours of the seabed, it looks like a very long, curving scar crisscrossed by vertical lines reminiscent of the stitching on a baseball.

At the places where plates crash together, the heavier plate slides slowly back down into the mantle, creating the highest and lowest spots on Earth. This geological process is called subduction. In the Pacific Ocean, where the Pacific Plate is slipping underneath the Philippine Sea Plate, the famous Mariana Trench has appeared – with a maximum depth of 10,994 m (36,070 ft), it boasts the deepest natural spot on Earth. Volcanoes often erupt along this type of boundary line between plates, because water contained in the plate

THE HIMALAYAS
Running east to west, Nepal's Rolwaling Valley is a little-visited section of the Himalayas that boasts glacial lakes, pristine waterfalls and many peaks exceeding 6000 m (20,000 ft).

slipping back into the mantle lowers the melting point of surrounding rock. It liquefies, rises – and erupts with great force. Chains of islands around the edges of the Pacific Ocean, including Alaska's Aleutian Islands, are one result of these eruptions.

Meanwhile, collision can also take Earth to heart-stopping heights. Formed by the convergence of the Indo-Australian and Eurasian Plates, the Himalayan and Karakoram mountain ranges bordering India, Pakistan, China, Nepal, Tibet and Bhutan continue to grow at a rate of over 1 cm (2/5 in) per year. The world's 10 highest peaks are located here, including Mount Everest, the world's tallest land-based mountain, with an official height of 8848 m (29,029 ft).

Sideways-sliding plates are responsible for many of the earthquakes recorded in the Ring of Fire –

◄ CUEVA DE LOS CRISTALES

Mexico's Cave of the Crystals is extremely hot and humid, so visitors can only spend a short time admiring its beauty.

a 40,000-km (25,000-mile) long zone of heightened geological activity along the Pacific Rim. One hot spot for earthquakes is the coast of California, where the North American Plate is slipping southwards and the Pacific Plate is moving northwards.

STARDUST, RECYCLED

Earth's outermost crust accounts for just 1 per cent of its total mass – yet it's packed with an astonishing variety of rocks and minerals. Some are eye-poppingly monumental, such as the 6286-m (20,623-ft) high granite cliffs of Pakistan's Great Trango Tower and the 12-m (39-ft) long gypsum crystals discovered recently in Mexico's Cueva de los Cristales. Others are infinitesimally small, like the quartz particles found on Florida's Siesta Beach – said to be the world's finest and whitest sand. Still others are exceedingly rare, such as the 5.1-carat red diamond unearthed in Brazil in 1990. Its estimated value is US$20 million.

LIMESTONE
California's Mono Lake is renowned for its outstanding tufa rock formations. Tufa is a unique type of porous limestone formed when calcium carbonate is deposited by springs of underground water.

Even rocks and minerals that don't seem glamorous – like the stones in your garden, the copper in your home's electrical wiring or the bone-building calcium in your breakfast yogurt – share the same fascinating origin. All are made from chemical elements assembled billions of years ago in nuclear reactions inside stars, and then released into the Universe in enormous clouds of gas and dust during huge star explosions called supernovas. Scientists have discovered 118 of these elements, but 99 per cent of the minerals on Earth are made up primarily of just eight: oxygen, silicon, aluminium, iron, calcium, sodium, potassium and magnesium.

Amazingly, these few elements are the main ingredients in more than 4000 known minerals on Earth. These include gemstones such as diamonds and rubies, precious metals like gold and silver as well as substances we use every day at home and at work. Silicon from quartz, the most common mineral on Earth, forms part of circuit boards and computer chips. Tin and indium are utilised in high-tech liquid crystal display screens. There's aluminium in soft-drink cans, graphite in pencils, talc in baby powder and tungsten in incandescent light bulbs; your toothpaste may contain calcium carbonate, limestone, sodium carbonate, fluorite, mica and zinc.

MINERALS VERSUS ROCKS

If you think of minerals as showy crystals in a fancy museum display cabinet and rocks as hard, brownish chunks found outdoors, it's time to take a closer look. Rocks actually contain one or more minerals, and may also include the remains of ancient plant and animal life. There are three types of rock, each telling a different part of Earth's history: igneous, sedimentary and metamorphic.

Igneous rock is hot, molten rock (magma) that has cooled and 'frozen' into solid shapes. Some was belched to the surface by volcanoes, but other igneous rock solidified below ground and was later exposed by the process of erosion – such as the 1588-m (5112-ft) high Devils Tower in Wyoming. Igneous rock makes up 95 per cent of the rock in the upper part of Earth's crust. There are 700 varieties; the most common is granite, but other types include basalt, pumice and glass-like obsidian.

Often sporting striped layers called strata, sedimentary rock is made up of sediment deposited over millennia in shallow seas and lakes. It may contain minerals from plants and animals, too – sometimes as beautiful fossils of ancient ferns or prehistoric land and sea creatures. This rock begins as the soft ground you feel when standing in a body of water. It becomes solid rock when the weight and pressure of water and sediment squeeze the layers of sand, silt and organic matter together. Water adds dissolved 'mineral cements' such as calcite and silica,

which act as a glue. Types of sedimentary rock include limestone, shale, sandstone, mudstone, chalk, coal, claystone and flint. According to a University of Oklahoma analysis, about 66 per cent of exposed rock on Earth's surface is a thin, sedimentary layer.

When subjected to heat, pressure and chemistry-altering fluids, the structure of rocks and the minerals they contain is changed significantly. Metamorphic rocks are sedimentary or igneous rocks that have undergone this type of transformation. The process may happen when rock is heated by magma or even by water from a hot spring, when rock is put under pressure as tectonic plates collide or if the rock is buried deep in Earth's crust. Examples of metamorphic rock include marble (made from limestone), slate (made from shale) and gneiss (made from granite and other rocks).

All types of rock are continually being modified by the environment around them. An igneous rock can be eroded by wind and weather, deposited in a stream bed and emerge, millions of years later, in a 'layer cake' of sedimentary rock. A sedimentary rock may be heated by a nearby volcano or pulled down towards Earth's mantle as tectonic plates meet – reappearing later as a metamorphic rock. Stone may look stable, but its only constant is change.

RAINBOW ROCKS
Zhangye Danxia Landform Geological Park in China boasts some of Earth's oddest rock formations. Over millions of years, colourful mineral grains have been pressed together into a layer cake of rocks such as sandstone, then tipped up by the forces of plate tectonics.

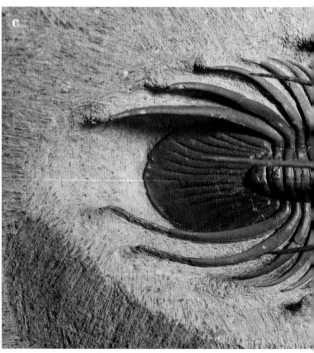

FOSSIL FINDS

Fossils record the structure of ancient creatures in amazing detail. (a) Archaeopteryx, a transitional genus between feathered dinosaurs and modern birds. (b) Prehistoric reptile. (c) Kolihapeltis, a genus of trilobite from the Early to Middle Devonian. (d) Prehistoric fish.

Earth through time

Four billion years ago, there was no life on Earth. Volcanoes spewed scalding, noxious gases. Asteroids, meteors and even small planets constantly bombarded the rocky surface, and heavy rain fell for hundreds of thousands of years. Yet within this inhospitable cauldron, the elements of life – carbon, hydrogen, nitrogen, oxygen, phosphorus and sulfur – were already swirling.

HOW DID THESE raw materials morph into today's riot of colourful, diverse, amazingly complex life on Earth? It's a puzzle that may never be solved. Scientists suspect that the basic elements joined forces in the atmosphere – perhaps energised by lightning – to form acids, sugars and other building blocks. But that's just one theory. Other experts think that amino acids – important precursors to life on Earth – came ready-made from outer space as hitchhikers aboard asteroids.

If the origin of amino acids is still an enigma, so is the next great leap forward – their joining together into gene-like strands of protein. Scientists debate whether the historic moment happened between microscopic layers of clay, at hydrothermal vents deep in the sea, on the ocean's surface or in thin, wet films on minerals. In any case, it was a breathtaking advance that paved the way for future life, ensuring its survival in a harsh, ever-changing environment.

Over time, the protein strands developed into one-celled organisms, with a protective cell wall surrounding the gene-like material. Just how that occurred remains a mystery, too. But this much is clear: these new creatures could feed themselves and reproduce. They were alive. And Earth would never be the same again.

ONLY THE STRONG SURVIVE

Buried in stone, the fossils of prehistoric creatures illustrate the astonishing story of evolution. The tale continues today. Briefly defined, evolution is the theory that all life on Earth shares a common, primordial ancestor. Tiny changes created by genetic variations – a longer fin or sharper teeth, for instance – might give one organism a survival advantage over their fellow creatures.

If the advantage were passed down to future generations, they would enjoy the same edge – and produce more offspring that were also equipped with the superior attribute. Eventually, this family's new and useful trait could become a feature of virtually all similar species within a given area.

SNOWBALL EARTH

Our planet has been frozen many times in its long history. The first deep freeze happened 2.4 billion years ago, as the planet cooled during a 250-million-year-old lull in volcanic activity. Chilly times returned 850 million years ago, during a 200-million-year-old cold snap aptly named the Cryogenian period. (*Cryos* is Greek for 'cold'.) Scientists suspect life may have triggered this freeze, by using up atmospheric carbon dioxide that helps keep the planet warm. Another ice age 460 to 430 million years ago prompted Earth's second-worst extinction event ever. Afterwards, land plants populated most corners of the globe – but their spread may have precipitated the next deep freeze (360 million years ago) by depleting Earth's carbon dioxide.

That's 'survival of the fittest' – the process that famed British naturalist Charles Darwin noticed among finches living in different spots on the Galápagos Islands. The birds all looked the same, except that each type had a different-shaped beak that helped them snare the food in the particular niche that they called home. Darwin named the phenomenon 'natural selection', shocking the world when his book *On the Origin of Species by Means of Natural Selection* was published in 1859. At first, the public muttered 'my ancestor wasn't an ape!' Yet by the 1870s, scientists began accepting Darwin's revolutionary ideas – though it was not until the 1930s and 1940s that natural selection became a mainstream concept.

AGAINST ALL ODDS

Since the beginning of its existence, life on Earth has faced an onslaught of major threats from climate-altering asteroid impacts, mass extinctions and ice ages. Despite, or perhaps because of, this changing environment, life continued to evolve and hang on – even in the toughest of times. The extensive fossil record reveals the timeline of the survival and development of life on Earth.

Between 3.5 and 2.5 billion years ago, microbes – such as the ocean-dwelling blue-green algae (also called blue-green bacteria) known as cyanobacteria – appeared and thrived. These creatures developed the ability to convert sunlight into usable, storable energy – the photosynthesis that almost all plants use today. Early microbes also became the architects of our oxygen-rich atmosphere, generating this gas as a waste product of photosynthesis. Evidence of their existence is found today in fossil formations called stromatolites, rocky bumps made from layers of microbes and grainy sediment.

Around 2 billion years ago, modern cells began to develop. Unlike early bacteria, these cells – called eukaryotes – contained important structures within their own membranes such as a nucleus with genetic

? EXTREME FACT
Around 250 million years ago, Earth's worst-ever mass extinction event wiped out 96 per cent of all species on the planet.

material, chloroplasts for photosynthesis and mitochondria that burn fuel for energy. These cells were established when different types of single-celled organisms engulfed others, Pacman-style.

From about 1.2 billion to 900 million years ago, multicelled life came into existence – and so did sexual reproduction. This breakthrough allowed genetic material from two creatures of the same species to combine, increasing the variation and survival odds for their species.

Between 550 and 320 million years ago, oxygen levels in the atmosphere rose due to photosynthesis, fuelling rapid advances in the diversity and sheer number of complex, multicelled organisms on Earth. Land plants evolved during this important era, and vertebrates – animals with a backbone – appeared for the first time, in the form of fish, amphibians and reptiles. *Tiktaalik roseae,* a 380-million-year-old fish with strong, bony fins, was found in the Canadian Arctic in 2006. Scientists say its leg-like fins suggest that life literally strolled onto dry land.

STROMATOLITES
Western Australia's Shark Bay has the world's most abundant collection of modern marine stromatolites. The cyanobacteria here are similar to those that created ancient stromatolites.

Some 250 million years ago, continental drift united all of Earth's landmasses to form the supercontinent Pangaea. The greatest mass extinction in history – caused by anything from an asteroid impact to a deficiency of oxygen in the atmosphere (scientists are still not sure!) – destroyed 96 per cent of life on Earth. Mammals survived as tiny, nocturnal creatures. Some sauropsids – the ancestors of dinosaurs and modern reptiles – also endured.

FROM DINOSAURS TO HUMANS

Dinosaurs of all shapes and sizes walked on Earth between 230 and 65 million years ago, surviving a mass extinction event that occurred approximately 200 million years ago. Flowering plants, bees and large mammals evolved some 150–100 million years ago, sharing the bounties of Earth temporarily with their dinosaurian companions. But cataclysmic climate change 65 million years ago – caused by an asteroid crash and possibly massive volcanic eruptions – led to the extinction of the dinosaurs. Or did it? Today's modern birds are descendants of ancient dinosaurs. A farmer in China's Liaoning province recently unearthed a fossil of a pheasant-sized feathered dinosaur – possibly flightless – called *Aurornis xui*, which was subsequently dated to 160 million years ago – making it the earliest known bird.

The great apes appeared just 14–2.5 million years ago. By 2.3 million years ago, *Homo habilis* had evolved – it was long considered the ancestor of modern humans. However, in 2008, the potential missing link between apes and humans – *Australopithecus sediba,* dating to 2 million years ago – was discovered in present-day South Africa. The fossil skeletons have ape-like long arms and strong fingers ideal for climbing trees, as well as flat feet and long legs – human-like traits perfect for walking upright on two legs. Modern humans, *Homo sapiens,* first appeared in Africa around 200,000 years ago, a mere drop in the ocean of time.

SIGNS OF EVOLUTION TODAY

Evolution is not just something that happened hundreds of thousands or even millions of years ago. There are many dramatic examples around us today that show how natural selection is still giving species an edge in the real world.

In the United Kingdom, the peppered moth is typically white with dark, pepper-like spots. But during the Industrial Revolution, light-coloured tree bark in London was soon coated in dark soot. The moths stood out, and were quickly eaten by hungry birds. A genetic variation produced darker moths that flourished because of their camouflage. When the pollution waned, white moths once again became more commonly seen.

Worldwide, more than 500 species of insects, spiders and mites have developed a resistance to pesticides thanks to natural selection. One, the two-spotted spider mite, attacks many types of fruit trees and berry bushes by sucking fluids from leaves. Pesticide resistance means farmers must constantly change the tactics they use to control these pests.

The Pacific leaping blenny of Micronesia is one of Earth's few species of walking fish. They can breathe through their gills and skin, and hop around near the water's edge between tides. This adaptation significantly expands the range in which they can look for food and mates, increasing the chances of survival for this species.

Only 35 per cent of the world's population, including most people of European ancestry and many from particular parts of Africa, are lactose tolerant – they possess a special enzyme that allows their body to digest cow's milk. This trait is thought to have developed 2000 to 20,000 years ago in groups that domesticated cattle and milked them. The advantage? Rather than waiting days or weeks for easier-to-digest cheeses and yogurts to be ready, humans could drink nourishing milk straightaway – the world's first fast food!

SMALLEST AND LARGEST

Today, 8.7 million different species of plants, animals, insects, aquatic life and bacteria are known to live on Earth, according to a 2011 United Nations report.

GIANT FOOTPRINT
Enormous dinosaurs such as Brachiosaurus *and* Diplodocus *roamed the coast of Western Australia near Broome, leaving behind large footprints.*

But the real number is far higher: 86 per cent of land species and 91 per cent of water species have yet to be discovered or named. The enormous number of known species covers a wide diversity of living things, from the bee hummingbird – the smallest bird in the world – to coast redwoods, the tallest trees on Earth.

Some ancient, one-celled organisms measured less than 20 microns, smaller than the width of a human hair. The oldest evidence of single-celled life on Earth is found in fossils dating back 3.5 billion years, which were discovered in Western Australia's North Pole Dome within the Pilbara region. The smallest known dinosaur is the 250-million-year-old Ashdown Maniraptoran, a bird-like creature believed to weigh just 200 g (7 oz) and measure 40 cm (16 in) in length, while the smallest humanoid is the hobbit-like *Homo floresiensis,* who stood about 1 m (3 ft) high and lived 95,000 to 17,000 years ago in Indonesia. Today, the smallest creatures in the world include Kitti's hog-nosed bat, which weighs just 2 g (0.07 oz) and is no larger than a bumblebee, and the fairy wasp – the length of one Costa Rican species is only two and a half times the diameter of a human hair.

The world's largest-ever land animal is known as *Argentinosaurus,* and it was named for the country in which the dinosaur was found. A farmer in Argentina first found this behemoth's 155-cm (61-in) tibia, or

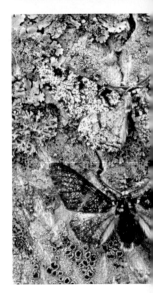

shinbone, in a sandstone formation in 1987. From this and a few other bones, palaeontologists estimate that this long-necked, plant-munching dinosaur measured 35 m (115 ft) from head to tail, and weighed nearly 100 tonnes (110 tons). But there may be an even larger, Brontosaurus like dinosaur waiting to be discovered in Western Australia – palaeontologists have located a footprint near James Price Point that measures an incredible 1.5 m (5 ft) in length! Today, the blue whale is Earth's largest living animal, measuring around 30 m (100 ft) in length and weighing an average of 150 tonnes (165 tons).

TERRIFYING TITANS OF ANTIQUITY

There were plenty of jumbo creatures in the ancient world that would have been frightening to meet face to face. Around 390 million years ago, a 2.5-m (8.2-ft) sea scorpion known as *Jaekelopterus rhenaniae* terrorised what is now Germany with its spiked, 46-cm (18-in) long claws. Throughout Earth's Carboniferous period, around 359 to 299 million years ago, 2-m (6½-ft) long poisonous centipedes scuttled alongside 1-m (3-ft) long land scorpions, while colourful dragonflies as big as seagulls buzzed overhead.

During the heyday of the dinosaurs – the Cretaceous period, from 145 to 65 million years ago – the first snakes appeared on the scene, and just a few million years later they had reached an enormous size. The fossilised remains of one, called *Titanoboa cerrejonensis,* was unearthed in Colombia in 2008. It was 13 m (43 ft) long and would have weighed about 1100 kg (2500 lb) – making it the biggest snake ever to have lived. The largest ancient bird is *Pelegomis chilensis,* a giant seabird with a wingspan of 5.2 m (17 ft). It lived 5 to 10 million years ago in what is now northern Chile.

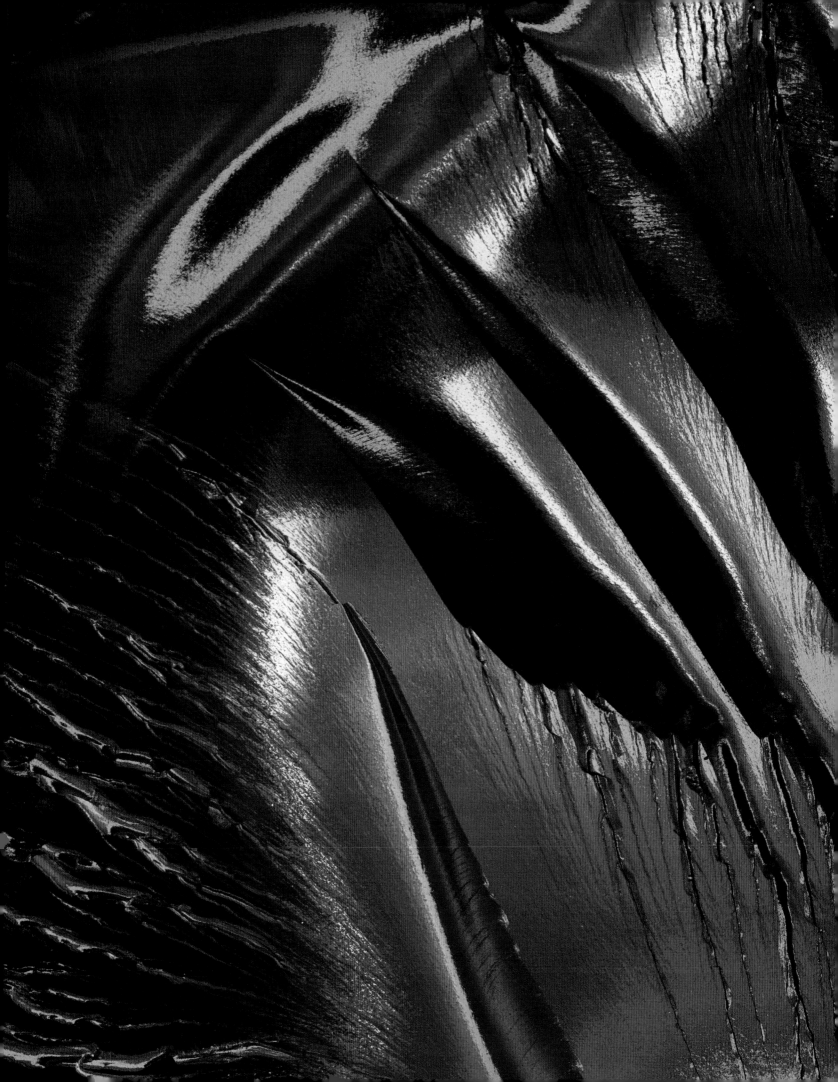

EXTREME FIRE AND MOVEMENT

Without a doubt, Earth is a restless planet. Giant plates of continental and oceanic crust float on a 'sea' of semimolten rock that boasts temperatures beyond imagining. The plates crash into each other or wrench apart, causing earthquakes and spewing magma in spectacular volcanic eruptions. Over millions of years, their movements have shaped the land – and the lives of people unfortunate enough to be in the wrong place at the wrong time. Earthquakes, eruptions and landslides can devastate cities in seconds, while in other regions the insidious action of water presents another hazard – sinkholes that can open up without warning and swallow a house whole.

CLOSE-UP OF LAVA
*Shimmering in the reflected light of still-seething lava, the folds
and fissures of this cooling lava reveal Earth's artistry at its best.*

SAN ANDREAS FAULT
This renowned fault has been shaping the landscape for some 28 million years. It is characterised by long escarpments, narrow ridges and streams that make a right-hand turn as they pass over the fault.

?

EXTREME FACT
If the San Andreas Fault, in California, continues moving at its current speed, Los Angeles will be level with San Francisco in 15 million years' time.

Faults and rifts

Earth's crust is like a giant jigsaw of interlocking plates that are constantly in motion. As the huge plates crash and grind against each other or slowly tear apart, they decorate the landscape with long, straight fractures and deep, steep-sided rift valleys.

THERE ARE EIGHT major and seven minor plates that make up Earth's crust, and these 'float' on the relatively denser and more malleable mantle below. Movement tends to be very slow, at less than 2 cm (⅘ in) per year (the rate at which fingernails grow), although some plates are moving faster – the Nazca Plate is travelling eastwards at a rate of 6 cm (2⅓ in) per year. Currently the fastest movement is where the western edge of the Pacific Plate is plunging below the Tonga and Indo-Australian Plates at a rate of 15 cm (6 in) per year. That's about the speed at which hair grows.

The forces moving the plates are immense, and since the rock that makes up Earth's crust is relatively brittle, it ruptures and forms cracks known as faults. As the rock breaks it releases energy, and this is felt as an earthquake. Faults can be 'dip-slip', where most of the movement is vertical or on an incline, either down ('normal') or up ('reverse' or 'thrust'). Faults can also be 'strike-slip' (or 'transform'), where most of the movement is horizontal as the blocks of rock slide against each other. These different fault types are seen around the edges of plate boundaries, depending on the movement of the plates.

TREACHEROUS EDGES

There are three types of plate boundaries: divergent, convergent and transform. Divergent boundaries arise when continental plates are moving apart, and they appear as deep gashes in Earth's crust known as rift valleys. Imagine tearing apart a fresh crusty loaf: the outer crust cracks and the inner bread stretches and thins as it pulls apart. This is like the middle of a rift valley – the centre is pulled thin and magma spews up through fissures to form new crust. Over time the gap widens, and a deep, steep-sided valley with a relatively flat bottom forms.

The spreading centres of ocean ridges also form along divergent boundaries. An example can clearly be seen by looking at the long rectangle of the Red Sea, west of Saudi Arabia. As the Arabian Plate moves north, the African Plate is moving north-west. The Red Sea is widening in the gap where the two

THE RED SEA
At the northern end of the Red Sea, the Gulf of Suez and the Gulf of Aqaba are like two tears in the landscape.

plates are pulling apart. Geologists predict that in time the two plates will be completely separated and Africa will be an enormous island.

Convergent boundaries occur where two plates push into each other. The heavier plate is forced under the lighter plate in a process called subduction. Mountains and stratovolcanoes form at these boundaries, as well as deep ocean trenches such as the Mariana Trench to the south of Japan. Subduction faults tend to be the site of the world's largest and most devastating earthquakes. As one plate sinks beneath the other, the forces of friction impede the movement. Sometimes a plate can get 'stuck' on another plate, but the two plates continue to move towards each other until finally the forces build up enough to push the 'stuck' plate on – with a corresponding large release of energy known as a megathrust earthquake. A recent example is the magnitude 9 earthquake off the coast of Japan on 11 March 2011.

The third type of boundary is known as a transform boundary, and this is where two plates slide against each other along a horizontal plane. Movement can be slow and creeping, or friction can impede the movement significantly so that energy builds up to breaking point, when it is suddenly released and causes an earthquake. During earthquakes the plates can slip several metres. A famous example of a transform fault is the San Andreas Fault in California.

TRANSFORMED LANDSCAPE

Viewed from the air, the magnificent San Andreas Fault looks like the gnarly backbone of some gigantic beast. It is exceptional because of its visibility and extent. Most of the faults that rupture Earth's crust can't be seen. The largest ones are under the oceans, like the Mid-Atlantic Ridge, while others are buried deep below ground. The San Andreas Fault, which hugs the California coastline for most of its length, is the world's largest overland fault zone, running 1300 km (800 miles) from Mexico to Oregon.

The fault is situated at the boundary of the North American and Pacific Plates. It's a 'strike-slip' (or 'transform') fault that has formed as the Pacific Plate to the west moves in a north-westerly direction relative to the North American Plate. Geologists refer to the San Andreas Fault as a shallow fault, although it extends in places to a depth of 16 km (10 miles). The rocks either side of the main fault line have ruptured, creating a complex system of interlocking smaller faults that are constantly shuffling, generating up to 10,000 earthquakes a year.

Different sections of the fault system move in different ways, with some areas travelling in a constant series of small movements. Other regions 'lock up' for a hundred years or more, eventually releasing the strain in powerful earthquakes that often have devastating consequences. During such an event the ground can shift by as much as 7 m (23 ft), as seen during the 1906 San Francisco earthquake. As a whole, geologists know that the fault has travelled more than 500 km (300 miles) by measuring the gap between geologically similar rocks on either side of the fault.

PREDICTING FAULT MOVEMENTS

When will the next big earthquake occur? To answer this, geologists constantly monitor whole fault systems (at least where they know them to be – there is always a chance of an unknown fault lurching into life). They look for 'seismic gaps' – places that have been quiet for long periods. The theory is that if a fault is quiet, it is 'locked' and building up energy ready for a large release. Geologists have noticed that, in general, a large earthquake occurs in the southern region of the San Andreas Fault roughly every 150 years. The last major earthquake in the Los Angeles area occurred in 1857, so it would seem that another one is due.

San Francisco residents may have a bit more time, since their last big earthquake was in 1906. They could have another 40 years' grace, although a significant quake could occur at any time (such as the magnitude 6.9 earthquake on 17 October 1989). Geologists predict that there will likely be foreshocks of about magnitude 5 before a bigger earthquake, though how much time residents will have to evacuate the area is unknowable.

The North Anatolian Fault that runs along the top of Turkey is a similar length to the San Andreas Fault and has generated some very destructive earthquakes. It is unusual in that there is a relatively predictable pattern to its rupturing. Geologists have observed that the earthquakes are progressing from east to west along the 1000-km (600-mile) fault. Since the 1939 earthquake in Erzincan, there have been seven major earthquakes along the fault line. It seems that as each segment moves, it passes the stress westwards and pressure builds up until the next segment ruptures. The most recent events were a magnitude 7.4 earthquake in Izmit on 17 August 1999, followed three months later by a magnitude 7.2 earthquake in Düzce. Geologists think that the next earthquake is likely to be near Istanbul – a worrying prospect for this highly populated city with many ancient buildings, such as the Hagia Sophia, constructed long before earthquake building codes.

A GOLDEN LINING

Though fault zones are the sites of many destructive earthquakes, they also offer some rather lucrative benefits. Regions of intense volcanic and seismic activity have long been known to be areas rich in minerals. This is because geothermal water carries minerals from Earth's depths and deposits them in rock nearer the surface. Since the water travels along faults, it often ends up depositing quartz and other trace minerals along these faults in 'veins'. Among the minerals deposited this way is the most precious of all: gold.

Gold is often found in quartz veins, though the precise mechanism for its deposition has been the source of debate. The conventional theory was that the gold was deposited as the water cooled and the quartz crystallised. However, geologists from The University of Queensland, Australia, have recently proposed that it is in fact the activity of faults that creates the gold deposits. When a fault ruptures, the sudden release in pressure allows water that is held within pockets of rock to expand. This sudden vaporisation precipitates out any gold it is carrying, as well as quartz, and it is deposited along the faults. The geologists say that although the amount of gold per earthquake is small, over time and numerous vaporisations large deposits of gold can build up. Even earthquakes of magnitude 4 can cause the vaporisation. It would mean that particularly active fault systems, such as New Zealand's Alpine Fault, could be generating significant gold deposits.

ANTIPODEAN FAULT ZONE

Perched astride the boundary of the Indo-Australian and Pacific Plates, it is no surprise that New Zealand is geologically active, with volcanoes, earthquakes and geothermal features in abundance. One of its most impressive elements is the razor-sharp Alpine Fault

that runs virtually the length of the South Island, from Blenheim in the north to Milford Sound in the south. The 650-km (400-mile) fault began to form 23 million years ago. As a single continuous fault (rather than a series of faults, like the San Andreas Fault) it is one of the world's longest, and certainly the largest that can be seen (other longer faults being on the seabed). It lies just to the west of the Southern Alps mountain range, and although the Alpine Fault is a 'strike-slip' ('transform') fault, the plates are also moving towards each other and causing uplift of the mountain range, currently at a rate of 7 mm (¼ in) per year.

The complex geology can be explained by looking at the movements of the tectonic plates around New Zealand. To the north, and under the North Island, the Pacific Plate is being forced under the Indo-Australian Plate, while to the south of the South Island the Indo-Australian Plate is being forced under the Pacific Plate – it's almost as though New Zealand is being twisted or wrung like a cloth. The Alpine Fault is in a highly charged transitional zone in the middle, and is both transform and convergent (termed 'obliquely convergent'), moving at an average rate of 38 mm (1½ in) per year.

The Alpine Fault has ruptured four times in the past 900 years, each time producing an earthquake of about magnitude 8. During those events, the fault shifted as much as 8 m (26 ft) horizontally, with up to 2 m (7 ft) uplift. Recent research by the Institute of Geological and Nuclear Sciences (known as GNS Science) looked back over 8000 years to gain an insight into how the fault behaves. They concluded that the average amount of time between big earthquakes of magnitude 8 is 330 years, with the shortest gap of 140 years and the longest of 510 years. The most recent event was in 1717. Geologists calculate that there is a 30 per cent

ALPINE FAULT
New Zealand's highest peak, Aoraki/Mount Cook, is part of the country's Southern Alps, which are growing larger every year as the nearby Alpine Fault causes an upwards movement in the landscape.

GREAT GLEN FAULT
Around a third of the length of the Great Glen Fault, in Scotland, is taken up by the 36-km (22-mile) long Loch Ness. This narrow lake was created around 10,000 years ago, at the end of the last ice age.

chance of the fault generating a major earthquake within the next 50 years. Such an earthquake would be significantly greater than Christchurch's recent earthquakes and would inflict the most damage to the west coast of the South Island, as well as Wellington, the country's capital city.

SLICING THROUGH SCOTLAND

Look at any map of Scotland and you will see a long, straight gash from Inverness on the east coast to Fort William on the west coast. It looks like a giant has taken a carving knife to Scotland, dividing the Northern Highlands from the Grampian Highlands to the south. But the straightness of the line points to its geological origins: a massive fault. Known as the Great Glen Fault, it sits in a landscape of broad, glaciated valleys and deep, tranquil lakes known as lochs. Perhaps its most famous landmark is Loch Ness, Britain's largest stretch of fresh water, which holds more water than all the lakes of England and Wales put together.

The fault extends further north-east into the North Sea, and to the south-west it clips the edge of the Isle of Mull before heading off towards Northern Ireland. It is an ancient 'strike-slip' fault that is thought to have formed 400 million years ago, but it could be older. The fault does still generate earthquakes, notably in 1888, 1890 and 1901. In 2001, Italian geologist Dr Luigi Piccardi posed the theory that sightings of the famous Loch Ness Monster coincide with seismic activity along the fault. He reasoned that the movement would be enough to cause rippling on the surface of the loch, which could be interpreted as evidence of the monster.

TEARING THE LAND APART

The Great Rift Valley is the longest gash in the Earth's surface, and it is even visible from the Moon. Running from Jordan through Kenya and Tanzania all the way to Mozambique in Africa, it is actually not one rift but a combination of several rift systems that are tearing the landscape apart. The region is the site of almost constant volcanic and seismic activity, tall sheer cliffs and broad flat valleys.

The northernmost rift is known as the Jordan Rift Valley, and below it is the Red Sea Rift, forming as the African and Arabian Plates separate. Further south is the massive East African Rift, which is often confused with the Great Rift Valley. It runs down eastern Africa for almost half the length of the continent, from the Gulf of Aden in the north to the Zambezi River in the south. The rift is forming as the Horn of Africa tries to sail off into the Indian Ocean. Slowly but steadily – at a rate of about 4 mm (⅙ in) per year – the African Plate is breaking apart, with most of Africa sitting on the so-called Nubian Plate while a new plate known as the Somalian Plate carries the Horn of Africa away.

Geologists predict that the Gulf of Aden, which currently borders the northern edge of the Horn of Africa, will one day flood the rift valley. Eventually the Horn of Africa will be a continental island, similar to Madagascar.

At the northern end of the East African Rift is a geologically complex area where three tectonic plates – the Arabian, Nubian and Somalian – are all pulling in different directions. The Afar Triple Junction, as the region is known, is the site of intensive volcanic activities. This is the home of Erta Ale, one of just a handful of volcanoes with a constantly bubbling lava lake, and the Dallol geothermal field, with its acidic hot springs and fumaroles.

The East African Rift divides into two branches that curve either side of the massive Lake Victoria. Several deep lakes have formed along the rift valley floor, including Lake Kivu and Lake Tanganyika, the deepest at a staggering 1470 m (4820 ft) in depth.

CUTTING DEEP

The world's deepest continental rift valley is the Baikal Rift Valley in north-eastern Russia. At the heart of it lies Lake Baikal, the oldest and deepest freshwater lake in the world. The rift began to form 25 million years ago when the Amurian Plate began pulling away from the Eurasian Plate.

Known as 'the blue eye of Siberia', Lake Baikal is 1637 m (5371 ft) deep. However, it is getting deeper, as the rifting continues at a rate of 2 cm (⅘ in) per year. The true depth of the rift is hidden beneath a thick layer of sediment at the bottom of the lake that extends a further 8 km (5 miles). This undisturbed sediment offers scientists a valuable insight into past environments, and core samples taken from the lakebed have shown many climatic changes over the past 250,000 years. The lake is also important for its wildlife; it is home to thousands of magnificent species of plants and animals, most of which live only in and around the lake.

THE CRADLE OF MANKIND

The East African Rift valley is famous for more than its active volcanoes and deep lakes. Palaeontologists have made several significant finds in the region, including Lucy, a 3.2-million-year-old *Australopithecus afarensis* skeleton, and human-like fossilised footprints that were made some 3.6 million years ago. More specimens of *A. afarensis* have been unearthed, thought to be the oldest hominids and the ancestors of modern humans, and these early hominid remains have helped scientists to understand how humans have evolved. Interestingly, scientists believe that when Lucy was alive, the East African Rift valley would have been lush grassland with plenty of fresh water and animals to hunt.

A SPREADING MIDDLE

The largest rift on Earth is the 10,000-km (6200-mile) long Mid-Atlantic Ridge, which began to form 200 million years ago. It runs north to south down the middle of the Atlantic Ocean, from just north of Greenland almost all the way to Antarctica. It marks the zone where the African and Eurasian Plates are moving eastwards, away from the North American and South American Plates, which are moving westwards.

As the continents move apart, magma pushes up from the mantle, creating a rise in the crust. It also spews out, filling in the gap between the diverging plates and causing the Atlantic Ocean to widen at a rate of about 2.5 cm (1 in) a year. The rugged peaks that have formed along either side of the central rift valley reach heights of over 2000 m (6500 ft).

WHERE TO SEE THE MID-ATLANTIC RIDGE

Þingvellir (Thingvellir) National Park located in south-western Iceland is the only place on Earth where you can take a walk down a mid-oceanic ridge. The national park covers a broad rift valley featuring dramatic cliffs, where the Mid-Atlantic Ridge – which runs down the middle of the Atlantic Ocean – rises above the sea.

EAST AFRICAN RIFT
A Samburu warrior looks out across the breathtaking eastern scarp of the East African Rift at Poro, Kenya. The cliffs here rise to 3000 m (10,000 ft) from the valley floor.

Earthquakes and tremors

With Earth's crust constantly on the move, huge forces build up along the boundaries of tectonic plates. When one plate slips, it releases energy in the form of an earthquake. Around 20,000 earthquakes are felt around the world each year, and the larger ones have the power to destroy buildings and lives in seconds.

E ARTHQUAKES ARE ONE of Earth's most lethal natural phenomena. A large earthquake can take thousands of lives and cause millions of dollars' worth of damage in just a few seconds. Worst of all, unlike volcanoes, which usually give some signs of an impending eruption, earthquakes generally strike out of the blue. There are regions where an earthquake is more likely, of course, most notably the notorious Ring of Fire (an area of exceptional seismic and volcanic activity that circles the Pacific Ocean), or anywhere near a plate boundary. For any given location geologists can even predict the probable size of an earthquake by looking at past events and local features in the rocks. But the exact timing and precise location are known only to Earth itself.

It is impossible to avoid Earth's shifting movements completely. Even places not normally associated with earthquakes can experience minor tremors. For example, people in the United Kingdom feel 20 to 30 earthquakes every year, though these are usually so small that they do not cause any damage. On a global scale, however, you can expect at least one earthquake of magnitude 8 or above every year. It's been estimated that earthquakes account for an annual death toll of around 10,000 people, not only from fallen buildings but also from the associated tsunamis, fires and landslides.

SHAKEN TO THE LIMITS

The most powerful earthquake ever recorded was the Great Chilean Earthquake of 22 May 1960. The source of the earthquake was off the Chilean coast, along the subduction zone where the Nazca Plate is being forced under the South American Plate. In a huge megathrust event, a 1000-km (600-mile) section of the fault ruptured, producing a magnitude 9.5 earthquake. Most of the damage occurred 15 minutes after the earthquake, when a tsunami deluged the Chilean coast from Lebu to Puerto Aisén.

As the tsunami travelled outwards across the ocean, it claimed at least 61 lives in Hawaii and caused thousands of dollars' worth of damage around the Pacific. The earthquake claimed between 2000 and 6000 lives in

?

EXTREME FACT
The magnitude 9.3 earthquake off Sumatra on Boxing Day 2004 speeded up Earth's rotation, shortening the day by exactly 2.7 microseconds.

◄

EARTHQUAKE DAMAGE
The magnitude 6.9 Great Hanshin Earthquake struck the Kobe area of Japan on 17 January 1995. The extensive devastation included buckled train tracks and powerlines that teetered precariously.

all. The death toll could have been much higher – fortunately, a strong foreshock rattled through the Chilean towns of Valdivia and Puerto Montt just half an hour before the main earthquake. It brought people running out of their houses, and they were still outside when the magnitude 9.5 earthquake struck. The massive shake brought down most of the dwellings, leaving 2 million people homeless – but alive.

MEASURING EARTHQUAKES

When an earthquake happens, energy is sent radiating out in all directions from its epicentre, a bit like ripples on a pond. There are three main types of wave, and they travel at different speeds and shake the ground in different ways. P-waves are the fastest, and so they are the first to arrive after an earthquake. They are compressional waves that expand and contract material in the direction in which they travel, like a concertina that is moving in and out. S-waves are slower than P-waves, and they move in an undulating 'S' shape, perpendicular to the direction of travel. These are the waves that cause up and down movements. P- and S-waves travel through bedrock, while additional surface waves travel along or close to the ground's surface. It is the surface waves that create some of the most peculiar effects of earthquakes, such as the elliptical movement caused by Rayleigh waves.

Geologists detect and measure earthquakes using seismometers. They position numerous machines in a network across a region, with each one recording the ground movement at its location. The information can then be pooled to gain an understanding of where the earthquake occurred and its strength. Geologists use the fact that P-waves are faster than S-waves to determine the location (or epicentre) of the earthquake. A seismometer that is close to the event will have P- and S-waves arriving at similar times, while a seismometer some distance away will have a gap between the arrival of P- and S-waves. By reading this information from a minimum of three different seismometers, geologists can determine the earthquake's exact location.

An earthquake's size can be quantified in several ways. The most common is its magnitude. This used to be expressed as a number on the Richter scale, based on the size of a readout from a seismograph and the distance from the epicentre. But the scale tended to underestimate the size of large earthquakes, so today geologists use the moment magnitude scale, which takes into account the rock's rigidity, the area of fault rupture and the average amount of movement.

An earthquake's strength can also be expressed as its intensity – this is a more descriptive measure of the observed shaking and damage caused at different locations. The Modified Mercalli Intensity scale rates this from 1 to 12, where 1 is 'Not felt', 6 is 'Strong – some objects topple over' and 12 is 'Completely devastating, with all buildings above and below ground damaged or destroyed.'

WHEN LESS IS MORE

It seems obvious that the greater the magnitude of an earthquake, the more damage it will cause – but this is not always the case. The residents of Christchurch, New Zealand, learned this the hard way on 22 February 2011, when a magnitude 6.3 earthquake destroyed the city's central business district and caused widespread damage, killing 185 people in the process. Just five months earlier, the city had survived a magnitude 7.1 earthquake virtually intact, with no lives lost. The February shake was an aftershock, yet it was more devastating than the main earthquake because it was shallower and closer to the city. The February earthquake was also extraordinary in that its peak ground acceleration was 2.2 G (over twice the force of gravity), which is the highest to ever occur beneath a city – and four times higher than Japan's magnitude 9 earthquake of 11 March 2011.

The Christchurch earthquakes are arguably the most monitored in history. Both earthquakes occurred on previously unknown faults, yet the whole of New Zealand has an extensive network of seismometers, coordinated by the Institute of Geological and Nuclear Sciences (known as GNS Science). After the September 2010 earthquake, a further 200 miniature seismometers were installed around the Canterbury region in the homes of volunteers. The instruments have captured extensive data about the earthquakes and the ensuing sequence of aftershocks.

The intensive monitoring has revealed some interesting characteristics that help to explain the ferocity of the February earthquake. Apart from its exceptional ground speeds and proximity to Christchurch, the earthquake was generated by a fault beneath the Port Hills that lie to the south-east of the city. The 14-km (9-mile) fault that ruptured is oriented south-west to north-east, which means it directed most of its energy north-westwards, straight at the city.

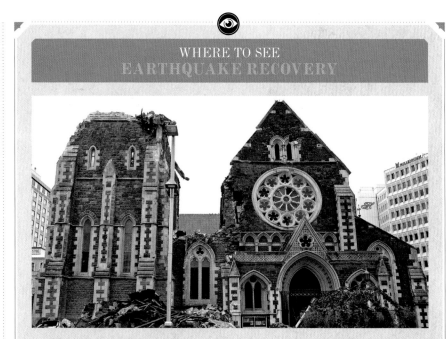

WHERE TO SEE
EARTHQUAKE RECOVERY

If you want to see what an earthquake-shattered city looks like, visit Christchurch in New Zealand. Compared with other earthquake zones, this one remains relatively civilised – and safe. Dangerous buildings have been removed or fenced off, but there is still plenty of earthquake evidence, most notably the ruined cathedral (pictured). Quake City in the central Container Mall offers information about the city's loss and recovery.

CHRISTCHURCH
Rubble covers cars in central Christchurch more than a week after the February 2011 earthquake. The total damage bill for this earthquake was over NZ$15 billion, more than double the amount held in New Zealand's Natural Disaster Fund.

Another effect that has rarely been documented before is known as the 'slap-down' or 'trampoline' effect. Seismograph readings during the February earthquake showed that the movement of the ground was more vertical than horizontal, and that greater speeds were recorded going up than down. This is because as the first waves of energy travelled outwards, they moved the weaker upper layers of the ground further than the stronger lower layers, separating them out. As the upper layers fell back, they 'slapped' against the lower layers that were still moving upwards, generating more energy that was carried to the surface. As well as intensifying the shaking, the 'slap-down' effect added to the liquefaction that occurred throughout the city. Such phenomena demonstrate that an earthquake's impact cannot be assessed on magnitude alone.

MEGATHRUST EARTHQUAKES

The most powerful earthquakes tend to occur along subduction zones, where one tectonic plate is being forced under another. They are known as megathrust earthquakes because they are the result of the lighter continental crust being thrust upwards as the heavy oceanic plate grinds beneath it. The Great Chilean

EARTHQUAKES ON THE QUIET

Subduction zones are known to be the sites of the most violent megathrust earthquakes, so imagine how surprised geologists were when they observed 'silent' earthquakes going on in the same zones. Tectonic plates are always in motion, but during a 'silent' or 'slow-slip' earthquake they move past each other faster than normal, yet still take weeks or even months to do it. If the same amount of slippage happened in seconds, it might generate a magnitude 7 earthquake – but these 'silent' earthquakes are not felt above ground. Geologists are puzzled by the mechanism of the 'silent' earthquakes, and whether they help lessen the chances of larger earthquakes by releasing some of the strain energy.

ALASKA

Anchorage was shaken to its core during the magnitude 9.2 Great Alaskan Earthquake of 27 March 1964 – the second-most powerful earthquake in living memory.

SUMATRA

Elephants were put to work in the city of Banda Aceh on the Indonesian island of Sumatra, removing tonnes of debris after the Sumatra–Andaman Earthquake and tsunami on Boxing Day 2004.

JAPAN

The destructive Tohoku Earthquake of 11 March 2011 was the first to be heard in space – a satellite passing overhead recorded low-frequency acoustic waves generated by the earthquake.

Earthquake of 1960 was a megathrust earthquake, as was the more recent magnitude 9 earthquake off the coast of Japan in March 2011.

Japan's earthquake, known as the Tohoku Earthquake because this was the region most badly affected, was the biggest in the country's recorded history (and the world's fourth largest). The epicentre was located on the seabed, where the Pacific Plate is being subducted beneath the North American Plate holding Honshu, Japan's largest island. The energy was released as the lighter continental plate pinged upwards like a diving board, displacing the seabed by 25 m (82 ft) along a region some 400 km (250 miles) in length. It created an enormous wave that took about 15 minutes to reach land before engulfing it.

The earthquake, as powerful as it was, did not destroy a single skyscraper in Tokyo, just 370 km (230 miles) to the south-west, as the buildings are modern and had been designed to withstand a high-magnitude earthquake. Yet 25,000 people in the Tohoku region are thought to have perished in the tsunami that devastated Japan's north-eastern coastal areas. As if the earthquake and tsunami were not enough, the people of Japan had to endure three aftershocks of more than magnitude 7 that day; there would be 60 others of more than magnitude 6 and hundreds of lesser tremors over the following year. The main earthquake was so huge it shunted the whole of Honshu eastwards by 2.5 m (8 ft).

Japan is particularly prone to earthquakes, as it sits astride the junction of four tectonic plates: the North American, Eurasian, Philippine Sea and Pacific Plates. It is part of the infamous Ring of Fire that runs around the edge of the Pacific Ocean. If you want to avoid earthquakes, you should try not to live anywhere along this belt (you'll also have a better chance of avoiding the effects of a volcanic eruption). In particular, you should stay away from Alaska because this region is one of Earth's most seismically active. According to the US Geological Survey (USGS), Alaska experiences a magnitude 7 earthquake on an almost yearly basis and can expect a massive magnitude 8 earthquake every 14 years or so.

LONG AND DEADLY

Much of the devastation caused by megathrust earthquakes is to do with their duration – they tend to go on for a long time. While buildings may withstand a short, sharp jolt, continuous shaking takes a heavier toll. The longest earthquake ever recorded happened off the coast of Sumatra on Boxing Day 2004. The shaking from the magnitude 9.1 event lasted an astonishing 10 minutes (most earthquakes are over in a matter of seconds). The shaking set off a colossal tsunami that caused widespread damage around the region. The earthquake was one of the most lethal in history, claiming over 200,000 lives. It also holds the record for the largest aftershock – at a whopping magnitude 8.7 – which happened three months after the main earthquake.

But the world's deadliest earthquake occurred in the Shaanxi province of China on 23 January 1556. The earthquake, which has since been estimated as magnitude 8, took the lives of around 830,000 people. There was damage spread over a huge area, and the earthquake was felt over 800 km (500 miles) away. It is thought that most deaths were due to the extensive collapse of dwellings. The event reduced the population by 60 per cent in some counties.

FORESHOCKS AND AFTERSHOCKS

Often an earthquake is heralded by a smaller foreshock –
a sign that the rocks are giving way to increasing strain.
A large foreshock saved the lives of thousands in the
Great Chilean Earthquake of 1960, while in 2011 Tohoku
received a warning in the form of a magnitude 7.2
foreshock two days before the main earthquake – yet
a significant number of earthquakes happen without
any warning at all. And the problem for geologists
is knowing when a foreshock has occurred. Without
the luxury of hindsight, deciding whether a rumble
is an isolated earthquake or the portent of a larger
earthquake to come is an almost impossible task. In
October 2012, six Italian scientists were convicted of
manslaughter after failing to predict the magnitude
6.3 earthquake that killed 309 residents of L'Aquila
on 6 April 2009. Locals had voiced their concerns
when numerous small tremors rattled through the

Haiti Earthquake of 12 January 2010 generated 33 aftershocks, while GNS Science data show that the magnitude 7.1 Christchurch Earthquake of 4 September 2010 generated over 12,000 aftershocks. This discrepancy is due to the fact that Haiti is poorly monitored, while the Christchurch earthquake sequence is probably the most monitored event ever. The location of the earthquake is another factor to consider, with earthquakes in remote areas or under the ocean being less monitored than those that occur near cities.

On 28 July 1976, the deadliest earthquake of recent times struck the city of Tangshan, China, just 150 km (90 miles) east of Beijing. The magnitude 7.5 earthquake that occurred in the early hours was followed by a huge magnitude 7.1 aftershock in the afternoon. Together, the two tremors killed between 250,000 and 650,000 people. There were reports of curious warnings in the days before the earthquakes, including excited chickens that would not eat and a well with rising and falling water levels. On the night before the earthquakes, villagers saw strange lights in the sky and heard booming sounds in the ground – phenomena that were also reported before the September 2010 earthquake in Christchurch.

WHEN MAN MAKES EARTH TREMBLE

In the United States, the USGS has been monitoring the country's seismic activity for decades. From 1967 to 2000, nationwide seismometers picked up an average of 26 earthquakes per year. However, in the three years between 2010 and 2012, the 'quake rate' rose to 300 per year! At first glance it would seem that the United States is experiencing some underlying seismic event, but that is not the case. The culprit is man – more specifically, it is the effect of injecting the ground with waste water from oil and gas extraction, a practice that has increased exponentially in the United States over the last few years.

Any major activity in the ground can cause an earthquake, from underground nuclear tests to the operation of geothermal power plants. Large dams are known to induce trembling as the immense weight of water bears down on the ground. The largest man-made earthquake is widely considered to be the one that struck China's Sichuan province on 12 May 2008. The magnitude 7.9 earthquake killed around 80,000 people and made 5 million homeless. It is thought that the nearby Zipingpu Dam, which holds over 300 million tonnes (330 million tons) of water, put pressure on a fault line, triggering the earthquake. One of the most damaging earthquakes in Australia – a relatively quiet country seismically – has been attributed to the effects of coal mining. The magnitude 5.6 Newcastle Earthquake of 28 December 1989 killed 13 people and racked up a bill of AU$4 billion. Academics have proposed that extensive removal of coal from the Newcastle region reactivated an old fault, resulting in the earthquake.

region in the weeks before the earthquake, but the scientists said in a press conference that there was 'no danger' just days before the earthquake struck.

Whether they have foreshocks or not, significant earthquakes are always followed by a sequence of smaller aftershocks. The size and number depend on the size of the main earthquake – the larger the main earthquake, the larger and more numerous are its aftershocks. Anyone who lives in an active earthquake zone will say that their particular earthquake has spawned the most aftershocks. It's very subjective, and in many cases the result of residents being highly attuned to even the slightest wobble.

In fact, it is difficult and rather meaningless to compare aftershock sequences between events, since they occur in different countries with different levels of monitoring. The number of aftershocks recorded depends on the network and sensitivity of local monitoring equipment. For example, according to the USGS, the magnitude 7

▲
HAITI
The Haiti Earthquake of 12 January 2010 destroyed much of the country's capital city, Port-au-Prince, including important historical buildings such as the cathedral.

◄
ITALY
Residents of L'Aquila, Italy, were left reeling after the April 2009 earthquake created a number of sinkholes and damaged up to 15,000 buildings.

Volcanoes and craters

At any given time, there are around 20 volcanoes in a state of eruption. Some volcanoes are particularly restless, though a quiet volcano cannot be termed dormant until 10,000 years have passed without incident. Yet an active volcano is not necessarily a dangerous one.

THE WORLD'S MOST active volcano, Kilauea, is one of the least treacherous. It is situated in the south-eastern corner of the Big Island, the youngest part of the chain of islands that make up Hawaii. Kilauea is a shield volcano that has formed above a 'hot spot', where magma exploits a weakness in Earth's crust and finds its way to the surface. The runny lava oozes out slowly and predictably, allowing people time to move out of its path.

Stratovolcanoes, on the other hand, are much deadlier. They form in regions where one tectonic plate is being forced under another; gaseous magma tends to erupt explosively, with catastrophic results. Russia's Kamchatka Peninsula has some of the most active stratovolcanoes on Earth. There are more than 100 active volcanoes strung out along the 700-km (400-mile) peninsula, with 30 that have erupted in recent times. Shiveluch is one of the region's largest and most explosive volcanoes, having produced 60 huge eruptions over the last 10,000 years. Its most recent eruption of 1999 is still ongoing, accompanied by an ominous plume of smoke emanating continuously from its peak. Its sudden and violent eruptions pose a threat to the towns of Klyuchi and Ust'-Kamchatsk that sit beneath it.

The largest and deadliest eruption in recorded history happened on 10 April 1815, when Mount Tambora, a stratovolcano on Indonesia's island of Sumbawa, blew its top. The explosion was later rated 7 (out of 8) – or super-colossal – on the Volcanic Explosivity Index (VEI). Fiery pyroclastic flows of gases, dust and rocks hurtled down the mountainside, killing thousands instantly, while around 80,000 people on nearby islands were killed by tsunamis and subsequent crop failures. The huge amount of ash ejected into the air had atmospheric effects all over the world; 1816 was called 'the year without a summer'. New York had frosts in June, and in Europe stormy weather brought about floods and crop failure, causing around 200,000 people to perish.

OUT OF THE BLUE

The most dangerous aspect of volcanoes is their unpredictability. When Mount Pelée on the Caribbean island of Martinique erupted on 8 May 1902, it wiped out the 30,000 inhabitants of Saint-Pierre within the space of just two minutes. The mountain had issued warnings, of course, but these were not fully understood at the time. Just two weeks earlier, Mount Pelée had shot a column of steam into the air and a series of tremors had shaken the region. Locals reported a strange mass exodus of insects and snakes off the mountain, and 50 people died from snakebites. We now know that the creatures were on the move because sulfurous gases were being emitted from the volcano – a sure sign of an imminent eruption. Three days before the blast, a local river had turned into a raging torrent of scalding hot, muddy water – a definite mark of rising magma.

Mount Pinatubo in the Philippines is another volcano that took people by surprise, when it woke from a 500-year slumber. The peak had been eroded, and the rich volcanic soil had encouraged a covering of lush vegetation – so the mountain no longer looked like a volcano. Locals had forgotten that there was a monster in their midst. This all changed in April 1991, when the monster stirred – a series of small steam explosions created a line of craters and dusted villages 10 km (6 miles) away in ash. Fortunately, officials responded quickly to these small explosions, and seismologists set up monitoring equipment on the mountain. They soon learned that magma was rising and pressure was building up beneath the mountain. By the time of the largest eruption on 15 June, around a million people had been evacuated from the mountain. Only 300 lives were lost. When it blew, Mount Pinatubo created a stupendous column of ash 35 km (22 miles) high and 18 km (11 miles) wide.

Today, most active volcanoes are closely monitored, and this enables prompt evacuation. Even so, there is nothing volcanologists can do to stop eruptions from happening and the chaos they cause. In 2010, Iceland's Eyjafjallajökull grounded airlines across Europe when it sent a huge plume of ash and dust into the air. The dust is harmful for jet engines, and the planes could not risk flying through it. In a similar situation, planes across the Southern Hemisphere were grounded in 2011 when ash and dust from Chile's Mount Puyehue circled the globe.

MOUNT MERAPI
The most active volcano in Indonesia, Mount Merapi is a stratovolcano that has been erupting on and off since 1548. In October and November 2010, a particularly violent series of eruptions killed more than 350 people.

MOUNT PINATUBO
After a series of minor eruptions, this large stratovolcano on the Philippine island of Luzon erupted on 15 June 1991, sending 5 cubic km (1 cubic mile) of material into the air. As pyroclastic flows roared down the mountain, those who had not been evacuated were forced to flee for their lives.

WHAT LIES BENEATH

Most of Earth's volcanoes are never seen because they are situated at the bottom of the ocean. Estimates of the number of submarine volcanoes range from 30,000 to a million, and on average their peaks lie some 2000 m (6600 ft) below the water's surface. Like land-based volcanoes, they form at the boundaries of tectonic plates and over hot spots. Deep-sea eruptions produce three-quarters of Earth's erupted magma and commonly occur along mid-oceanic ridges, such as the lengthy Mid-Atlantic Ridge that runs north to south down the middle of the Atlantic Ocean.

Enormous submarine volcanoes are occasionally discovered as improved technology allows us to explore the ocean depths in more detail. Kawio Barat, off the coast of Sulawesi in Indonesia, was found in 2010. It is completely submerged and rises 3500 m (11,500 ft) from its base to its peak, which is 1800 m (5900 ft) below the surface. An even larger volcano was reported in August 2013. Previously, scientists had believed that Tamu Massif, located in the north-western Pacific Ocean, was made up of several volcanoes. However, new research points to it being the work of a single vent. The volcano reaches 4000 m (13,100 ft) in height, but is gently sloping due to thin and runny lava that has created an enormous base some 310,000 sq km (120,000 sq miles) in area – making it the world's biggest volcano.

ISLANDS IN DISGUISE

Sometimes what looks like an island is in fact the top of a huge volcano. The tallest volcano in the world – and the tallest mountain from base to summit – is Hawaii's Mauna Kea. Its true height is hidden because most of it is submerged, with just 4205 m (13,796 ft) standing above the water. But when you take the underwater part of the volcano into account, it is a staggering 10,203 m (33,474 ft) from seabed to peak, substantially taller than Mount Everest's official height of 8848 m (29,029 ft).

It can take thousands of years for a permanent volcanic island to form. Consequently, to witness a permanent island being created from scratch is incredibly rare – but that is what happened in 1963 off the southern coast of Iceland. Surtsey was born through a series of violent eruptions that began on 8 November. As the volcano neared the surface of the sea, there was less water pressure bearing down on it and the eruptions became more explosive, sending grey plumes of steam and ash 6 km (4 miles) into the air. It took only a week for the volcano to break the surface, some 130 m (430 ft) from the seabed. It continued erupting and growing in size until 5 June 1967. At its tallest it was 170 m (560 ft) above sea level and about 2.5 sq km (1 sq mile) in area.

OCEAN VOLCANO
In March 2009, a submarine volcano erupted about 10 km (6 miles) off the coast of Tonga's main island, Tongatapu, sending plumes of steam, ash and smoke up to 20 km (12 miles) into the air.

EXTREME FACT

The loudest noise in recorded history was made by the Krakatau eruption in 1883. The sound was heard 5000 km (3000 miles) away in Alice Springs, Australia.

MOUNT ETNA
Europe's largest volcano, Mount Etna on the Italian island of Sicily is famous for its paroxysmal eruptions (explosive lava fountains). Its eruption history stretches back 500,000 years.

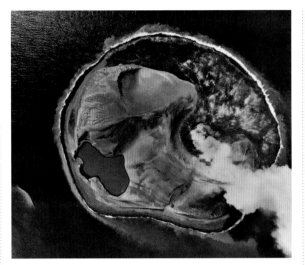

SURTSEY

Surtsey, off the coast of Iceland, may seem barren – but over 60 plant species have colonised the island since 1963.

Surtsey has offered scientists a unique opportunity to study how islands are colonised by plants, insects and birds. The first flying insect, probably carried on the wind from Iceland, was spotted in 1964, and sea rocket, a pioneer plant, was found growing on the shore in 1965. Birds were seen using the island as a place to perch almost as soon as it cooled, and in 1970 the discovery of nests on the island showed that black guillemots and fulmars had started to breed there. As the island has shrunk in stature during its lifetime, it is providing geologists with information about the processes of erosion. It is now roughly 120 m (390 ft) in height and half its original area, though geologists believe the island is holding its own and will be around for many years to come.

LIQUID ROCK

One of the most terrifying aspects of a volcano is the angry red lava that can suddenly flow down from its summit, destroying everything in its path. Lava flows arise when molten rock (magma) from beneath Earth's crust pushes its way to the surface and breaks free. As the steaming lava river snakes down the mountainside, igniting any vegetation it touches, it's clear that this liquid is hot – but just how hot is hard to comprehend. The temperature of lava flows can range from 700°C to 1200°C (1300°F to 2200°F). There is nothing that can withstand such heat.

A spectacular sight during an eruption is when lava spurts out like a water fountain before it flows down the side of the volcano. The highest fountains yet recorded were produced by Mount Etna in Italy, during an eruption in 1999. The fountains were an estimated 1500–2000 m (5000–6500 ft) tall, which is higher than a stack of four Empire State Buildings!

Though they are dangerous and destructive, lava flows are not normally the deadliest characteristic of eruptions. This is because in most instances they move at a speed of around 10 km/h (6 mph) an hour, and people are able to flee the descending limbs of lava. But when the lava is thin and runny, its effects can be swift and fatal.

LAVA LIKE WATER

The deadliest lava flows belong to the Democratic Republic of the Congo's Mount Nyiragongo. This is because of the volcano's unique structure – a steep-sided crater lake measuring about 1.2 km (¾ mile) in width and 800 m (2600 ft) in depth, containing very fluid lava – and its proximity to heavily populated areas.

On 10 January 1977, when a fissure appeared in the side of the crater, the lake drained in the space of an hour, sending rivers of its particularly fluid lava gushing down the slopes. It is thought that the lava reached speeds of over 100 km/h (60 mph), making it impossible to outrun. It happened in the night – taking many people by surprise – and hundreds were killed.

MOUNT
NYIRAGONGO
*In the Democratic
Republic of the Congo
lava in this crater
lake is rising once
again, posing a great
threat to nearby
residents.*

The contents of the crater lake built up again, and on 17 January 2002 another part of the volcano complex fractured, sending out rivers of lava once more. The volcano claimed more than 100 lives on that occasion, and a large, unstoppable lava flow cut the nearby town of Goma in two.

LARGEST AND LONGEST

Iceland is the site of what is thought to be the largest deposit of lava in recent times. The violent eruption of Laki that began on 8 June 1783 opened up several immense craters, which exuded almost 15 cubic km (3½ cubic miles) of lava that romped wildly over the land, devastating a vast region of around 500 sq km (200 sq miles). Huge volumes of sulfurous fumes killed off much of the country's livestock and ruined the crops, leading to a famine that wiped out around a quarter of the population. The gases hung in the air over Europe for five months, causing weather anomalies, crop damage and respiratory illnesses.

As lava travels it gradually cools. The outer part forms a kind of skin, eventually solidifying. Sometimes large channels harden on the outside, while the lava continues to flow inside. Over time, the lava may drain away or the volcano becomes extinct and leaves behind a series of cave-like tubes. The world's longest and deepest continuous lava tube is Kazumura Cave, a 68-km (42-mile) tunnel on the eastern flank of Kilauea in Hawaii.

But the longest stretch of lava flow is found at the Undara lava tube system in Queensland, Australia. The monumental series of tunnels and caverns are the remnants of a volcano that was active 190,000 years ago. The volcano deposited an enormous 23 cubic km (5½ cubic miles) of lava in long lobes and channels, with the longest arm extending 160 km (100 miles) to the north-west.

WHERE TO SEE
MOVING LAVA FLOWS

The best and safest place to see flowing lava is at Kilauea on Hawaii's Big Island. The volcano is in continuous eruption, and there are regular helicopter flights and boat trips to see the red-hot lava plunge into the sea. For the more daring, Sicily's Mount Etna performs fairly frequently with loud and fiery eruptions. The volcano's current level of activity determines how close you can get.

REMNANTS OF EXPLOSIONS

In the Crater Highlands area of north-eastern Tanzania, there is a rather unique kind of wildlife sanctuary unlike anything else in the world. Where once churned the angry heart of a volcano, there is now a wide, flat plateau that is home to almost every species of animal native to eastern Africa, including the endangered black rhinoceros.

Ngorongoro Crater is a vast basin covering some 260 sq km (100 sq miles), enclosed by a rim that is around 600 m (2000 ft) high. Such craters, which are also known as calderas, form when a massive eruption destroys the top of the volcano and ejects so much magma that the ground beneath it sags and the volcano slumps back into itself. In the case of Ngorongoro, it is thought that the crater formed about 2 million years ago. It is believed to be the largest intact caldera in the world.

DANGEROUS CRATER LAKES

Sometimes when a volcano blows its top, the remaining caldera gradually fills with water to become a lake. A breathtaking example is the 600-sq-km (230-sq-mile) Lake Taupo, formed after the eruption of Mount Taupo on New Zealand's North Island some 27,000 years ago. But even larger is Lake Toba in Sumatra, the result of a gigantic eruption that happened around 75,000 years ago. The lake is an impressive 100 km (60 miles) long and 30 km (20 miles) wide, and was created when the volcano emptied its magma chamber in the largest eruption of the last 2 million years.

Though often stunningly beautiful, crater lakes can pose a significant hazard to populations living nearby, if the volcanoes beneath them are still active. For example, Lake Nyos in Cameroon became known as the 'Killer Lake' in 1986, when it belched out a cloud of noxious gases that killed thousands of people and livestock within hours.

Mount Rainier, in the Cascade Range of Washington State, has a crater lake that poses another kind of danger: the possibility of a deadly mudflow, known as a lahar. The lake is high up on the mountain and overlaid by ice. Geologists have noticed that sulfurous gases from the volcano have been leaking through underground passages, forming sulfuric acid that is constantly eating away at the rock. Should the caldera wall collapse, the lake would drain – sending water, ice, rocks and mud gushing down the mountainside to deluge the towns below. There is evidence that this happened about 500 years ago, with a 25-tonne (28-ton) rock having been carried 50 km (30 miles) away in the lahar.

LIVING INSIDE THE CRATER

Surprisingly, there are many places where villages and even towns exist inside a volcanic crater. Set in the deep blue waters of the Aegean Sea is the Greek island of Santorini, popular with tourists for its sun-drenched beaches and quaint white-washed stone buildings. But the island's crescent shape is a clue to the inherent dangers of this place. Viewed from the air, it is clear that Santorini is part of a massive caldera, where the central part has flooded to form a lagoon. The island is all that remains after a massive volcanic eruption in approximately 1613 BC. Such large eruptions are thought to be infrequent, with the next one due in 10,000 years or so. However, the region is still active with occasional earthquakes and eruptions, the most recent in 1950, which emanated from the submerged central vent.

In Panama, El Valle de Antón is perhaps the oldest town situated within a caldera. It is thought that the region has been inhabited for the last 10,000 years, and the town currently has in excess of 3000 residents. The walls of the caldera reach up to 880 m (2890 ft), creating a natural enclosure. The enormous crater

▲
SANTORINI
The steep cliffs of the picturesque Greek island of Santorini rise up to 300 m (1000 ft) from sea level. They form part of the wall of a large flooded caldera that measures 12 km by 7 km (7 miles by 4 miles).

formed 35,000 years ago when the volcano erupted, and for several thousand years the region was covered by a vast lake until a fissure in the crater rim caused it to drain. Like most farmland in the shadow of a volcano, the soil is fertile – perhaps this is why the region has long supported settlements. Fortunately for the people of El Valle de Antón, the volcano has long been dormant.

THE VOLCANO BELT

Running around the edge of the Pacific Ocean is a region of exceptional seismic activity known as the Ring of Fire. It is an appropriate name, since 75 per cent of the world's volcanoes are located on it. Earthquakes are prevalent here, with 90 per cent of all tremors emanating from somewhere around the belt.

The reason why the Ring of Fire is so active is because it marks the zone of subduction where the Pacific Plate is plunging beneath the lighter continental plates that surround it. The oceanic plate melts as it sinks down into the mantle, and the magma finds its way up to the surface, eventually building up enough pressure to explode in an eruption. Some of the largest eruptions in recorded history have been from volcanoes on the Ring of Fire, including Tambora and Krakatau (1815 and 1883, Indonesia), Katmai (1912, Alaska) and Pinatubo (1991, Philippines). It is no coincidence either that most of the world's supervolcanoes are located there, too.

APOCALYPTIC ERUPTIONS

Geologists know that in the past Earth has been subjected to eruptions on a colossal scale thanks to enormous supervolcanoes. There is evidence of these super-eruptions all over Earth, the most recent occurring around 75,000 years ago at Lake Toba in Sumatra.

Super-eruptions have a Volcanic Explosivity Index (VEI) of 8, which is the top of the scale. It means that the volcano must have ejected at least 1000 cubic km (240 cubic miles) of ash and rocks – that's 1000 times more ejecta than the Mount St Helens eruption in 1980. Though such eruptions are rare, there is always the chance that one could happen again. If it did, you could expect worldwide devastation and chaos. It would mean that an area equivalent to the size of North America would be covered in ash. This would kill people and livestock, and inhibit agriculture in that region, while any ash travelling further afield in the atmosphere would block out the Sun and lower global temperatures for several years after the event. Again this would affect agriculture, leading to widespread famine.

With no super-eruptions in recorded history, geologists have had to base their predictions on evidence gathered from ash deposited by previous eruptions. They think that a super-eruption happens somewhere in the world every 100,000 years on average. With the last one occurring 75,000 years ago, it would seem we have 25,000 years to prepare. But there is no room for complacency, since the mechanism of these eruptions is poorly understood.

In response to understandable public concern, geologists have identified a handful of likely suspects that might be capable of a super-eruption. They include the United States' Yellowstone Caldera (Wyoming), Long Valley Caldera (California) and Valles Caldera (New Mexico), as well as Toba (Indonesia), Taupo (New Zealand) and the Phlegraean Fields (Italy). But it is all speculation, since there could be an as yet unidentified caldera ready to explode. Even if the timing and location were known, there is nothing we could do to halt an eruption. In the best-case scenario, there would be enough time to evacuate an area – but think of the logistics of evacuating a region the size of North America!

YELLOWSTONE'S TICKING TIME BOMB

Beneath Yellowstone National Park in Wyoming lies a supervolcano, capable of spewing out huge amounts of ash, rock and magma in a gigantic eruption. Currently, the volume of magma beneath Yellowstone is roughly the same as the volume of water in Lake Superior! Volcanologists are monitoring the volcano for signs of an imminent eruption, such as bulging, gaseous emissions and earthquakes. They believe that a major eruption is unlikely to happen any time soon, but cannot rule out the possibility. If it did, the consequences would be dire: around 80 per cent of the United States would be covered in a thick layer of ash, and global temperatures could drop by up to 15°C (27°F).

DOLINA GEIZEROV
Part of the Volcanoes of Kamchatka World Heritage Site, in Russia, Dolina Geizerov is the world's second-largest geyser field. The area also features hot springs and fumaroles.

Geysers and mud pools

When ground water comes into contact with hot magma, a variety of geothermal phenomena can result, from scalding geysers and mud pools to steaming fumaroles. The landscapes produced are often strange and dangerous, and they are commonly found near volcanoes and fault lines, where Earth's heat is closest to the surface.

G EYSERS ARE a natural marvel: heat from deep within Earth bursts forth in a fountain of boiling water. There are only a handful of places on Earth where you can see geysers, because they only occur when a set of very specific conditions is met. There must be a source of intense heat, such as a magma chamber, that is near Earth's surface; there also needs to be plentiful ground water; but perhaps the most important ingredient is an underground network of fissures and cracks in the bedrock that become pressure-tight water chambers, where superheated water and steam collect before being released in the characteristic showy display.

The first recorded geyser, and the one that has given its name to the phenomenon, is The Great Geysir in Iceland's Haukadalur Valley. *Geysir* means 'to gush', and that's exactly what The Great Geysir has done, at regular intervals, for several hundred years. Records begin to mention the geyser in 1294. In those days, people thought it had strange, supernatural origins, and they travelled from all over Europe to see it. Its eruptions were powerful, sometimes attaining a height of around 100 m (330 ft).

In 1846, a visiting German scientist, Robert Bunsen (the co-developer of the Bunsen burner), came up with the theory of how the geyser works. His theory remains the accepted model for all geysers. The sudden, forceful upsurging of scalding water is the result of geothermally heated water being trapped beneath a layer of cooler water that acts like a pressure cooker. The water at depth cannot move upwards and so reaches a temperature that is above boiling point. Eventually, bubbles of superheated steam power their way to the surface, pushing out the cooler water. With the pressure relieved, the heated water below expands suddenly and violently, producing the magnificent eruptions. The interval between eruptions depends on the rate at which water fills the underground chambers and how long it takes to heat up.

EXTREME FACT

There are only around 1000 active geysers in the world, and half of them are found in Wyoming's famous Yellowstone National Park.

The Great Geysir fell dormant in 1935 and then awoke in 2000. The changes in its activity, as with all geysers, are likely due to shifts in the local rocks, which affect the movement and collection of ground water. This is understandable in the seismically active regions where geysers commonly occur. Today, The Great Geysir still performs its gushing fountains, but they are much more infrequent and generally reach only 10 m (33 ft) in height; the nearby Strokkur geyser is more reliable, with eruptions of up to 20 m (65 ft) every four to eight minutes.

GEOTHERMAL WONDERLANDS

Dolina Geizerov (Valley of the Geysers) on the east coast of the Kamchatka Peninsula in Russia has more than 200 active geysers and numerous hot springs. Many of its geysers are unusual in that they emerge from the ground at haphazard angles, instead of

straight up, and over the years the mineral-rich water has created large terraces beneath the steaming outlets. Another impressive collection of geysers can be seen at El Tatio in Chile's Atacama Desert. It is the largest geyser field in the Southern Hemisphere, with numerous mud pots, hot pools and around 80 active geysers. The eruptions are frequent, but relatively small, with an average height of less than 1 m (3 ft).

Both these geyser fields are remarkable, but both pale in comparison with the geysers of Yellowstone National Park. Sprawling over the north-western corner of Wyoming (with a tiny portion in neighbouring Montana and Idaho), most of Yellowstone is in fact a vast caldera formed by a series of massive volcanic eruptions, the last of which occurred 640,000 years ago. A large magma chamber still seethes beneath the park and powers the region's numerous geothermal features. Yellowstone holds the record as the largest geyser field in the world, supporting around 10,000 geothermal features. Visitors to the park can see fumaroles, hot springs and mud pools as well as some of the most impressive geysers on the planet.

OLD FAITHFUL

The eruptions of Yellowstone's famous geyser Old Faithful are magnificent at any time of the day. Between 14,000 and 32,000 litres (3700 and 8400 gallons) of exceptionally hot water are expelled during each eruption.

STANDING TALL

Yellowstone's Steamboat Geyser is currently the tallest in the world, with its water jet sometimes reaching a height of 120 m (400 ft). The eruptions can last between four and 40 minutes, with a finale of huge steam clouds that give the geyser its name. It is a cone geyser, with its water jet emerging from a cone of rock deposit known as geyserite. Although the water jet can reach great heights, it is very unpredictable. On 31 July 2013, it erupted for the first time in eight years. In the past there have been intervals of 50 years between eruptions, and in 1964 it was particularly active with 29 eruptions.

Grand Geyser, as its name suggests, is the most spectacular of Yellowstone's predictable geysers. It is a fountain geyser – meaning that it erupts out of a pool of water – and its jet can attain a height of up to 60 m (200 ft). Eruptions happen every eight to 12 hours and last about 10 minutes. Visitors are advised to watch out for a second burst, as this is usually much more exciting than the first.

Yellowstone is also home to the most famous geyser of all: Old Faithful. Its name came from its frequency and reliability when it was first discovered in 1870. Even so, you can hardly set your watch by it: its eruptions occur every 35 to 120 minutes, with a current average interval of 74 minutes. Though some people say it is slowing down, this steady old cone geyser is as reliable as it ever was, and its eruptions still reach 30–55 m (100–180 ft) in height. After decades of study, park rangers can estimate the time of Old Faithful's next eruption by the duration of the last one. So, after a short eruption of say two minutes, a visitor would need to wait about an hour for the next one. But after a four-minute eruption, the wait could be 90 minutes.

HOT SPRINGS

Conditions for a hot spring to arise are not as specific as for geysers, and consequently hot springs are found all over the world – even in areas that are not generally considered seismically active, such as the famous spa at Bath in the United Kingdom. The formation of a hot spring begins when rainwater percolates down into the ground, through porous rocks. As it descends it picks up a variety of minerals, depending on the type of rock and soil through which it travels. The temperature of Earth increases with depth, so the deeper the water percolates, the hotter it becomes. The water then finds a rapid way back to the surface, often following a fault line in the rock, emerging as a hot spring. A rapid ascent is vital, otherwise the water would cool down before it reached the surface.

The temperature and chemical composition of the spring water depends on the path it has taken under the ground. When it reaches the surface, natural basins in the bedrock may capture the water, forming a hot pool. Some, like the springs in Bath, are a pleasant 34–37°C (93–99°F), while others are much hotter. The temperature of surface pools cannot go above 100°C (212°F) for long because that is the boiling point of water, when it turns into steam. But there are many pools that simmer at 97–98°C (207–208°F). These dangerously hot pools tend to be located within geologically active regions, such as Indonesia and Japan. They are far too hot to bathe in – you would be boiled alive.

INTO THE FRYING PAN

One of the world's most extraordinary geothermal landscapes is at Rotorua on New Zealand's North Island. The geothermal field is relatively recent, having formed after the eruption of nearby Mount Tarawera in 1886. Among its boiling mud pools, steaming vents and smoking craters is the world's largest hot pool, called Frying Pan Lake.

Surrounded by native forest, and billowing clouds of steam and noxious gases, the flat-bottomed lake does

A RAGING TOWER OF SCALDING BLACK WATER

The tallest and most ferocious geyser ever recorded was New Zealand's Waimangu Geyser, which became active in 1900. *Waimangu* is Maori for 'black water', and the geyser regularly formed an inky black tower over 150 m (500 ft) high. Occasionally the water topped 450 m (1500 ft), easily dwarfing Auckland's 328-m (1076-ft) Sky Tower. The geyser was part of the geothermal field that formed after the explosion of Mount Tarawera in 1886. A small tourist industry sprang up around the geyser, but the eruptions hurled scalding material with such ferocity that in 1903 four people were killed after venturing too close. In 1904 the geyser began to wane, and by the end of the year it had stopped.

PAMUKKALE

People have bathed in the warm waters of Pamukkale, in south-western Turkey, since the time of the Ancient Greeks and Romans. To protect its precious terraces, Pamukkale is now a World Heritage Site.

FOUNTAIN PAINT POT

The mud here in Yellowstone National Park is a mixture of clay minerals and silica particles. Heavy rain or snow often gives the mud a watery consistency, but an extended dry period thickens the mud.

indeed resemble a frying pan – and there is definitely something cooking. The lake sits in part of the crater formed by the 1886 eruption, and spans an area of almost 40,000 sq m (430,000 sq ft). It is fed by several acid springs, and the water temperature is around 50°C (122°F). The pool is too hot and acidic to swim in, but the Rotorua region has numerous spas that offer relaxing bathing.

There are also parks in the region that allow access to natural hot pools and mud pools, but the landscape is not without its dangers. Wardens in the various parks monitor the pools and fence off those that have become dangerously hot, but there is only so much they can do. In 2007 and 2008, a number of lone bathers died after inhaling hydrogen sulfide gas, leading to the local coroner advising that people always travel to the pools in pairs. Then in a tragic 2010 accident, a 10-year-old boy slipped into a fenced-off boiling mud pool. The pool was 75°C (167°F), and the boy suffered burns to 95 per cent of his body before dying a few days later.

Mud pools form where steam and gases, generated by the volcanic heat source below, rise to the surface beneath natural rainwater ponds. The acidic gases attack the surface rocks, forming clay, which mixes with the pond water to produce a bubbling, hot slurry, or mud pool. The consistency of the pools varies with rainfall, and the temperature can be boiling hot. The largest mud pool in New Zealand is at Wai-O-Tapu,

south of Rotorua. But the largest mud pool in the world is the Fountain Paint Pot in Yellowstone National Park. This stunning pool has a striking appearance in shades of red, brown and yellow, which is due to the oxidation of iron compounds in the clay.

CASTLES MADE FROM CALCIUM

Minerals dissolve more easily in hot water, but as the mineral-rich spring water cools down on reaching the surface, the minerals are deposited, sometimes creating breathtaking landscapes. Imagine a strange fairytale castle on the side of a cliff, with sparkling white ramparts and balconies. This is Pamukkale – which means 'cotton castle' – in Turkey's Cokelez Mountains. At the top of the cliff, numerous hot springs continuously spout water that has travelled through the local limestone bedrock, picking up calcium carbonate along the way. As the water trickles down the side of the cliff it evaporates, leaving its pure white calcium deposit in the form of travertine – the same substance that forms stalagmites and stalactites in caves.

Over the years the deposit has created a series of shallow basins, some protruding 20 m (65 ft) from the cliff face. The overall effect is magical, with the basins full of turquoise-blue water, overflowing past 'frozen' white cascades and puffy mounds that resemble cotton wool. Similar structures, called the Pink and White

Terraces, used to exist near Rotorua in New Zealand. Formed from precipitation of silicates and salt, the terraces were described as the 'eighth wonder of the world', but they were destroyed by the Mount Tarawera eruption of 1886.

LETTING OFF STEAM

Fumaroles are another common feature of geothermal fields. They are essentially vents that allow underground steam and gases to escape to the surface. Fumaroles can form temporarily, such as after an eruption when hot debris has been strewn down a volcano and the heat needs to escape. As the region cools, the fumaroles disappear. Others are more permanent because they sit above a geothermal heat source. They are similar to geysers, but they do not have large underground chambers of water.

Fumaroles are usually located on hillsides above the watertable, and the small amount of water that comes by is quickly flashed into steam and forcefully emitted alongside gases such as carbon dioxide, hydrogen chloride and hydrogen sulfide (with its characteristic rotten-egg smell). Yellowstone National Park has thousands of fumaroles of various sizes. Roaring Mountain, as its name would suggest, vents off a tall column of steam and gases with a loud hissing noise; Black Growler Steam Vent emits the hottest vapours in the park, reaching 138°C (280°F).

A LAND OF ACID AND HEAT

Dallol geothermal field in Ethiopia's Danakil Desert is a strong contender for the most hostile place on Earth. Numerous hot springs and fumaroles scatter the land, spurting almost pure acid and sulfurous fumes in temperatures that can reach 60°C (140°F) in the shade. The extreme heat (the region is considered one of the hottest places in the world) quickly evaporates any water, concentrating the acid and causing salts to be deposited in strange formations, including stacks, terraces and small egg-shaped structures.

The sulfur in the deposits gives the place an eerie appearance in luminous shades of yellow and green, while iron compounds add red and russet tones. The overall effect is a surreal landscape that looks like an alien planet. You wouldn't want to put a foot wrong in such an environment, since the salt encrustations can be just a few centimetres thick in places – with seething pools of almost pure sulfuric acid below. Coupled with its remote location, the inhospitable nature of the region probably explains why it is so little studied. Geologists who do venture there have to take breathing apparatus because even the air is saturated with sulfur.

The Dallol geothermal field sits within the Danakil Depression, a rift valley that is forming parallel to the Red Sea as the Nubian Plate (part of the African Plate)

WHERE TO SEE
MUD POOLS AND HOT SPRINGS

Rotorua on New Zealand's North Island lies on an ancient caldera within the Taupo Volcanic Zone. The main geothermal region is Whakarewarewa, which is famous for its bubbling mud pools (pictured), spouting geysers and cascading terraces. There are 500 hot springs and seven active geysers, the largest of which is Pohutu, which reaches over 20 m (65 ft) in height.

pulls away from the Arabian Plate. In the past, the Red Sea has flooded into the region and deposited sea water, which has evaporated and left behind thick bands of salt deposits. As the plates pull apart, fissures form in the rock and magma rises to the surface, providing a constant heat source for the many geothermal features and occasionally spewing out lava in effusive eruptions.

LIFE ON THE BOIL

You would think that nothing could survive in the extreme temperatures of hot springs, but several types of microorganisms have managed to adapt to the heat. Known as thermophiles (heat lovers), the microorganisms form mats around the edges of pools; they are often colourful, with different types adapted to different temperature ranges. This is clearly demonstrated in the Grand Prismatic Spring at Yellowstone National Park. A rainbow effect is seen around the pool, with rings of red, orange, yellow and green. The reddish organisms prefer the coolest water, while the yellow and green organisms have adapted to progressively hotter water (about 73°C [163°F]). None can live in the centre of the pool, which reaches 87°C (189°F) and stays a deep blue.

The microorganisms contain chlorophyll (green), with which they photosynthesise, and carotenoids (orange, yellow or red), which protect them from the

FUMAROLE

Ijen is a volcano on the Indonesian island of Java. A fumarole here ejects highly sulfurous gases, leaving behind a build-up of yellowish sulfur deposits that are mined by the local community.

DALLOL

The terraces at Dallol, in Ethiopia, may look similar to those at Turkey's Pamukkale, but you wouldn't want to take a dip here – the water is dangerously acidic, and there are ever-present toxic fumes.

ultraviolet rays of the Sun. The ratio of chlorophyll to carotenoid determines the organism's colour, and it changes with the seasons, with less carotenoids required in winter when the Sun is weakest. So for the best displays of colour, it is best to visit the Grand Prismatic Spring in summer.

These and other specially adapted thermophilic microorganisms have led to advances in biotechnology by providing the heat-tolerant enzymes needed for a technique known as Polymerase Chain Reactions. Such reactions are used in laboratories to magnify DNA. There are many applications for the technique, from forensic analysis to the diagnosis of disease. The organisms have also been of great interest to NASA scientists because they offer insights into the earliest life forms on Earth and give clues as to how life may survive on other planets.

ONSEN: A JAPANESE BATHING TRADITION

As Japan is a geologically active region, it is no surprise that there is an abundance of hot springs throughout the country. The Japanese have been making use of the free heat for thousands of years, developing a deeply embedded culture concerned with soaking in the steaming hot pools. The Japanese word for a hot spring is *onsen,* and the term also refers to the bathing houses and spas that have been built around the springs. There are thousands across Japan, from outdoor natural rock pools to large spa complexes with private tubs as well as single-sex and communal bathing. In all instances, the ritual is the same: the bather must strip naked and shower off any dirt and grime; once cleansed, the bather may enter the onsen and enjoy its restorative powers.

In addition to visiting onsen for relaxation purposes, Japanese people are convinced of the hot water's healing potential – much of which is associated with the types of minerals that it carries. Balneotherapy – the traditional treatment of disease with baths – is widely practised. In fact, there is evidence to show that regular bathing in hot pools can improve conditions such as rheumatism, neuralgia and skin diseases, depending on the precise composition of the water. After World War II, 50 hot-spring hospitals were established across the country.

Onsen are tightly regulated in Japan, and the water must contain at least one of 19 recognised minerals (such as sodium, magnesium, calcium, iron, sulfur or potassium). The mineral composition varies, and an onsen will usually describe itself according to the prominent mineral in the water, such as an iron onsen, sulfur onsen or hydrogen carbonate onsen.

Beppu, on the east coast of Japan's island of Kyushu, is a favourite onsen destination for holidaymakers. It is famous for its high concentration of onsen, many of

them having a sacred significance. In addition to the bathing pools, there are scalding hot pools known as the 'nine hells of Beppu'. Although bathing in them is impossible, all the pools have a striking appearance. Among them is Oniishibozu Jigoku (Shaven Monk's Head Hell), a boiling mud pool named after the appearance of large mud bubbles as they break the surface; Umi Jigoku (Sea Hell), a luminous turquoise pool; and Chinoike Jigoku (Blood Pond Hell), its deep red water the result of a high concentration of iron.

SOME LIKE IT HOT

Humans are not the only animals to make use of geothermal heat. In the Nagano Mountains on the island of Honshu, Japanese macaques have learned the benefits of a long, hot dip. Every winter since 1963, the monkeys have been making their way down from the steep-sided cliffs to the valley floor at Jigokudani onsen to immerse themselves in the hot water. It is thought that they discovered the relaxing 43°C (109°F) water when a female went in after some food thrown there by a keeper. She came back and was soon joined by other members of the group. Now it is a yearly spectacle and a chance for the monkeys to escape the bitterly cold winter climate. The area is very remote, but for the intrepid tourists who do make it to the park in winter, there is the unusual sight of bathing monkeys, who look oddly human as they hang their limbs out of the pools and sit, red-faced, enjoying the heat.

Scrubfowls in the Pokili Wildlife Management Area of Papua New Guinea have also learned how to use Earth's heat. Nearby Mount Pago fuels the region's geothermal field, and the birds have discovered that they can dig nests in the hot ground in which to incubate their eggs. In Sulawesi, Indonesia, another geothermally active area, the maleo does the same thing. This strategy means that the birds do not have to sit on the nest, allowing them the freedom to forage. Once buried, the eggs need no further parental input. The chicks develop large claws that they use to break out of their shell and dig their way out of the nest.

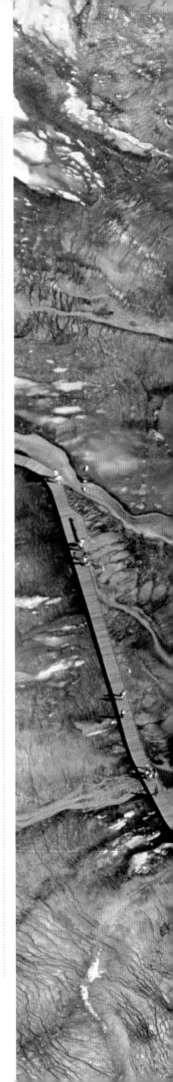

MONKEY MAGIC
Japanese macaques (also known as snow monkeys) live in an exceptionally cold region – the average winter temperature here is just -10°C (14°F). Some – but not all! – monkeys like to warm up in the waters of Jigokudani onsen, and they sit in the hot spring for up to two hours each day.

Sinkholes and landslides

We think of the ground beneath our feet as being solid, but this is not always the case. Subtle processes can eat away at bedrock or change the stability of a slope, leading to a sudden and catastrophic failure. The sinkholes, landslides and mudflows that result often have disastrous consequences.

I T WAS LATE in the evening on 12 August 2013, when holidaymakers staying at the Summer Bay Resort in Florida became concerned about a series of loud crashes and bangs. Tracing the noise to windows that were buckling and breaking, hotel staff decided to evacuate the building. It was lucky that they did, for just half an hour later the central part of the building collapsed as the ground beneath it simply fell away. Over the course of five hours, stunned guests watched in horror as around a third of the resort slipped into a sinkhole some 30 m (100 ft) wide and at least 5 m (16 ft) deep. This was just the latest in a series of sinkhole collapses in Florida. In March of that year, a sinkhole had opened up beneath a house in Tampa, swallowing a man who was asleep in bed. His body was never recovered.

Florida is prone to sinkholes because of its underlying geology: it sits on a bed of limestone, a sedimentary rock formed from the compacted remains of shells and microskeletons deposited on an ancient seabed millions of years ago. Though hard and tough like any other rock, it is more soluble than most and can be gradually dissolved by the weak acids found in rain and ground water. Over time, the gradual dissolution of the limestone forms voids and caverns beneath the ground.

ACID ATTACK

As rain falls through the atmosphere, it absorbs enough carbon dioxide to make a weak solution of carbonic acid. Limestone comprises a series of layers ('strata'), which normally has cracks and lines of weakness – and these are the first areas to be attacked by the acidic water. Slowly but surely, the rock is eaten away; cracks widen, and potholes and shafts form. Overland streams may seem to 'disappear' as they plunge down into a gully cut through the limestone and then flow through an underground network of caves.

?

EXTREME FACT
According to the British Geological Survey (BGS), landslides in the United Kingdom are on the increase – a trend also seen around the world that may be linked to climate change.

❱❱
FLORIDA
Located only a few minutes from Walt Disney World, the Summer Bay Resort was a popular place for families to stay – until it succumbed to one of the many sinkholes that have recently opened up in the Florida landscape.

Sinkholes arise when limestone dissolves underground, leaving a large chamber beneath a thin 'roof'. Anything built on such a structure is vulnerable, as the ground beneath can collapse without warning. In Florida, the limestone is overlain by clay-rich topsoil that has some natural cohesion. This means that it will hold together for a time, even though there is a gaping hole beneath it. But should there be a change in the watertable (due to heavy rainfall or as a result of overextraction from aquifers), the clay can loosen and fall into the void, taking any buildings with it. The trouble is knowing where these holes are forming. Often the first sign is when you come home to find your house is in a hole.

KARST LANDSCAPES

Terrain that has been created by the dissolution of soluble rocks such as limestone is known as karst. Some of the largest sinkholes in the world are found in karst landscapes, especially in China. If you ever wanted to hide the Empire State Building, Xiaozhai Tiankeng (Heavenly Pit) in Chongqing province would be an ideal place. Thought to be the world's deepest sinkhole, at 662 m (2172 ft), Xiaozhai Tiankeng has a width of about 600 m (2000 ft) at the top that narrows to 300 m (1000 ft) across at its base – the Empire State Building would easily fit inside, with over 200 m (650 ft) to spare.

Another deep sinkhole is found in neighbouring Guangxi province. Dashiwei Tiankeng is 400–600 m (1300–2000 ft) across and 613 m (2011 ft) deep. Both

GREAT BLUE HOLE
Belize's picturesque sinkhole is situated in the middle of the Lighthouse Reef. Jacques-Yves Cousteau named it as one of the world's top dive sites.

Dashiwei Tiankeng and Xiaozhai Tiankeng harbour unique communities of plants, which have sprung up from the thick layers of debris that have fallen into the sinkholes. Isolated by the steep walls for thousands of years, the plants include many rare and unique species. Amazingly, these special oases of life remained largely unexplored until the 1990s.

There are other stunning examples of karst topography throughout the world, including the 500-m (1650-ft) deep Minyé sinkhole on the island of New Britain, Papua New Guinea, and the impressive series of sinkholes in Tamaulipas, Mexico, known as the Sistema Zacatón. Here, acidic water that has been heated by volcanoes has helped to create around 20 water-filled sinkholes, the most impressive being El Zacatón – the world's deepest water-filled sinkhole, at 339 m (1112 ft).

Yet another surprising landscape can be seen (from the air) over Venezuela's Sarisariñama tepui. The steep-sided tabletop mountain is covered in lush greenery, apart from a series of large sinkholes that punctuate the surface as though a giant has punched holes through the jungle deep into the rock. These sinkholes are unique because they have formed in sandstone, rather than limestone.

IK KIL CENOTE
Not far from the important Mayan site of Chichen Itza, Mexico, this 60-m (200-ft) wide sinkhole is popular with swimmers, who share the cool and refreshing water with a school of friendly black catfish.

MAYAN TREASURE TROVES

The water-filled sinkholes of Mexico's Yucatán Peninsula are called cenotes. They were important to the ancient Mayans because they were the region's only sources of fresh water. The Mayans believed that Chac, the god of rain and sustainer of life, lived within the deep pools, and they would offer ritual sacrifices there. Archaeologists have retrieved important artefacts from numerous sinkholes in the region, including items made from jade, gold and copper. They have also found skeletons with marks denoting human sacrifice. The cenotes are popular with divers, and archaeologists fear that many finds may already have been removed illegally from the ancient sites.

The Caribbean islands are underlain by limestone reefs; consequently, they are prone to sinkholes, too. The most notable is the giant underwater sinkhole near Belize known as the Great Blue Hole. Almost perfectly circular, it resembles a giant eye with a dark centre thanks to the deep hole, which plunges 124 m (407 ft) into the limestone beneath.

LEAKAGE AND LIQUEFACTION

Sinkholes can result from human activities, such as the collapse of mine shafts and the overextraction of ground water, and sometimes they can form after chronic leakage from underground sewers or stormwater pipes. Two astonishingly large holes that formed under Guatemala City are thought to be at least partly due to water leaking from sewage pipes as well as the effects of poor drainage after heavy rain. These holes are not true sinkholes because they did not occur in soluble bedrock, although the way they developed is similar. The 'piping pseudokarsts', as they are known, formed as leaking water below ground gradually washed away the volcanic ash and debris on which the city is built. The first collapse in 2007 took only three lives, while the second in 2010 killed around 15 people; both resulted in widespread evacuation.

The violent vibrations of earthquakes are the source of another type of sinkhole that can swallow cars and topple buildings. In short, liquefaction is when soil behaves like a liquid – and you can imagine what that means for a building's foundations. When saturated sandy or silty soil is vibrated violently, as happens in an earthquake, the particles lose their cohesiveness and any water in the soil is forced up through them

to form a sloppy mush. Water continues up to the surface, and is followed by the silt, forming grey mud mounds. Roads often turn into muddy rivers, and anyone foolish enough to try to drive their car through the mud risks falling bonnet first into a hidden sinkhole.

LAND ON THE MOVE

The largest landslide ever witnessed took place on 18 May 1980, when the northern flank of Mount St Helens in Washington State headed downslope. Triggered by a magnitude 5.1 earthquake, the landslide involved the removal of about 3.7 cubic km (almost 1 cubic mile) of rock – and the subsequent release of pressure allowed magma and gases that had been building within the volcano to blow. Just 30 seconds after the landslide the volcano erupted, sending pyroclastic flows down the volcano to add to the destruction caused by the landslide. According to the US Geological Survey (USGS), the landslide destroyed 250 homes, 47 bridges, 24 km (15 miles) of railway track and nearly 300 km (185 miles) of highway. The rock and debris thundered down the mountain at around 25 km/h (16 mph) – impossible to outrun, though there were reports of people who managed to drive away from the oncoming flow. Though massive, the landslide took only 57 lives because the volcano had given many warning signs and the mountain had been mostly evacuated.

In December 1920, the people living in the Ningxia province of China were not so lucky, when a magnitude 7.8 earthquake in Haiyuan County set off a series of devastating landslides. The shaking went on for an excruciating 10 minutes, setting loose an area of 50,000 sq km (19,000 sq miles). The world's deadliest landslides to date, they buried whole villages and claimed over 100,000 lives. Landslides are commonly

NEW ZEALAND
Liquefaction caused much of the damage in the Christchurch earthquakes of 2010 and 2011. The grey mud created sinkholes under roads that sucked down any cars in their vicinity.

GUATEMALA
The infamous hole that suddenly formed in Guatemala City on 31 May 2010 measured 20 m (65 ft) across, and 30 m (100 ft) deep. When it collapsed, it took a three-storey building with it.

VENEZUELA
The seaside city of Caraballeda suffered some of the worst damage during the 1999 landslides. Deposits of boulder-strewn debris were up to 6 m (20 ft) deep in some places.

associated with earthquakes, but they have other triggers, too. A landslide occurs when a slope becomes unstable, and this depends on the material in the slope and its steepness. Heavy rainfall, floods and rapid snowmelt can trigger landslides, as can mismanagement of the land through deforestation or poor drainage.

A STEEP PRICE TO PAY

When a precarious glacier collapsed at the top of Mount Huascarán – the tallest peak in the Peruvian section of the Andes – in 1962, it unleashed a torrent of ice, rock and debris that completely destroyed the village of Ranrahirca and killed over 4000 people. Heavy rain was the trigger for the devastating landslides in the Vargas State of Venezuela in December 1999. Over three days, a storm dumped 1000 mm (40 in) of rain over the region, causing thousands of landslides along the coast and an estimated 30,000 deaths. The damage to infrastructure and buildings was enormous, leaving a repair bill of US$2 billion.

Even if they don't claim lives, landslides are always costly – houses, roads and more need to be rebuilt, and there is also the expense of digging out the mud, rock and debris and carting it away. One of the costliest individual landslides ever measured was the April 1983 event in the town of Thistle, Utah. The landslide was triggered by exceptionally high rainfall in the region, and as the land slumped it dammed up the nearby Spanish Fork River, forming a lake. The huge economic loss, estimated in excess of US$688 million, was due to the fact that the landslide cut off two major highways and the main cross-continental railway line. Large expenses were incurred by industries that relied on these three thoroughfares, and there were additional financial tolls involved in rerouting the roads and building a tunnel for the railway line to avoid the landslide and lake.

LAHARS: THE DEADLIEST MUDFLOWS

Landslides and mudflows caused by torrential rain or shattering earthquakes are bad enough – yet there is an even worse kind of mudflow produced by volcanic eruptions. Known as lahars, the boiling mudflows are created when the hot gases, rock and ash from an erupting volcano melt the snow and ice at the summit. The lahars rush down the mountainside at a frightening speed, stripping vegetation and picking up soil and large boulders on the way. They soon become an unstoppable and deadly force.

Nevado del Ruiz is a stratovolcano in the Cordillera Central region of the Colombian Andes. Standing 5389 m (17,680 ft) tall, its peak is continually shrouded in a thick covering of snow. The November 1985 eruption of the volcano had a modest Volcanic Explosivity Index (VEI) of 3, yet it sent more than 25,000 people to their deaths.

PINATUBO LAHAR
In the first few years after the 1991 eruption of Mount Pinatubo, in the Philippines, enough mud and debris washed down the mountainside during the annual monsoon season to fill 300 million tip-trucks.

The eruption owes its fatal consequences to the lahars that came down the mountainside at 60 km/h (40 mph). By the time the mudflows had travelled through some of the narrow river valleys on either side of the volcano, they were around 50 m (160 ft) deep and carrying a lethal cargo of boulders, trees and other debris. First to succumb was the town of Chinchiná to the west, where 2000 people perished, and then followed Armero, located to the east. Tragically, Armero's inhabitants had been told by officials to stay put, and while a few did escape to higher ground, at least 20,000 of them remained in their houses – and died there, encased in a river of grey mud.

Though most lahars are associated with an eruption, they can continue years after the blast as seasonal rains wash deposited ash and pumice down into the surrounding settlements. A heartbreaking example is Mount Pinatubo in the Philippines. The volcano famously erupted in 1991, sending a gigantic plume of ash into the air that was large enough to alter the world's climate. But for the people who lived near the mountain the misery would continue for years, as every monsoon season, from May to October, brought with it thick torrents of 'secondary lahars' to bury their houses. Composed of fine ash, the lahars had the consistency of wet cement, and would dry as hard and heavy as concrete. By 1997, the secondary mudflows had destroyed more than 100,000 homes. With few resources, the villagers could do little more than rebuild their homes on top of their buried houses.

MOVING A MOUNTAIN

Landslides from prehistoric times make some of our modern-day landslides look tiny by comparison. Heart Mountain in Wyoming is a remnant of a huge landslide that took place around 50 million years ago. Geologists' suspicions were aroused when they took samples of rock from Heart Mountain and found that they were older than the rock that sits beneath it.

Further investigation revealed that the mountain was once part of a large slab of limestone, several kilometres thick, 10–20 km (6–12 miles) wide and more than 55 km (34 miles) long, that detached itself and slid downslope, breaking into several pieces. For a while geologists were puzzled about how the mass could have moved tens of kilometres along a fault line that is on an incline of less than 2 degrees. The answer could be down to the sheer weight of the mountain. In 2005, geologists came up with the theory that when the rock started to move, the inevitable friction heated up the limestone, releasing carbon dioxide that – under the extreme heat and pressure – formed a fluid and lubricated the passage of the rock.

Some of the largest landslides on Earth have taken place under the ocean. The biggest is thought to be the Agulhas landslide off the coast of South Africa. Geologists believe that it comprises a volume of some 20,000 cubic km (4800 cubic miles), with a run-out distance of over 140 km (90 miles). Other significant submarine landslides include the Storegga Slides in the Norwegian Sea. There is evidence of three large landslides in the region; the last one occurred around 8000 years ago, when a colossal 3500 cubic km (840 cubic miles) of sediment slipped from the edge of the continental shelf. It would have caused a large tsunami that affected anyone living along the west coast of Norway, the east coast of Scotland, the Shetland Islands and the Faroe Islands. Geologists are uncertain about the triggers for such massive events, but they think it may be earthquakes or the release of gas hydrates from within the sediment.

LANDSLIDE IN THE MAKING

While geologists continue to investigate the large landslides of the past, they are keeping a watchful eye on a site in the Canary Islands where a significantly large landslide could be on the cards. Cumbre Vieja is a volcano on the island of La Palma. In the year 2000, geologists identified that the western flank of the volcano is unstable, and should there be an eruption it will likely slide into the sea.

With a volume of around 500 cubic km (120 cubic miles), the landslide would generate a megatsunami, the effects of which would be felt throughout the Atlantic. A 600-m (2000-ft) wave would deluge the coast of Africa within an hour, while those on the eastern seaboard of the United States would have six hours in which to brace themselves for the onslaught. Needless to say, it would be a devastating event, with thousands of lives lost and destruction on an unprecedented scale. Controversy remains, however, as to whether the flank of the volcano will fail suddenly, causing the megatsunami, or will slip gradually into the sea with less lethal consequences. Only time will tell.

EXTREME LAND

Nearly a third of the world's surface is covered by land. It first formed over 4 billion years ago, and powerful forces have been reshaping it ever since – creating the incredible variety of landforms that exist today. Remote islands, giant dunes, soaring mountains and crystal-packed caves – these are just some of the record-breaking features that make Earth's surface a place of such astonishing extremes. Dry land holds many records in the living world as well. Life may have started in the oceans, but land habitats are home to by far the most species, including the tallest, heaviest and oldest living things that have ever existed on Earth.

BAMBOO FOREST
In Japan, bamboo is a symbol of strength and prosperity. It is often planted en masse around sacred places as a protection against evil.

Mountains and cliffs

Revered and feared throughout the ages, mountains and cliffs have a magnetic attraction for anyone seeking the ultimate in extremes. The world's highest peaks are well documented, but cliffs are harder to classify – many are in remote regions, and some of the biggest may still be awaiting discovery.

T HERE IS NO scientific dividing line between mountains and hills, and no official figure for the total number of mountains on Earth. However, like people, mountains tend to stick together: some are solitary, but far more belong to mountain chains. Every continent has its mountains, but three great chains in Asia – the Himalayas, the Karakoram and the Hindu Kush – include nearly all of the 100 highest peaks in the world. These chains were formed when India collided with Asia about 50 million years ago, squeezing dry the ancient Tethys Sea. In the collision, seabed rocks were crushed and forced upwards, like the crumpled wreckage of a crashed car. Today, that wreckage towers over the low-lying plains of southern Asia, and its jagged peaks are still growing at a rate of over 1 cm (²/₅ in) per year.

THE DEATH ZONE

Fourteen of the world's top 100 mountains soar into the 'Death Zone', the name given by climbers to altitudes above 8000 m (26,000 ft). Here, atmospheric pressure is only a third of the value at sea level, so it takes three lungfuls of air to deliver the same amount of oxygen as a single one lower down. Muscles act more slowly, thinking becomes confused, and every step holds the potential for disaster if a misjudged foothold gives way. Humans can survive in the Death Zone, but without supplementary oxygen, every hour is a calculated risk. Success on the way up does not guarantee a safe descent; after reaching a summit in the Death Zone, many climbers die on their way down.

The 14 Death Zone mountains each have their own character and mood. Mount Everest, the world's highest land-based mountain, stretches furthest into the zone, with its summit at 8848 m (29,029 ft). The summit was first reached in 1953, although the first ascent without extra oxygen was not until 1978. Today, several hundred mountaineers make the ascent each year, creating perilous bottlenecks during the Himalayan 'weather window' – the few weeks each spring before heavy snowstorms signal the start of the annual monsoon. Mount Everest's peak lies on the world's highest

PERILOUS K2
Expedition members climb a blustery ridge on the Chinese side of K2, the most hazardous route to the summit.

border, between China and Nepal. Even in spring, the temperature here can be colder than a kitchen freezer, and the peak is often raked by hurricane-force winds. The average stay at the summit is less than 30 minutes, although in 1999 a Nepalese Sherpa managed to stay here for a record-breaking 21 hours.

Notorious for its extreme weather and avalanches, K2 is the world's second-highest mountain, with an official height of 8611 m (28,251 ft). Named after a survey label on a nineteenth-century map, it is the highest point in the Karakoram chain, and one of the world's most hazardous climbs. However, the most treacherous of all 14 'eight-thousanders' is Annapurna I, the tallest of a cluster of peaks in the Himalayas of Nepal. Measuring 8091 m (26,545 ft), it is the tenth-highest mountain in the world, and was first climbed in 1950 – the first time that the Death Zone had been breached. The two climbers who reached the summit both survived, but many others have not been so lucky. Out of every 10 climbers that have scaled Annapurna I, four have died in the attempt.

ANCIENT PEAKS

Mountains look timeless, but appearances can be deceiving: some chains – like the Himalayas – are in their first flush of youth, while others are extremely

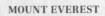

EXTREME FACT

High up on Mount Everest, there are bands of limestone six times older than the rest of Everest. Some of them contain fossilised seashells – proof that the limestone was once part of an ancient seabed.

▲

**BARBERTON
MOUNTAIN LAND**

*Properly known as the
Barberton Supergroup
geological formation,
this important region
in South Africa has
been nominated for
inclusion on the
UNESCO World
Heritage List.*

▶▎

**APPALACHIAN
MOUNTAINS**

*This ancient mountain
range runs for about
2400 km (1500 miles)
down the east coast
of North America,
from Newfoundland
in Canada to
Alabama in the
United States.*

old. The world's oldest rock formations are in northern
Canada and south-western Greenland, but the oldest
intact mountain range is thought to be the Barberton
Mountain Land in South Africa, a group of grass-covered
peaks that date back about 3.5 billion years.

If the planet's history could be squeezed into 24 hours,
the Barberton range would appear at about 5.20 am –
long before any of the continents that exist today. These
modest-looking mountains are no more than 1800 m
(5900 ft) high, but, in addition to their great age, they
have another claim to fame: their rocks harbour fossil
bacteria that are among the earliest known signs of life
on Earth. These ancient microbes date back 3.2 billion
years, and are so small that 2000 of them would only
just stretch across a full stop. However, despite their
simple structure, they had everything it took to survive,
to grow and, most importantly of all, to reproduce.

MOUNTAINS OLD AND NEW

A colossal gap in time separates Barberton's ultra-
ancient mountains from ones in their middle age.
The Appalachian Mountains, in present-day North
America, erupted into life about 460 million years ago,
or about 9.30 pm on Earth's 24-hour clock. Created by
the collision of two tectonic plates, they started out as
towering volcanoes, before being worn away into the
rounded contours that they have now. Australia's Great

EXTREME TOP 10
HIGHEST MOUNTAINS ON LAND

1 MOUNT EVEREST (NEPAL, CHINA)
8848 M (29,029 FT)

2 K2 (PAKISTAN, CHINA)
8611 M (28,251 FT)

3 KANGCHENJUNGA (NEPAL, INDIA)
8586 M (28,169 FT)

4 LHOTSE (NEPAL, CHINA)
8516 M (27,940 FT)

5 MAKALU (NEPAL, CHINA)
8485 M (27,838 FT)

6 CHO OYU (NEPAL, CHINA)
8188 M (26,864 FT)

7 DHAULAGIRI I (NEPAL)
8167 M (26,795 FT)

8 MANASLU (NEPAL)
8163 M (26,781 FT)

9 NANGA PARBAT (PAKISTAN)
8126 M (26,660 FT)

10 ANNAPURNA I (NEPAL)
8091 M (26,545 FT)

Dividing Range came into being about 300 million years ago, or roughly 10.20 pm, followed closely by Russia's Urals, located at the boundary between Europe and northern Asia.

As chance would have it, all these ranges run roughly north to south, giving them a wide range of different climates. Mount Washington, in the northern reaches of the Appalachians, is credited as having the world's worst weather, through a combination of icy temperatures and high winds. On 12 April 1934, this mountain entered the record books with the highest wind speed ever measured outside a tornado – 372 km/h (231 mph). It held the record for over 60 years, until a 1996 Australian cyclone snatched it with a wind speed of 408 km/h (254 mph).

Compared with these mature mountains, the world's biggest and most imposing chains are newcomers on the scene. In places, North America's Rocky Mountains date back to about 80 million years. The European Alps and Himalayas formed even more recently, as the final 20 minutes of Earth's 24-hour clock ticked away. These last two ranges are still growing fast – in the next 50 million years, Himalayan-size peaks could develop in Europe, dwarfing the towering alpine summits that exist today.

BLASTS FROM THE PAST

Earth's moving tectonic plates have created most of the world's mountain chains. But scattered across the globe – sometimes far from plate boundaries – Earth's newest peaks blast their way into the record books. Tallest of all is Mauna Kea, one of the volcanoes on Hawaii's Big Island, which has been in a constant state of eruption for most of the last million years.

Mauna Kea began life as a volcanic vent on the Pacific Ocean seabed. Since then, it has not only managed to rise almost 6000 m (19,700 ft) to reach sea level, but it has also grown by a further 4205 m (13,796 ft). Its total height is now well over 10,000 m (33,000 ft) – far higher than Mount Everest, and the greatest base-to-summit height of any mountain on Earth. Mauna Kea has achieved this at an average rate of 1 m (3 ft) per century, although this figure disguises bursts of even faster growth when it was young. Although this enormous volcanic mountain last erupted nearly 5000 years ago, it is currently classified as dormant.

With its gentle slope, Mauna Kea is a mountain to be walked up rather than climbed. Bizarrely, it is one of the few mountains on Earth with specific warnings for scuba divers: hiking up it within 24 hours of diving can bring on a dangerous attack of decompression sickness, better known as the 'bends'.

Mount Kilimanjaro – another volcanic giant – soars way above the plains of Tanzania, where its famous snow-clad summit seems to float above the clouds. This emblem of Africa started to form about 750,000 years

GIANT GROUNDSELS
Dendrosenecio kilimanjari *is the species of giant groundsel that is found on Mount Kilimanjaro, in Tanzania. These plants grow more branched with age.*

EUROPEAN ALPS
Two male Alpine ibex lock horns – with a female watching – in front of the Mer de Glace, one of the longest glaciers in the French Alps at 7 km (4 miles) in length.

MOUNT KILIMANJARO
The mountain's well-known snowy covering is rapidly diminishing – about 80 per cent has been lost in the last century. It could be ice-free in as little as 20 years.

ago, and it is currently 5895 m (19,341 ft) high. Its complete isolation makes it the tallest freestanding land-based mountain in the world. Despite being close to the Equator, Mount Kilimanjaro is high enough to have glaciers – although in today's warming climate, their ice is rapidly melting away.

GARDENS IN THE SKY

Despite the colossal destruction that they can cause, volcanoes are often much more fertile than other mountains. Their ash is rich in mineral nutrients, which is why their slopes are often covered with thick vegetation. Isolated volcanoes like Mauna Kea and Mount Kilimanjaro have their own distinctive plant life, including giant versions of plants that normally grow knee-high. They include silverswords, which grow on volcanic cinders in the Hawaiian Islands, and Mount Kilimanjaro's giant groundsels, which look like cabbages perched on poles. These mountain-proof plants can grow at altitudes of over 3000 m (10,000 ft), where less specialised species would struggle to survive.

Silverswords get their name from their rosette of sharply pointed leaves, which are covered in silvery hairs. The hairs protect the leaves from the night-time cold, and they stop the plant from losing too much water to the dry air. They also work like a sunscreen, fending off harmful ultraviolet light. Giant groundsels have a different way of preserving themselves. Their leaves open up in the morning, and close again at dusk. This protects them from Mount Kilimanjaro's challenging climate, which is like summer during the day, and winter after dark.

THE HIGHEST TOWN ON EARTH

Asia's mountains hold most of the world's altitude records, but they fall well short of being the longest mountain range on Earth. That title – on land at least –

MACHU PICCHU

Located on an Andean ridge around 2400 metres (7900 ft) above sea level in Peru, Machu Picchu stands as testament to the engineering brilliance of the Incas. Every enormous block of stone was hand cut and carried up the mountainside, and most buildings were constructed without mortar – the blocks were carved to fit together perfectly.

is held by South America's Andes, which stretch over 7200 km (4500 miles) from Colombia to the tip of Tierra del Fuego. No other mountain range has such a variety of landscapes, including tropical forests, hyper-arid deserts, ice fields and sky-high plateaus. Famous as the home of the Incas, the Andes concealed the secret Incan stronghold of Machu Picchu until American archaeologist Hiram Bingham rediscovered it in 1911.

The highest Andean peak, Aconcagua in Argentina, attracts climbers from around the world. However, in the Andes, you don't have to be a mountaineer to be high up. The inhabitants of the world's highest capital city, La Paz in Bolivia, live and work at an altitude of up to 4100 m (13,500 ft) – which can leave visiting tourists panting for breath. The Andes are also the setting for the world's highest permanent settlement, a town called La Rinconada in Peru. La Rinconada lies at approximately 5100 m (16,700 ft), which is only slightly lower than the base camps at Mount Everest. At these heights, new arrivals often fall victim to acute altitude sickness, known locally as *soroche*. In the Andes, the traditional treatment is tea made from coca leaves – a brew that dates back to Incan times.

La Rinconada is far too high for farming, but it holds a much greater attraction – the chance of finding gold. For over 500 years, hard-working miners have carved tunnels under the Andes' glacial ice here, and in the sixteenth century, one writer reported chunks of gold being unearthed that were as large as a human head.

LONGEST MOUNTAIN CHAIN

The Andes make up the longest mountain chain on land, but they are dwarfed by the Mid-Oceanic Ridge – a winding chain of submerged mountains that stretches around the world. The Mid-Oceanic Ridge is about 65,000 km (40,000 miles) long, or just over 1½ times the circumference of Earth. The Atlantic section of the ridge was the first to be discovered: in the 1850s, engineers laying the first transatlantic cable noticed that the ocean was shallower in the middle than on either side. The presence of undersea mountains was confirmed in the 1950s, when the floor of the Atlantic was surveyed for the first time.

Today, the precious yellow metal is found only in small flecks, but thousands of miners still brave the thin air, hoping to strike it rich.

The Andes also hold another important record: the world's highest point on land, when measured in a direct line from the centre of Earth. That point is on the tallest of four major summits of Mount Chimborazo, a huge dormant volcano that is the highest mountain

in Ecuador. The summit known as Whymper has an altitude of 6310 m (20,702 ft), which is about 2500 m (8200 ft) lower than the summit of Mount Everest. However, unlike Mount Everest, this Andean mountain is almost on the Equator – a region where Earth bulges outwards as it spins. This equatorial bulge puts Mount Chimborazo's summit 6384 km (3967 miles) from Earth's centre, which is about 2 km (1¼ miles) further than Mount Everest's summit.

MOUNTAIN MAMMALS

Animals have their own ways of surviving at extreme altitude, with its mix of thin air, intense sunshine and bone-chilling night-time cold. In the Andes, herds of llamas roam the Altiplano, or central plateau – a region bigger than New Zealand, with an average height of nearly 4000 m (13,000 ft). Distant relatives of camels, llamas have dense wool that keeps out the cold, and blood that is much better at taking up oxygen compared with animals that live lower down.

Llamas are domesticated animals that have long been raised for their meat and wool, but the smaller and more graceful vicuña is nearly always wild. In Peru, these shy and easily startled animals range almost as far as the 5500-m (18,000-ft) mark – almost 1000 m (3300 ft) higher than the North American mountain goat, and half the standard cruising altitude of commercial aircraft. Where most mammals would

be left fighting for breath, vicuñas trot rapidly over the dry Andean grassland without a problem.

Despite their talent for the high life, vicuñas are beaten into second place by the Himalayan yak – an ultra-hardy grazer that can weigh half as much as a small family car. Roaming the Himalayas and the Tibetan plateau further north, yaks occasionally live as high as 6000 m (20,000 ft), although the iciness of winter brings them further down. With their long coat and thick, wrap-around layer of body fat, they can cope with temperatures far below freezing, but they start to suffer from heat stress if the thermometer climbs above a modest 15°C (59°F).

VICUNAS

MOUNTAIN LIFE

*Animals and birds have developed a range
of useful adaptations to help them cope with
the cold and rugged nature of mountain
environments, from specialised hooves
and thick coats to enlarged hearts
and enhanced lung capacities.*

YAK

CONDOR

HIGH FLIERS

Birds have a natural advantage in living high up, because their lungs are extremely efficient and their feathers are superb protection against the cold. In 1973, an African Rüppell's griffon vulture collided with a plane at 11,300 m (37,000 ft), setting an altitude record over 1¼ times the height of Mount Everest. This unlucky accident may have been a freak, but swans have sometimes been seen at nearly 9000 m (29,500 ft), migrating high above the sea.

In the Andes, condors live at elevations of up to 5000 m (16,400 ft), where they nest on remote mountain ledges. In the Himalayas, bar-headed geese regularly migrate over high mountain passes, climbing to nearly 6500 m (21,300 ft) and clearing the entire mountain range in as little as eight hours. These hardy migrants are often quoted as the bird world's highest fliers, but sightings show that the lammergeier goes higher still.

The lammergeier is a true mountain bird, with a unique way of life. Instead of feeding on dead flesh, it grabs large bones in its talons, flies into the air and then drops the bones on rocks far below. With luck, the bones then shatter, letting the vulture feed on the marrow inside. Lammergeiers live in mountain ranges from the European Alps as far as north-eastern China, and some birdwatchers have reported seeing them on Mount Everest at 7500 m (24,600 ft).

This eye-popping altitude is probably the upper limit for animals with backbones, but ones without them – or invertebrates – may sometimes end up higher still. In summer, strong updraughts suck tiny flying insects high into the sky, sprinkling some of them on the tallest mountain peaks. Spiders can also achieve lift-off – instead of flying, they drift at the end of long strands of silk. In 1924, two species were found at 6700 m (22,000 ft) on Mount Everest, and others may even survive higher up.

MIGHTY MONOLITHS

Climb up a typical mountain, and the chances are you'll notice several different types of rock. Monoliths are different: they are made of a single kind of rock, in an enormous and imposing mass. The largest and most famous of these 'island mountains' is Australia's Uluru, or Ayers Rock, which rises to a height of 348 m (1142 ft) above a flat and almost featureless plain. Made from hard, terracotta-like sandstone, it changes hue as the day wears on – at sunrise it is deep fiery red, but it can look almost violet when the sun sets.

Uluru's iron-rich sandstone is arranged in parallel layers, tipped up by almost 90 degrees so that they dive vertically into the ground. Beneath the surface, they form part of a rock layer up to 5 km (3 miles) deep, so most of this landmark is actually buried out of sight.

Monoliths also include volcanic plugs – steep-sided columns of hardened magma that are left behind when extinct volcanoes wear away. One of the biggest is

WHERE TO SEE
THE HIGHEST OVERHANG

Mount Thor, on Canada's Baffin Island, has an overhang of 105 degrees. This means that from the 1675-m (5495-ft) high summit, climbers can abseil 1250 m (4101 ft) through empty space – the longest free drop in the world. Thrill-seekers are tempted to BASE jump from Mount Thor, but the activity is banned because it is difficult for emergency services to reach this isolated spot.

Shiprock in New Mexico, whose sheer sides rise nearly 500 m (1600 ft) above the desert floor. Another North American monolith, El Capitan in Yosemite National Park, is made of solid granite, and has an almost sheer face 900 m (3000 ft) high. Once considered unclimbable, it is now a favourite race against the clock, and has recently been scaled in the incredible time of less than 2½ hours.

OVER THE EDGE

Majestic, overwhelming, beautiful and frightening, cliffs are some of the most awe-inspiring sights on Earth. The world's longest cliff face is on the south coast of Australia, where the Nullarbor Plain meets the turbulent waters of the Great Australian Bight. Here, along a 400-km (250-mile) battlefront, ocean waves constantly pound the Nullarbor's limestone, creating one of the world's wildest and loneliest coasts, with very few places where a boat can safely land – consequently, there are many historical shipwrecks in the region.

The Nullarbor cliffs are up to 100 m (330 ft) high, which is relatively tiny when compared with some of the largest inland cliffs. Many climbers and geologists award the top position to the world's ninth-highest mountain, Nanga Parbat in Pakistan. Its almost-sheer Rupal Face drops a stunning 4.5 km (2⅘ miles) from its summit to its base. Without any trees to betray its scale, this immense drop is difficult to grasp: it is over five times as high as the Burj Khalifa in Dubai, currently the tallest building in the world.

Also in Pakistan, the fabled Trango Towers have some of the world's tallest near-vertical cliffs, acknowledged to be among the hardest climbs in the world. Despite this, two Australian climbers scaled the summit of Great Trango Tower in 1992, and performed a simultaneous BASE jump from near the top, at an altitude of over 6000 m (20,000 ft). Despite tumbling as they fell, they managed to successfully deploy their parachutes – one of the biggest, fastest and scariest cliff descents ever made.

Revered by the Navajo people, Shiprock is a 30-million-year-old volcanic plug that is situated in north-western New Mexico. Radiating out from the monolith are six wall-like sheets of igneous rock known as dykes, the most prominent of which measures 9 km (6 miles) in length.

GRAND CANYON
Bright morning light beautifully illuminates the colourful rock layers – including quartzite, dolomite, granite and basalt – that are found within Arizona's magnificent Grand Canyon.

?

EXTREME FACT
Every year, the Colorado River washes enough sediment out of the Grand Canyon to fill 2 million full-size trucks.

Canyons and gorges

Some canyons and gorges are only just wide enough to squeeze through, but others have enough standing room for every human being on Earth. Together, they are a testament to the incredible power of flowing water, as it grinds down rocks and then sweeps them away.

I T'S NOT THE biggest. It's not the deepest. It's not the oldest either. But for sheer visual impact, the United States' Grand Canyon easily ranks as one of the most stunning geological features on Earth. Set in a high rocky plateau in Arizona, it snakes its way east to west for over 400 km (250 miles), collecting side branches that are major canyons in their own right. To create this enormous canyon, the Colorado River has excavated 4000 cubic km (1000 cubic miles) of rock – enough to cover the whole of New South Wales in a layer 5 m (16 ft) deep.

ANATOMY OF AN ICON

The Grand Canyon falls away with heart-stopping suddenness from the ground on either side. Its central section is up to 1800 m (6000 ft) deep, a drop so great that it even affects the seasons – spring arrives inside the canyon while the plateau is still covered in snow. Seen from its rim, the canyon showcases a fantastic variety of landforms from cliffs and flat-topped mesas to crumbling terraces and lofty spires. Coloured in all the warm shades of the spectrum, these formations give the canyon its iconic status, and make it one of most instantly recognised natural sites in the world.

The Grand Canyon was known for millennia by Native Americans. One tribe – the Ancestral Pueblo – walled off small caves, creating granaries set high in the canyon walls. Reached by narrow pathways and ladders, these large granaries doubled as storerooms and hide-outs, protecting both them and their food supplies from the weather, wild animals and thieves. The first Europeans to see the canyon arrived in 1540, but a long gap followed before pioneers and settlers moved into the area in the second half of the nineteenth century. During this era, hundreds of the canyon's features were given their current names. Many of these names, such as Indian Gardens or Cremation Canyon, mark historical sites. Others, such as the Shiva Temple or Tower of Babel, are fanciful comparisons, while some record oddities of the canyon's shape. Echo Peaks, for example, were named in 1871, when a shot fired at the cliffs produced 22 echoes before the sound finally faded away.

ANCESTRAL PUEBLOAN GRANARY
Nankoweap Canyon is a side branch of the Grand Canyon, and the site of a well-preserved Native American granary.

REVEALING THE PAST

The Grand Canyon is a unique window on the world's geological history, revealing a complete sequence of rocks that stretches back almost 2 billion years. The oldest and deepest rock layer is called the Vishnu Schist. Stacked up above it, like a colossal sandwich, are nearly 40 contrasting bands of sandstone, limestone and shale, each dating from a different time in Earth's distant past. These rocks were originally laid down as seabed sediment, but they were forced upwards when the Rocky Mountains formed. This uplift created the Colorado Plateau – the 3-km (2-mile) high upland that the Colorado River travels across on its journey to the sea.

Compared to these ancient rocks, the canyon itself is a youngster on the geological scene. Scientists debate its exact age, but it may have developed in as little as 6 million years. As luck would have it, the perfect ingredients for canyon building were in place: a fast-flowing river running through a high rocky landscape, and a dry climate that prevented plants stabilising slopes with their roots. Once the river started carving its way downwards, it became trapped in its own ever-deepening cut, sweeping rocks and silt downstream.

Today, the Colorado River averages less than 100 m (300 ft) across – a mere stone's throw compared to the

canyon itself, which measures up to 29 km (18 miles) from rim to rim. The Colorado River created the main channel, but the rest is due to countless side streams, which spread out like a network of veins. In summer, many of these streams are dry. However, sudden thunderstorms can turn them into violent torrents, capable of carrying away car-sized boulders as they surge downhill. Each time this happens, the canyon widens by a few more centimetres, and the Colorado River eventually clears the debris away.

CANYONS OF LATIN AMERICA

There are many ways of measuring canyons and gorges, and many claimants to the title of longest, deepest or widest in the world. One important distinction is between enclosed canyons, which are sunk into plateaus, and open ones, which run between tall mountain peaks. Enclosed canyons are measured from their rim, but with open ones, depth figures are often taken from the very highest point of land along the canyon. It's a crucial difference, and one that can give open canyons a massive head start in the record stakes.

The Grand Canyon is the world's largest enclosed canyon, but compared to open canyons, it quickly loses its place at the top of the list. In the Americas, Mexico's Copper Canyon is far longer than the Grand Canyon, and also deeper as well. Instead of being carved out by one

CANYON UNDER ICE

The longest canyon in the world is buried beneath the Greenland Ice Sheet. Measuring 750 km (470 miles) from end to end, it is almost twice as long as the Grand Canyon, and up to 800 m (2600 ft) deep. Scientists discovered it by surveying Greenland's ice sheet with radio waves, which travelled through the ice and were reflected by the bedrock underneath. A giant river formed the canyon over 4 million years ago, before the ice sheet reached the size it is today. It runs from south to north, emptying into the Arctic Ocean.

COLCA CANYON
An Andean condor glides along on the updraught emanating from Peru's Colca Canyon. Other birds found here include the giant colibri (a large hummingbird), the mountain caracara and the Chilean flamingo.

river, it was created by six, giving it a total length of several thousand kilometres. Parts of it are over 2500 m (8200 ft) deep, although, like most open canyons, its walls are sloping, rather than sheer. Impressive though this is, even deeper canyons exist in Peru. Cotahuasi Canyon drops over 3300 m (10,800 ft), while Colca Canyon plumbs even greater depths, measuring over 4000 m (13,000 ft) from the mountains that flank it to the canyon floor.

On their high slopes, these Peruvian canyons are brown and barren, but deeper down, the landscape changes to a bright green. Here, the rugged ground is covered with laboriously constructed farm terraces that date back to long before Incan times. Until the mid-twentieth century, people in these canyons were entirely self-sufficient, and few ever ventured into the outside world.

ASIAN MEGA-CANYONS

High mountains and deep canyons go hand in hand, because water has more cutting power if it rushes steeply downhill. Every time its speed doubles, its energy jumps by a factor of four, giving it even more strength to carve through any obstacles in its way. The world's youngest mountain ranges have the highest and steepest drops, and it is here that many of the world's deepest canyons and gorges are found.

Peru's canyons cut through the Andes Mountains – the longest land-based mountain range in the world. Colca Canyon, near the city of Arequipa, is sometimes cited as the deepest canyon on Earth. However, despite its immense size, it is no match for the biggest canyons in the Himalayas, where rivers start even higher up, and gather the torrential run off from the summer's monsoon rain. Flushed with this water, their energy is enormous, and the results are on a massive scale.

One of these mega-canyons was cut by the Yarlung Tsangpo River, which drains a large part of southern Tibet. It surges through a 250-km (150-mile) chasm on its way to much lower ground in India and Bangladesh, where it changes its name to the Brahmaputra River and empties into the Bay of Bengal. In the Yarlung Tsangpo Grand Canyon, the river thunders between peaks up to 7500 m (25,000 ft) high, in a narrow cut that is deep enough to swallow 12 Empire State Buildings standing on top of each other, with some extra room to spare. Little known to outsiders, it is one of the most dangerous whitewater rivers on Earth. In the canyon, there is no local river traffic, and very few kayakers have ever been brave enough to venture into its churning currents, which rush downhill faster than an athlete can run.

THE BIG THREE

The Yarlung Tsangpo Grand Canyon measures about 5500 m (18,000 ft) from its highest point to river level, which is almost exactly three times the Grand Canyon's maximum depth. Its narrowness fully qualifies it as a gorge, and it is often regarded as the deepest in the world. However, also in the Himalayas, the Kali Gandaki Gorge is another contender for the title. Located in central Nepal, it separates two of the world's tallest mountains – Dhaulagiri I and Annapurna I – which gives it a maximum depth of over 6000 m (19,600 ft), and makes it one of the most awe-inspiring trekking routes in the Himalayan range.

These two gorges form part of a trio, and, according to some measurements, the third outdoes them both. Created by one of Asia's mightiest rivers, the Indus Gorge divides another pair of towering peaks, Pakistan's Nanga Parbat and Rakaposhi. At this point, the Indus River is only about 1000 m (3300 ft) above sea level, while Nanga Parbat has an altitude of 8126 m (26,660 ft).

YARLUNG TSANGPO RIVER

Snow-covered Gyala Peri – one of the tallest mountains at the eastern end of the Himalayas – looms over the Yarlung Tsangpo River as it tumbles wildly through one of the most fearsome canyons on the planet.

history stretching back more than 250 million years. Often described as Africa's Grand Canyon, it has many similar landscapes, with abrupt cliffs and rocky terraces sunk into an arid plateau. For over 150 km (90 miles), the river meanders through a winding ravine, but unlike the Colorado River, its active canyon-cutting days are largely a thing of the past. In the dry season, the river comes to a halt, leaving just a chain of shallow pools that slowly evaporate in the hot desert air.

Africa's biggest – and its most dangerous – gorge is 4500 km (2800 miles) north-east of Fish River Canyon as the crow flies, in the highlands of Ethiopia. Here, the Blue Nile churns its way through a 400-km (250-mile) long trough before it enters the Sudan and finally joins the White Nile at Khartoum. As deep as the Grand Canyon, the Blue Nile Gorge is much too treacherous for passenger boats, and before the late twentieth century, the only permanent crossings were two antique bridges made from mortar, brick and stone. Despite its name, the river itself is often a deep coffee brown, and in the upper reaches of the gorge, black volcanic rock lines the river's edge.

SLOT CANYONS

At the other end of the size spectrum, slot canyons compress some of the world's most amazing vistas into the minimum amount of space. Formed by rushing water, they are typically cut into soft sandstone, and they can be less than 1 m (3 ft) wide, but dozens or even hundreds of metres deep. Unlike other canyons, they sometimes look unimpressive from outside, but they have a spellbinding beauty when seen from within, with sculpted walls that look more like a swirling fluid than solid rock. Some slot canyons contain running water all year round, but ones in desert regions are less predictable, and also more hazardous – after months of drought, they can suddenly flood after heavy rain.

Hidden in Australia's Blue Mountains, just a few hours' drive west of Sydney, some of the wildest and wettest slot canyons draw extreme sports enthusiasts from all over the world. Like giant outdoor plumbing, they drain water from flat-topped plateaus, funnelling it in vertical conduits as it plunges downhill. Camouflaged by trees and ferns, and buried deep in shade, these channels are less like classic canyons and more like vertical caves.

Opinions differ about whether it is a true gorge or a valley, but its peak-to-river depth is four times greater than the Grand Canyon, a figure unequalled by any other canyon or gorge on Earth.

RUNNING WILD

The list of the world's greatest canyons also includes spectacular chasms in China and Africa. In southern China, Tiger Leaping Gorge gets its name from a local legend, which tells how a tiger cleared the Yangtze River in a single bound. This would have been an extraordinary feat, because even at its narrowest the gorge is still 25 m (80 ft) wide, but the myth sits well with the stunning scenery, where the Yangtze River squeezes between two peaks that are over 5000 m (16,500 ft) high. Further downstream, many of the Yangtze's gorges have been dammed, but Tiger Leaping Gorge remains untamed.

In south-western Africa, Namibia's huge Fish River Canyon is one of the oldest in the world, with a geological

INDUS RIVER

After surging through what is perhaps the world's deepest gorge, the Indus River appears to be dwarfed by the towering peaks of the Karakoram range before it eventually flows into the Arabian Sea.

CLAUSTRAL CANYON

Lush ferns flourish between the narrow walls of Claustral Canyon, deep in the heart of Australia's Blue Mountains. This canyon features three abseils that drop into cold pools – a wetsuit is a must in this chilly environment.

With so much water on the move, the only way to explore these slots is to start at the top, and travel with the flow. The longest canyons drop over 600 m (2000 ft) in a series of waterfalls interspersed with rocky pools, so the descent is like reverse mountaineering, with long abseils and little chance to dry off on the way down.

INNER WORLDS

The American Southwest has the greatest concentration of dry slot canyons anywhere on Earth. One of the most famous – Antelope Canyon in Arizona – attracts thousands of visitors every year. Approached through a narrow slit in a rocky slope, it opens out into a fantasy world, where the Sun plays on waves of intricately banded sandstone, creating a constantly changing backdrop during the course of the day. Despite its rather magical appearance, it can be a very dangerous place. In 1997, 11 people drowned here during a flash flood triggered by a thunderstorm nearly 10 km (6 miles) away.

Buckskin Gulch, in southern Utah, is over 20 km (12 miles) long, which makes it one of the longest slot canyons on record. It is also remarkably deep: in some sections, the walls tower nearly 150 m (500 ft) above the narrow passageway below. Even on a hot day, hiking in this narrow chasm can be a chilling experience, because – unlike in Antelope Canyon – the Sun rarely reaches as far as the sand-covered floor.

BIRD'S-EYE VIEW

Canyons and gorges can be major barriers for land animals, but they are almost ideal habitats for raptors, or birds of prey. Soaring high over slopes or swooping close to cliffs, they use their extraordinarily sharp vision to scan the ground for signs of food. In the Himalayas, griffon vultures patrol gorges in search of dead remains, while eagles and buzzards concentrate on living prey. Australia's largest raptor – the wedge-tailed eagle – is also at home in this kind of habitat, and so is Verreaux's eagle, a specialist predator from Africa. This black-and-white eagle feeds almost entirely on rock hyraxes – guinea pig-shaped animals that live among boulders and in scree. Hunting alone or in pairs, the eagle usually zeroes in on its prey by flying low down, but it sometimes knocks hyraxes off cliffs, diving down to snatch them up once they have hit the ground.

Griffon vultures can have a wingspan of over 2.5 m (8 ft), which makes them some of the largest raptors in the world. But in South America, the Andean condor is bigger still. This enormous scavenger has wings measuring 3.2 m (10½ ft) from tip to tip – the largest of any land bird. It soars over mountains and canyons in search of large carcasses, and nests on inaccessible ledges up to 5000 m (16,500 ft) high. These legendary birds normally keep their distance from people, but in Peru's Colca Canyon they can be seen at eye level as they

WHERE TO SEE
SLOT CANYONS

One of the most famous slot canyons is a natural passageway known as the Siq (pictured), in the ancient Jordanian city of Petra. Slot canyons are also common in the American states of Utah, Colorado, Arizona, New Mexico and Nevada, as well as in Australia's Blue Mountains and Purnululu National Park.

sail over the canyon's upper slopes, with their primary flight feathers outstretched like the fingers of a hand.

When European settlers first arrived in California, similar birds flew over canyons and mountains in what is now the American Southwest. California condors fed on the remains of large mammals, such as mountain goats and deer, and for a while they did well on the carcasses of horses – animals that once lived in North America, and which European settlers reintroduced. But during the twentieth century, their numbers plunged, and by 1987, only 22 wild birds were left. The decision was made to bring all of them into captivity, and an emergency breeding program began.

Today, California condors can be seen once more, soaring over the Grand Canyon and other sites where they have been released. The species is not out of danger, but the total population has climbed to over 400 – a remarkable turnaround for a bird that once teetered on the brink of extinction.

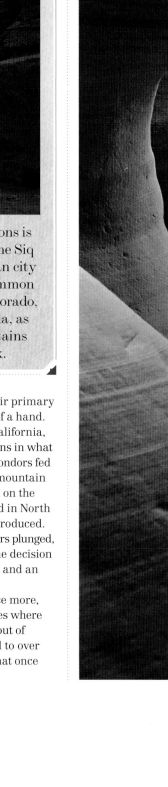

ANTELOPE CANYON
Located on Navajo land in Arizona, the two sections (upper and lower) of Antelope Canyon are accessible only with a permit and on a guided tour.

ICE CAVE
The superb Dévoluy Mountains in France boast over 600 caves, and even feature an underground glacier. The caves are popular with adventurous spelunkers.

Caves and caverns

Hidden beneath Earth's surface, caves and caverns are often places of breathtaking beauty, with spellbinding rock formations that can take millennia to grow. New cave systems are discovered every year, but, even so, less than 10 per cent of the world's caves have been fully explored.

I F YOU FIND confined spaces difficult to cope with, the lure of the unknown is unlikely to tempt you underground. You are not alone. In fact, scientific studies show that up to a third of the human population feels the same way about being shut in, whether it's in small windowless rooms, crowded elevators or caves. But strangely enough, cavers don't only have to fight off claustrophobia – sometimes the spaces they explore are so enormous, they struggle to conquer their fear of the unknown.

LOST IN SPACE

Imagine a subterranean passage that widens into a giant chamber, big enough to swallow a six-lane highway. The walls and roof retreat beyond the reach of your lights, leaving nothing but an oppressive emptiness in their place. In conditions like these, it's easy to be unnerved by the sheer scale of the darkness, and by the notion of millions of tonnes of rock perched high above your head.

In January 1981, thoughts like these crossed the minds of a group of British cavers during an expedition in the Gunung Mulu National Park, in Sarawak, Borneo. The cavers were exploring the Gua Nasib Bagus, or Good Luck Cave, when they discovered a chamber that no one had entered before. At the time, they could only guess at its dimensions, but as they moved forwards across its floor, it became clear that this huge void was on a wholly unprecedented scale.

The cave they discovered – known as the Sarawak Chamber – is by far the biggest known cavern in the world. Laser measurements show that its dimensions are about 700 m (2300 ft) long by 400 m (1300 ft) wide, with a height of at least 70 m (230 ft). In terms of floor area, it is the biggest uninterrupted enclosed space anywhere on Earth, with enough room to accommodate the White House, Westminster Abbey and the Sydney Opera House at the same time.

The world's largest cave passage is also in Southeast Asia, close to Vietnam's border with Laos. Called the Hang Son Doong, or Mountain River Cave, it is 150 m (500 ft) wide, and an incredible 5 km (3 miles) long. This single passage could house 20 of the world's largest aircraft carriers, with plenty of room to spare.

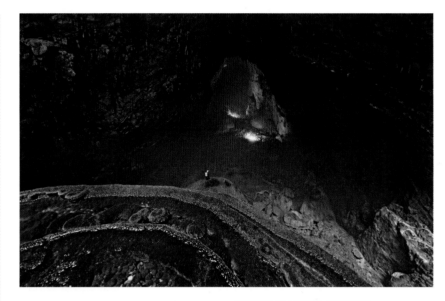

HANG SON DOONG
Slippery algae covers some of the surfaces in this enormous cave passage in Vietnam. There is even a jungle growing in a section of the cave where the roof has collapsed.

EXTREME FACT
Instead of being formed by water, New Mexico's Carlsbad Caverns were carved out by dilute sulfuric acid, which created over 50 km (30 miles) of passageways.

HOW CAVES FORM

Like most of the world's caves, the Sarawak Chamber is set in limestone – a rock that has been formed from ancient sediment in lakes and shallow seas. Although limestone feels hard, it is slightly soluble, particularly in anything that has a hint of acidity. Drop some vinegar on it, and the rock's surface turns cloudy as it starts to dissolve. Lemon juice has a similar effect. Even rainwater can eat into it, because rain absorbs carbon dioxide as it falls, turning it into a weak acid by the time it hits the ground.

Cave-bearing limestone layers are full of natural joints and cracks. Rainwater finds its way into the smallest of these openings, widening them out so it can flow downwards by the steepest and shortest route. Vertical cracks gradually expand to form pit caves or potholes, while sloping ones become narrow conduits that funnel water downhill. As these sloping passages widen, their roofs often weaken, and sometimes they collapse. If this happens near the surface, it can create an open shaft or sinkhole, but if it is deep enough, a rock-filled chamber is formed. The water then works away at the fallen rubble, enlarging the chamber and creating a cavern underground. Where the water drips through the darkness, it deposits crystals of calcite, a translucent

EXTREME TOP 10
LONGEST CAVE SYSTEMS

1 MAMMOTH CAVE (KENTUCKY, UNITED STATES)
644 KM (400 MILES)

2 SAC ACTUN AND NOHOCH NAH CHICH (MEXICO)
310 KM (193 MILES)

3 JEWEL CAVE (SOUTH DAKOTA, UNITED STATES)
267 KM (166 MILES)

4 OX BEL HA (MEXICO)
243 KM (151 MILES)

5 OPTIMISTICHESKAYA (UKRAINE)
235 KM (146 MILES)

6 WIND CAVE (SOUTH DAKOTA, UNITED STATES)
225 KM (140 MILES)

**7 LECHUGUILLA CAVE
(NEW MEXICO, UNITED STATES)**
222 KM (138 MILES)

8 HÖLLOCH (SWITZERLAND)
200 KM (124 MILES)

**9 FISHER RIDGE CAVE
(KENTUCKY, UNITED STATES)**
195 KM (121 MILES)

10 GUA AIR JERNIH (SARAWAK, MALAYSIA)
189 KM (117 MILES)

mineral with a distinctive pearly sheen. This steady dripping creates a wonderland of calcite formations, from hanging stalactites that are as thin as a pencil to curtain-like flowstones dozens of metres across.

Caves keep growing as long as water travels through them, sometimes capturing entire rivers that disappear underground. But in many cave systems, the water eventually finds a lower route through the rock, leaving old caves high and dry. Over thousands of years, the flow is gradually turned off, until the caves – together with their calcite formations – are suspended in the vastness of subterranean time.

INTO THE INTERIOR

Unlike the above-ground world, caves are brimming with shadowy frontiers. Many of them are still poorly known, and – according to some estimates – only one in 10 of the world's cave systems have been found and explored completely. Cave scientists – or speleologists – can predict where caves are most likely to occur, but it takes perseverance to discover new cave systems, and often a dose of good luck.

In 1900, two brothers in South Dakota made a find that speleologists dream about, when they discovered a curious hole in a rocky hillside. The hole was too small to climb into, but a strong current of cold air

⌃
FLOWSTONE

Part of the Verneau cave system in France, Gouffre de la Baume des Crêtes possesses one of the world's finest flowstones – a delicate calcite veil that seems to hide the entrance to another realm.

was blowing out of it. Intrigued by their find, they widened the hole with dynamite, and then made their way inside. To their amazement, they found a labyrinth of passages and low chambers richly decorated with calcite, which glittered like gems in the light of their lamps.

Their discovery, named the Jewel Cave, was declared a National Monument in 1908, but even half a century later, only 3 km (2 miles) of the cave had been mapped. At this point, a group of climbers and geologists began to comb the cave's furthest reaches, and the network of known passages soon expanded to 25 km (16 miles) in length. Since then, our knowledge of the Jewel Cave system has grown almost exponentially. It now has a known extent of 267 km (166 miles), which makes it currently the third longest in the world.

RIVER CAVE
Explorers illuminate a large underground river passage in New Britain, an island of Papua New Guinea. The island is famous for its extensive cave systems.

MAMMOTH CAVE

Thanks to the tireless work of dedicated speleologists, cave records change almost yearly – and the list of longest and deepest caves is constantly under review. Known caves keep getting longer, and new systems are discovered every year, particularly in the tropics. However, despite some stunning recent discoveries, nothing has yet emerged to challenge the ultimate record holder: the Mammoth Cave system, in Kentucky, is easily the world's longest, with a mapped extent more than double that of any other system presently known.

The Mammoth Cave has a large main entrance, and a long history of human use dating back over 5000 years. In the early 1800s, the system was mined for saltpetre, a key ingredient of gunpowder. As its fame spread, it also became a tourist attraction, and finally a national park. Over many decades of exploration, the system's known length has steadily increased to about 644 km (400 miles). However, its actual extent is still unknown. Some speleologists estimate that it could be as much as 1000 km (600 miles), or 2½ times the length of the London Underground, one of the biggest subway systems in the world.

Mammoth Cave contains a wealth of spectacular features, but it owes its amazing length to an accident of geology. In this part of Kentucky, the cave-bearing limestone is covered by a cap of tough sandstone, which protects the oldest caves and stops them being worn away. Over millions of years, the watertable inside the limestone has gradually dropped, creating a maze of passageways stacked up like a multistorey car park. Nearest the surface are dry caves that were carved out long ago, while further down are the newest caves, which are still growing today.

HIDDEN DEPTHS

Despite its stupendous length, the Mammoth Cave system isn't the deepest in the world. Far deeper caves exist in other regions where soluble rock is exceptionally thick, letting water carve out record-breaking cave systems as it cascades underground.

In 1956, cavers broke a crucial psychological barrier when they descended over 1000 m (3300 ft) into the Gouffre Berger – one of the deepest caves in France, and an early candidate for the record of deepest in the world. Climbing this far down is fraught with hazards, particularly in wet shafts where falling water is all around. The Gouffre Berger's tunnels are not technically difficult, but heavy rain on the surface can rapidly flood some parts of the cave. Five people have lost their lives here during sudden floods, giving it an unenviable reputation as one of the world's most dangerous caves.

Another French cave, the Gouffre Mirolda, eventually beat this depth record, setting a new low of 1626 m (5335 ft) in 1998. But even this depth is dwarfed by the

MAMMOTH CAVE
According to the useful mnemonic, stalactites 'hold on tight' – looking up at the dagger-like stalactites hanging from the ceiling in the Mammoth Cave in Kentucky, the observer can be thankful that they rarely fall.

current record holder, the Krubera-Voronja Cave in Georgia's Caucasus Mountains – a region riddled with chasms that have only recently been explored. In 2004, a team of over 50 cavers dropped into its modest-looking entrance, high up in mountain pastures. Shouldering over 5 tonnes (5½ tons) of equipment, including 3 km (2 miles) of rope, they climbed down a series of shafts, following an active watercourse that finally resurfaces near the shores of the Black Sea.

During their four-week expedition, the team set a new record by travelling down 1800 m (5900 ft) – a feat that they likened to climbing Mount Everest upside down. A water-filled sump ultimately blocked their downward progress, but soon afterwards, another team discovered a way past this obstacle. These cavers became the first in history to breach the 2000 m (6500 ft) barrier – equivalent to six Eiffel Towers stacked on top of each other.

GOUFFRE BERGER

In 2012, intrepid cave explorers descended over 1100 m (3600 ft) into France's infamous Gouffre Berger cave. At the bottom, they encountered intricate passageways – some very narrow – as well as subterranean waterfalls and pools.

UNDERGROUND ARTISTRY

Cave explorers often encounter spectacular rock formations of a kind never seen above ground. These natural decorations, known as speleothems, often mimic living things, but their strange and beautiful shapes are entirely due to the way water dissolves away the rock, and then re-deposits its minerals in a completely brand new form. Limestone rocks, being extremely soluble, often contain abundant caves, full of calcite (calcium carbonate) speleothems sprouting from the ceiling, walls and floor. The calcite deposits grow slowly as time goes by, but their size and shape depends on many different factors, including their position, age, the water flow and the concentration of dissolved minerals in the water. Speleothems reach their greatest size where water seeps into a cave at a steady rate over thousands of

years. Most speleothems are creamy white, but some are stained by impurities; iron, for example, gives them a wide range of red, orange or brown hues.

The most common speleothems are stalactites, which grow like icicles from cave ceilings, and stalagmites, which sprout from their floors. Amazingly, stalactites and stalagmites both start with a single drop of water, which leaves a minute ring of calcite on a cave's ceiling, and a much wider splash of calcite on its floor directly underneath. The world's largest known stalactites are over 20 m (65 ft) in length, but stalagmites can be much bigger because they sit securely on the ground. Several caves have stalagmites over 50 m (160 ft) high, and the largest-known specimens – in Vietnam's Mountain River Cave – measure 75 m (250 ft) from their tip to their base, which is as tall as a 22-storey building. A stalactite and stalagmite can eventually grow together to form a column or pillar. The immense variety of other natural cave masterpieces includes shawls or lace-like mineral curtains formed as water trickles down the cave wall, slender yet hollow cave straws, delicate twisty helictites, giant wedding-cake-like flowstones and calcite-rimmed water-filled basins as big as swimming pools.

CRYSTAL PALACES

Most cave decorations are found in limestone, or in closely related rocks such as marble or dolomite. But nature's subterranean artistry does not stop here. In some parts of the world, caves are encrusted with mineral crystals, ranging from delicate hair-like growths to giant beams weighing as much as a bus.

The most common kind of crystalline caves are made from halite, better known as salt. Halite may not look like the salt you sprinkle on your food, but if you touch the walls of a salt cave with wet fingers and then place your fingers in your mouth, the taste is exactly the same. Natural salt deposits form when shallow lakes and seas evaporate, leaving their salt behind. In some parts of the world, water then seeps through the salt layers, creating passages with crystalline growths on their walls. Halite usually forms six-sided crystals, but these decorations include twisting fibres and salt 'flowers'. Unlike limestone stalactites or stalagmites, halite formations grow from a weak base – which means they can drop off easily if touched. They also grow quickly, allowing salt caves to change over days or weeks, rather than over thousands of years.

Cave crystals also include rhodochrosite, a pink mineral that is sometimes used in jewellery, and quartz (also known as rock crystal). But the most spectacular crystals of all are formed by gypsum – a soft mineral that is used to make plaster of Paris. Gypsum crystals are usually smaller than a fingernail, but given the right conditions, they can grow to a stupendous size.

In the year 2000, workers digging a tunnel broke into a surprising subterranean chamber beneath northern Mexico's Naica Mine. Inside it, they found some of the largest natural crystals in the world, thrown together like tree trunks in a chaotic forest. Made of selenite – a kind of gypsum that forms crystalline slabs – the biggest of them are 12 m (39 ft) long and weigh about 50 tonnes (55 tons).

Mexico's incredible Cueva de los Cristales, or Cave of the Crystals, is a stifling cavern warmed by volcanic heat. Visitors can only spend a few minutes here, because the temperature hovers at over 55°C (131°F) and the humidity is nearly 100 per cent. But half a million years ago, the chamber was flooded with hot mineral-rich water, and it was in these unusually stable surroundings that the crystals began to form. The crystals stopped growing in the 1980s, when mining operations drained the rock, revealing one of the greatest wonders of the subterranean world.

SPELEOTHEMS

Tham Kaew, or Jewel Cave, in Thailand's Khao Sam Roi Yot National Park is well named – the rock formations here glitter like diamonds because they consist of innumerable calcite crystals.

SÓTANO DE LAS GOLONDRINAS

To reach the debris- and guano-littered floor of this enormous pit cave in Mexico, visitors abseil 333 m (1093 ft) through empty space from the low side of the entrance. This breathtaking journey can take up to an hour.

GOING DOWN

Pit caves or potholes are vertical shafts found in a cave system. Some caves contain none, while others – such as Georgia's Krubera-Voronja Cave – have several in a row. Spectacularly big examples include the Vrtoglavica Cave in Slovenia, which has a record-breaking shaft 603 m (1978 ft) deep, and Mexico's enormous Sótano de las Golondrinas, or Cave of the Swallows, which is one of the widest cave shafts in the world. This huge pit flares outwards beneath an overhanging rim, creating a vast bottle-shaped space so big that a hot-air balloon once touched down inside. A favourite site for vertical cavers, who abseil over 300 m (1000 ft) to the bottom, it also attracts BASE jumpers, who leap off the rim and parachute to the floor.

It takes up to two hours to climb out of the Cave of the Swallows using a rope and friction clamps; those who are unprepared would find it difficult to clamber out at all. Even the smallest of pit caves can become deadly traps. Camouflaged by plants, their mouths are like snares, waiting to gulp down anything that does not see them in time. Some pit caves have been catching animals for thousands of years, and they are still active today.

TRAPPED!

Natural Trap Cave, located in the Bighorn Mountains of Wyoming, is a 25-m (80-ft) pit set in rugged limestone country, or karst. During the last ice age, huge numbers of prehistoric animals blundered into its clutches, creating an extraordinarily detailed record of North America's living past. Bones from over 30,000 animals have been found on its floor, including mammoths, American lions, bison, bears and dire wolves – the name given to an extinct species of wolf with a much more powerful bite than the wolves alive today.

The active period of the Natural Trap Cave dates back to between 12,000 and 20,000 years ago. But in Australia's Nullarbor Plain, shallow pit caves have

been trapping animals for far longer than this. Leaena's Breath Cave – so-called because air currents make it 'breathe' in and out – has ambushed the continent's native animals for most of the past million years. Among the incredible haul of fossils are the remains of giant wombats and kangaroos, as well as marsupial lions. Unrelated to true lions, these massively built predators were Australia's largest-ever meat-eating mammals, with jaws like bolt-cutters, and powerful thumbs with large claws, which might have been used for slashing open prey.

Like many of Australia's large mammals, marsupial lions died out about 50,000 years ago. However, Leaena's Breath Cave is still at work, although not quite on the same scale as in the past. Birds fly through the narrow entrance to feed or to rest. The lucky ones are caught and set free by researchers, but others never find their way back out to the sunlight.

LIFE BELOW GROUND

Fortunately for the world's animals, caves like these are few and far between. Instead of trapping wildlife, caves are more often used as important breeding sites or habitats. Some of their animals are daily visitors, but others stay underground all their lives. These permanent cave-dwellers – known as troglobites – include fish, salamanders and spiders, as well as

BRACKEN CAVE BATS

In spring, millions of Mexican free-tailed bats migrate from their winter home in Mexico to this special cave in Texas, where the females give birth. It can take up to three hours every night for the adult bats to leave the cave in search of food.

crustaceans, centipedes and insects. Many are restricted to individual cave systems, and, in a world without light, most are completely blind.

Compared to the outside world, the food supply in caves is extremely meagre, so troglobites cannot afford to waste any energy on unnecessary activities. They move very slowly, and often spend hours at a stretch doing nothing at all. In most caves, the humidity and temperature change very little throughout the year, so troglobites do not have to use precious resources to keep themselves moist or warm. Some are predators, feeding on other troglobites, but even so, their way of life ultimately depends on food that comes from outside. Cave fish and salamanders feed on scraps of organic matter that are washed underground by streams, while many cave insects are scavengers, feeding on dead remains. These include droppings that are left by bats and birds, as well as their corpses, and the occasional feast provided by animals that wander into caves, get lost and die.

Troglobites find their food mainly by smell and by touch – even a tiny change in air currents can guide them to a tasty meal. For these animals, life in the subterranean slow lane has one advantage: they often survive for an extraordinarily long time. Cave crayfish can breed long after their hundredth birthday, and some of them live to 175 – about 10 times as long as crayfish above ground.

◤◣

SAC ACTUN

From the accessible Gran Cenote – the main entrance to Sistema Sac Actun, or White Cave System in Mexico – divers can make their way through a number of exquisitely decorated caves and passages flooded with crystal-clear water.

FLOODED LABYRINTHS

Some cave systems are permanently flooded, and can only be explored by diving. They include the Sac Actun and Nohoch Nah Chich caves in Mexico, whose combined length of 310 km (193 miles) makes them the second-longest cave system in the world. Cave diving is one of the world's most dangerous extreme sports, requiring careful preparation and steady nerves. The risks involved are so high that divers usually carry twice their planned air requirements, two separate sets of guide lines and three independent sets of lights.

SEEING WITH SOUND

In prehistoric times, caves were used as refuges by some large and dangerous carnivores, including cave lions and cave bears. In Africa, they are still the haunt of leopards, and Kitum Cave in Kenya is even visited by elephants in search of salt. But across most of the world, the most common cave visitors are flying ones that roost and breed underground.

Bats navigate by echolocation – the animal equivalent of sonar – which lets them fly deep into caves without colliding with their walls. Cave-dwelling bats nearly always breed in colonies, and most of them feed on insects, taking to the air as the sun sets. In some caves, this mass exodus is an astounding spectacle, featuring some of the biggest concentrations of mammals anywhere on Earth. One of the largest bat colonies, found in Bracken

KITUM CAVE

Elephants have visited Kenya's Kitum Cave for centuries, using their tusks to scratch salt off the walls; this may have increased the size of the cave. Other animals such as hyenas scavenge any salt chunks that the elephants have not eaten.

Cave in Texas, is home to about 20 million Mexican free-tailed bats, which pour out of the cave's entrance like a dense cloud of smoke. Incredibly, each nursing mother finds its own pup when it returns at dawn, homing in on it first by its calls, and then by its personal scent.

Most birds nest near cave mouths, because, unlike bats, they are unable to navigate in the dark. However, there are some remarkable exceptions to this rule. In Southeast Asia and Australia, cave swiftlets use high-pitched clicks to find their way underground, while in South America, fruit-eating oilbirds do the same. Their clicks are only part of their vocal repertoire, because they also make blood-curdling wails and screams. The oilbird is the world's deepest cave-dwelling bird: thanks to its special type of sonar, it can twist and turn through narrow passages, building its nest up to 750 m (2500 ft) underground.

Deserts and dunes

Deserts are defined by extremes. Heat and drought make them some of the harshest places on Earth, where plants and animals battle with a punishing climate every day of their lives. Within deserts, Earth's surface is laid bare in an endless variety of landscapes from glistening saltpans to seas of shifting sand.

O NCE EVERY 50 to 100 years, something extraordinary happens near the desolate town of Yungay, in northern Chile. The sky darkens, and it pours with rain. After decades of almost total drought, flash floods churn up the barren grey dust and grit that make this region eerily like the surface of the Moon.

Yungay is in the heart of the Atacama Desert, a 900-km (550-mile) long plateau wedged between the Pacific Ocean to the west, and the Andes Mountains to the east. The Atacama's fringes receive enough rain or fog for drought-resistant plants, but its hyper-arid core is the driest place on Earth, and one of the few without natural wildlife of any kind. Ultra-hardy bacteria have been detected in the desert's rocks, but apart from them, nothing grows and nothing rots. Instead, organic matter dries out and becomes mummified: bury an orange and it will still be there decades later, a fragile and dehydrated shell. Human remains are even more durable. On the Atacama coast, the Chinchorro people preserved their dead by removing their internal organs and replacing them with earth. Thousands of years later, many of these 'mummies' have been dug up, and their skin and hair are still intact to this day.

LIFE IN EARTH'S HOTTEST PLACE

Deserts cover about one-third of the world's land area, in a pattern that slowly shifts over time. Like the Atacama, many of them are in the subtropics, where large masses of dry, high-pressure air prevent rain clouds forming. The Atacama has a relatively cool climate, but continental deserts – at the centre of big landmasses – scorch in the highest temperatures anywhere on Earth.

The Sahara is by far the biggest of these hot deserts. Spread across nearly a dozen countries in northern Africa, it covers an area about the size of the whole United States. Like the Atacama, parts of the Sahara are hyper-arid, although water deep below ground shows that its climate was much wetter thousands of years ago. A region of stark and austere beauty,

it is studded with remote oases, immense sand dunes and mountains that seem to hover like islands in the shimmering desert air.

Together with California's Death Valley, the Sahara shares the much-contested record of the hottest place on Earth. In 1922, the Libyan town of Al-Aziziya recorded the world's hottest air temperature – a searing 57.8°C (136°F), which is high enough to liquefy candle wax. Nearly a century later, this figure has been questioned, but there is no doubt that large parts of the Sahara easily exceed 50°C (122°F) in the summer months. In the blinding sunshine, the ground-surface temperature

? EXTREME FACT

Some 36 million years ago, giant penguins lived on the Atacama Desert's coast. Standing up to 1.5 m (5 ft) tall, they had spear-like beaks for impaling their prey.

is higher still. In conditions like these, walking in bare feet is highly dangerous, and dehydration can set in within 30 minutes, particularly if there is a strong wind blowing. Small wonder then that most Saharan animals – including jackals, scorpions and fennec foxes – are active only at night.

However, there is an astonishing exception to this rule. When the daytime heat is at its most intense, the Saharan silver ant comes out of its underground nest to search for food. Like many ants, it makes a living by scavenging for the dead bodies of other insects. It braves the fiery temperatures because this is exactly the time when the fewest predators are about. Saharan silver ants are some of the world's most heat-tolerant animals, capable of operating for several minutes in surface temperatures of up to 70°C (158°F). They have a special navigational system that keeps track of their movements, allowing them to return to the safety of their nest by the shortest and fastest route, instead of retracing their steps.

ATACAMA DESERT
*Chile's Valle de la
Luna (Valley of the
Moon) is one of the
bleakest sections of
the Atacama Desert.
Its lunar landscape
features dry lakes,
wind-worn rocks and
saline formations.*

MERCURY FALLING

When night falls in deserts, temperatures often plummet. Without any cloud cover, the ground soon radiates its store of daytime heat. In the northern Sahara, winter nights often bring ground frost, and on high ground – such as the remote Ahaggar Mountains – even a rare dusting of snow. Freak snowfalls have even been known in the Atacama, when cold polar air manages to push northwards towards the tropics. In 2011, up to 80 cm (30 in) of snow fell on the mountains bordering the Atacama plateau, stranding trucks and cars while their shivering drivers waited for help.

Instead of melting, desert snow sometimes evaporates straight into the air. Over a period of days or weeks, the snow cover gradually shrinks until none is left. Evaporation also lies behind virga – rain or snow that vanishes before it touches the ground. Like a mirage overhead, virga promises precious moisture, snatching it away before the promise is fulfilled.

GAPS IN THE MAP

With little or no vegetation, deserts are a geologist's paradise. Heat and frost crack open exposed rocks, while flash floods and strong winds shape the landscape. Dry riverbeds – known as wadis or creeks – snake across the desert like veins, occasionally channelling water from rare periods of rainfall into lakes that may fill once a century or less. Cliffs and pinnacles rear up into the sky, while deep canyons cut through the surface, revealing rock layers that can be millions or even billions of years old.

Features like these stand out on desert maps, together with other landmarks that were crucial to travellers in the days before GPS. Oases, escarpments and bluffs all act as useful signposts, and so do isolated desert trees. Until 1973 – when it was hit by a truck – the Tree of Ténéré, in northern Niger, was an important marker for camel trains heading north across the Sahara, and a welcome sign for ones heading south. The tree – an acacia – was one of the most remote in the world, and probably survived by tapping a reserve of ground water deep below the surface. A well dug nearby encountered its roots 35 m (115 ft) below the surface, but even this is not a record: that goes to a tree known as *Boscia albitrunca*, which grows in southern Africa. One specimen, in the Kalahari Desert, had roots that were 68 m (223 ft) deep – the same length as six conventional North American school buses parked in a row.

Beyond lone trees and oases, the desert map often turns blank, and it can stay that way for hundreds of kilometres. In many cases, this void is actually filled by desert pavement – a hard, rock-strewn mosaic that can be as flat and featureless as a tabletop, stretching as far as the eye can see. Known by a variety of regional

names, from reg in the Sahara to gibber in Australia, its origin is uncertain, although it probably forms when the wind blows away smaller particles, leaving the larger ones behind. The rocks that make up these pavements are often dark and shiny. Few are bigger than a clenched fist, but they can be difficult to lever up because they have been cemented in place for hundreds or thousands of years.

The other kind of blank is exactly the opposite: seas and mountains of shifting sand.

SAND ON THE MOVE

Think of deserts, and you most likely think of sand dunes – the backdrop to countless photos and films. Sand actually covers less than a quarter of the world's deserts, although some, such as the Rub' al Khali, or Empty Quarter, in Arabia, and the Simpson Desert in Australia, have more than their fair share. The Rub' al Khali is the biggest sand desert on Earth, covering an area that is larger than France. After dark, satellite images of the region show flares from oil wells, as well as some scattered cities and towns. But most of the Empty Quarter remains exactly that: a place of few settlements, almost no permanent roads and some of the longest dunes in the world.

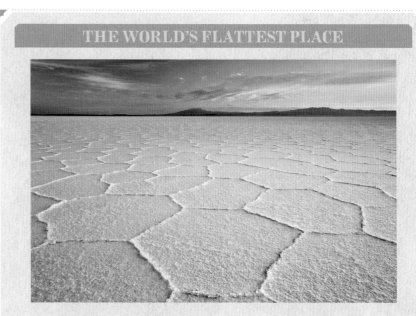

THE WORLD'S FLATTEST PLACE

In deserts, stormwater sometimes forms shallow lakes, which evaporate in the sun. The water vanishes, but any salt that it carries is left behind. Over hundreds or thousands of years, the result is a dazzling and dead-level sheet of salt crystals, known as a saltpan. The world's largest saltpan, and its flattest place, is the Salar de Uyuni in south-western Bolivia. It covers over 10,000 sq km (4000 sq miles), which is about the same size as Cyprus or Jamaica. Despite its huge area, its height varies by less than 80 cm (30 in).

No two dunes are the same, but they all fall into distinct family groups depending on wind strength, directional consistency and the quantity of sand available. In sandy areas with steady winds, dunes may form unbroken parallel ridges that snake their way across the ground for up to 200 km (125 miles). Common in the Empty Quarter, as well as in central Australia, these dunes force travellers to move along the valleys between them, or face an exhausting succession of hard climbs and steep descents.

Where sand is scarcer, crescent-shaped barchan dunes appear. With their pointed ends leading the way, they march across the ground at speeds of up to 100 m (330 ft) a year. Barchans look uncannily like gigantic versions of microscopic living things, and they have the same aptitude for engulfing their 'prey' – little can be done to stop them, as houses and palm trees are smothered in their relentless advance. In Tunisia, these implacable marauders are slowly engulfing a famous film set used in *Star Wars,* and identical dunes can be seen crawling across the face of Mars.

GIANT DUNES

The world's most massive dunes form in places where the wind direction varies throughout the year. Called star dunes, they have all the majesty of real mountains, with sharp ridges radiating outwards from one or more summits. Measuring them is difficult: Dune 7, in south-western Africa's Namib Desert, tops out at nearly 400 m (1300 ft), but the Cerro Blanco – or White Hill – in Peru's Sechura Desert rises over 1170 m (3840 ft) from the dusty desert floor. It's a three-hour climb to the top of Cerro Blanco, but sandboarders can make the return trip in minutes, sliding down the dune's steepest slopes at a hair-raising 60 km/h (40 mph).

Some of the world's strangest star dunes are located deep in the Badain Jaran Desert, in northern China. Measuring up to 500 m (1600 ft) in height, they make a deep throbbing sound in high winds. The sound registers over 105 decibels – that's about the same volume as a chainsaw held a few metres away. The Italian traveller Marco Polo described the booming dunes 700 years ago, a claim that was met with scepticism at the time. But the dunes of Badain Jaran are not alone: singing, throbbing or humming dunes are scattered all over the world, from the Sahara to the deserts of California. The sound is produced when dry sand starts to slip, and the stationary dune beneath it acts like a giant amplifier.

MAKING TRACKS

A big dune can contain millions of tonnes of sand, and an unimaginably vast number of individual grains. During the day, the slopes are often featureless, but it can be a very different story at dawn. Wake up at

WHERE TO SEE
OASES

With their year-round water, desert oases brim with life. San Pedro de Atacama, an oasis in Chile, is surrounded by the world's driest desert, while Egypt's Farafra Oasis (pictured) is south of the famous White Desert. Palm Valley, in Australia's Red Centre, is full of rare plants.

sunrise, and you have a good chance of spotting the many telltale signs of dune wildlife on the move.

Zigzagging tracks show the path of darkling beetles, which search the dunes for smaller insects and other specks of food. With their lightweight bodies and six slender legs, they scuttle lightly over the sand like tiny clockwork toys. Scorpions leave two rows of prints, separated by a central furrow where they drag their tails. At the first sign of danger – or food – their tails curve forwards over their bodies, readying their famous venomous sting. Deserts are classic scorpion territory, and species from the Sahara include the most dangerous in the world. The deathstalker, or African gold scorpion, has the most potent venom, but the fat-tailed scorpion is larger and more aggressive, and can kill an adult human with a single jab. Without treatment, death occurs in six to seven hours.

As well as surface tracks, dunes sometimes bear the stamp of reptiles that cruise below the surface like small submarines. Shovel-nosed snakes, from the American Southwest and Mexico, have extra-smooth scales and recessed jaws, while the Saharan sandfish – which is actually a kind of lizard – has short legs that it folds by its sides. Both use their specialised bodies to swim through the sand with wriggling movements, emerging onto the surface to hunt but submerging within seconds if they are threatened.

INTO THE INTERIOR

Some of the world's deserts – such as the Atacama and Namib – are only a short walk from the sea. At the other extreme, Central Asia's deserts are in the heart of the world's biggest continent, and as far from the sea as it is possible to be. Earth's most landlocked spot, in the Gurbantünggüt Desert of north-western China, is over 2600 km (1600 miles) from the nearest coast, and with it, the nearest source of rain-bearing winds. Like its much bigger neighbour – the Gobi Desert – it lies far outside the tropics. Summers here are warm, but winters are bitterly cold, with temperatures often dropping below -30°C (-22°F) for weeks at a time.

Stretching across China and Mongolia, the Gobi Desert is as big as Australia's Northern Territory, and over five times the size of the United Kingdom. Much of it comprises high-altitude plateaus, but it also includes the Turpan Depression – the world's third-lowest land-based point, where ancient irrigation systems nurture fields of a vivid and startling green. Apart from this, the Gobi's landscapes are bleak and severe. Gravel plains stretch away to distant horizons, while ranks of sand-scoured hills, called yardangs, look like the hulls of upturned boats, with their prows pointing into the wind.

THE FLAMING CLIFFS

In 1922, the American palaeontologist Roy Chapman Andrews set off on the first of several expeditions from Beijing to the Gobi, using a caravan of over 70 camels, and a small fleet of automobiles. His aim was to find fossils of early humans – a mission that drew a blank. Instead, at a site in Mongolia called the Bayn Dzak, or Flaming Cliffs, he unearthed a treasure trove of dinosaur remains. They included a beak-jawed plant-eater called *Protoceratops,* the fast-running predator *Velociraptor* and – even more astounding – several nests of dinosaur eggs. One of the nests was covered by the bones of a meat-eating dinosaur, which looked as though it had died while stealing the eggs. Many years later, the predator – called *Oviraptor,* or 'egg thief' – was officially cleared of blame: a beautifully preserved embryo inside a crushed egg showed that the nest was its own.

Andrews carried out a total of five expeditions, before bandits and political instability forced him

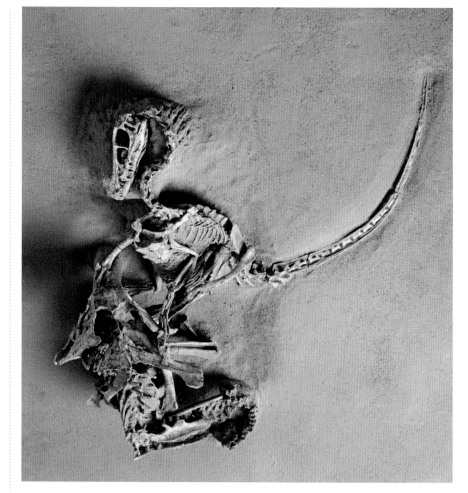

DINOSAUR FIGHT
The 1971 discovery of a Velociraptor *and* Protoceratops *encounter, which had remained hidden in sand since the Late Cretaceous period, was the first proof that palaeontologists had of actual dinosaur predation.*

to withdraw. In the decades that followed, Russian and Polish teams travelled further into the Gobi, and made some stunning discoveries of their own. The most famous was unearthed in 1971. Instead of one dinosaur, it consisted of two – a *Velociraptor* and *Protoceratops* locked in mortal combat. *Velociraptor* was armed with lethal claws that slashed its would-be prey, but *Protoceratops* defended itself by gripping its opponent's right arm in its powerful beak. The duel was inconclusive, because the struggling pair were suddenly swamped by a dune collapse, which buried them in an avalanche of sand. Frozen in time, they remained entombed for the next 84 million years.

THE STING OF SANDSTORMS

With nothing to hold it in place, desert dust and sand is easily swept up by daytime winds. The result is a dust storm or sandstorm – a dangerous and sometimes frightening event that brings all movement to a halt. You don't have to live in a desert to experience the after-effects of storms like these, because once fine particles are airborne, they can travel thousands of kilometres. The Gobi generates dust that coats buildings, streets and cars in faraway Beijing, while the Sahara

creates enormous plumes of dust that are blown out into the Atlantic, or northwards as far as the British Isles. Dust storms periodically hit cities in Australia and in the American Southwest, while the world's dustiest place – Chicha, in northern Chad – has dust storms on over 100 days a year. Incredibly, superfine dust from here reaches as far as the Amazon, where it is washed out of the air by the region's heavy rain.

Compared to fine dust, heavier sand grains do not travel so far, but their hard edges scratch and scrape any solid objects in their path. Car windscreens and headlights are peppered by thousands of tiny pits, and even solid rocks are slowly gnawed away. Most of the sand stays near ground level, so this sculpting creates mushroom-shaped rocks perched on slender 'stalks'. Over thousands of years, the stalk narrows and finally breaks, sending the rock above it toppling onto the desert floor.

THE ULTIMATE DESERT

Until the twentieth century, most geography books listed the Sahara as the biggest desert in the world. But as Antarctica was mapped and explored, it became clear that this was not true. Antarctica is not only the coldest continent, but the driest one as well. Heavy snow often falls on the coast, but at the South Pole, the average annual snowfall is almost nil. Even measuring snowfall is difficult, because most of it consists of 'diamond dust' – small ice crystals blown in on the wind, often under a clear blue sky.

The South Pole is 2800 m (9200 ft) high, so the air here is thin as well as cold. As a result, it contains far less moisture than in other deserts further north. These bone-dry conditions make working difficult: scientists at the South Pole Station suffer from cracked skin and chapped lips, and without proper protection – and plenty of water – they can get sunburned, frostbitten and dehydrated in just a few hours.

As well as being the world's largest desert, Antarctica is the only one that consists of glacial ice. It contains two-thirds of the world's fresh water – that's enough to cover the Sahara in a layer 3 km (2 miles) deep. Only one part of Antarctica is entirely free of snow and ice: the McMurdo Dry Valleys, where a hyper-arid desert has existed for over 2 million years.

'A VALLEY OF DEATH'

The McMurdo Dry Valleys are among the driest and most desolate places on Earth. Discovered by the polar explorer Robert Falcon Scott in 1903, they were originally gouged out by glaciers, which then retreated and left them bare. Ever since then, they have been kept clear of snow by ferocious winds. The steep cliffs and valley floors bear no outward signs of life, apart from mummified remains of seals and

EXTREME TOP 10
WORLD'S LARGEST DESERTS

1 ANTARCTIC DESERT (ANTARCTICA)
13,830,000 SQ KM (5,340,000 SQ MILES)

2 ARCTIC
13,727,000 SQ KM (5,300,000 SQ MILES)

3 SAHARA (AFRICA)
9,400,000 SQ KM (3,629,000 SQ MILES)

4 ARABIAN DESERT (ARABIAN PENINSULA)
2,330,000 SQ KM (900,000 SQ MILES)

5 GOBI DESERT (ASIA)
1,300,000 SQ KM (502,000 SQ MILES)

6 KALAHARI DESERT (AFRICA)
900,000 SQ KM (347,000 SQ MILES)

7 PATAGONIAN DESERT (SOUTH AMERICA)
670,000 SQ KM (259,000 SQ MILES)

8 GREAT VICTORIA DESERT (AUSTRALIA)
647,000 SQ KM (250,000 SQ MILES)

9 SYRIAN DESERT (MIDDLE EAST)
520,000 SQ KM (201,000 SQ MILES)

10 GREAT BASIN DESERT (NORTH AMERICA)
492,000 SQ KM (190,000 SQ MILES)

ANTARCTIC
DESERT

Bull Pass links Wright Valley and McKelvey Valley, part of the McMurdo Dry Valleys. Two small frozen lakes clearly stand out in this otherwise barren and windswept environment.

penguins that have wandered into the valleys by mistake. Some of these macabre relics are thousands of years old. Why these animals were drawn here, up to 20 km (12 miles) from the sea, no one really knows.

Scott thought that this eerie region was entirely lifeless – 'a valley of death' was how he described one of these gigantic rocky troughs. It is not hard to see why. Blasting out of the centre of Antarctica, the wind here can reach over 300 km/h (185 mph) – one of the fastest sustained wind speeds anywhere on Earth. The soil is little more than gravel and grit, and winter temperatures can drop below -55°C (-67°F), staying there throughout the long polar night. But amazingly, life does exist here, and the more scientists look, the more of it they find.

To see some of it, all you need to do is crack open a rock. Here, a few millimetres beneath the surface, specialised bacteria live in a world sealed off from the wind. Many of them grow by harnessing the energy in sunlight, although conditions are so cold that they are active for only about five or six weeks each year. Living alongside them are Antarctic lichens – the world's toughest multicellular life forms, with a life span often many centuries long. Together, the bacteria and lichens stain the rock a muddy green – colourful evidence of a thriving ecosystem in the strangest and remotest desert on Earth.

Trees and forests

From the fringes of the Arctic to the hot and steamy tropics, forests are the richest land habitats on Earth. They contain the world's tallest, biggest, oldest and heaviest living things, as well as millions of kinds of animals that depend on trees for their livelihood.

 ONG BEFORE THE age of the dinosaurs, evolution stumbled across something that completely changed life on Earth. It wasn't a new way of moving, or of catching prey, but an extremely strong and durable construction material. Unlike any man-made substance, it could grow and repair itself, and it could withstand enormous stresses and strains without breaking or being torn apart. In time, this new material proved to be a key asset for many living things, giving them a huge advantage in the struggle to survive.

This phenomenal substance is still here today – as you read this, the chances are that some is just an arm's length away. Without it, there would be no shrubs, no trees and no forests, and none of the extraordinary wildlife they contain. Botanists define it as secondary xylem, but it is far better known as wood.

FOSSIL FORESTS

Wood makes fabulous fossils, which is one reason why the record of the world's tree cover stretches far back in time. In places as far apart as Argentina and Australia, petrified forests show where trees once stood, before they were gradually turned into stone. These ancient forests were buried by volcanic ash or waterborne sediment, and dissolved minerals infiltrated the trees' cells. These minerals then crystallised, preserving every tiny detail of the cells' original shape. The results – aeons later – are amazingly lifelike replicas of tree trunks, in fossil forests that date back tens or hundreds of millions of years. Some of them are enormous: Arizona's Petrified Forest – one of the world's largest – covers an area of desert bigger than the whole of Singapore. Here, thousands of fossilised trunks are cracked open by winter frosts, just as if a chainsaw had cut them up.

?

EXTREME FACT
Ginkgo trees are living fossils – they have remained relatively unchanged for over 200 million years.

ARIZONA'S PETRIFIED FOREST
The tree fossils found here date back to the Late Triassic period, 237–201 million years ago.

Fossil forests can be found in many other places where no trees exist today. Great Britain has a number of fossil forests that are only visible at low tide, while on the Canadian Arctic island of Axel Heiberg, the mummified or dried-out remains of ancient trees lie on the open tundra. The oldest fossil forest discovered so far comes from Gilboa, in New York State, where ancient tree stumps were dug up over a century ago. A complete trunk was found much more recently, helping scientists to piece together trees that date back over 380 million years – that's about 150 million years earlier than the first dinosaur, and 220 million years before the first bird.

FIGHT FOR LIGHT

Before wood evolved, most land plants lived in marshy places, and few of them were more than knee-high. But once it existed, trees spread inland, and they began the equivalent of a space race as they competed for a share of the light. During this race, trees developed an astonishing variety of shapes, and some of them became the tallest living things in the entire history of Earth.

Over millions of years, the maximum height record has changed hands many times. Today, it is held by coast redwoods – breathtakingly beautiful conifers that grow in a narrow strip of central and northern California, where fog rolls in from the nearby Pacific Ocean. The tallest of these trees, named Hyperion,

currently measures just over 115 m (377 ft) in height, making it taller than the Statue of Liberty, and about 70 times the height of the naturalist who first climbed it in 2006. This magnificent redwood is estimated to be up to 800 years old, and it would be even higher were it not for woodpecker damage, which has removed the very tip of the tree.

Between the 1850s and 1950s, coast redwood forests were heavily logged, and it is only recently that they have been protected by a national park. Left to grow naturally, they are often densely packed, and – even by conifer standards – their trunks are amazingly lean and straight. High above the ground, their leaves intercept the fog that rolls in from the ocean, creating a constant drip of moisture that helps them to grow so tall. The biggest coast redwoods are in deep gullies, but Hyperion's exact position is being kept secret, to avoid the damage that too many admiring visitors might cause.

THE TALLEST-EVER TREES

Although coast redwoods currently hold the height record, the tallest conifer ever measured may have been a Douglas fir. In 1895, a huge specimen was felled near the Canadian city of Vancouver, and its height was put at 127 m (417 ft). In 1897, *The New York Times* mourned the passing of an even taller tree, which allegedly reached 142 m (466 ft) before it was cut down and measured on the ground. There are some doubts about both records, but, even so, Douglas firs still reach tremendous heights today.

Another contender for the tallest tree title comes from a very different part of the world. Known as the mountain ash or swamp gum, it is a broadleaved eucalyptus rather than a conifer. Mountain ashes grow on high ground in mainland Australia and Tasmania, and are currently the tallest broadleaved trees in the world. In the past, they may have broken an even more significant record as the biggest-ever plants.

Like coast redwoods and Douglas firs, mountain ashes have been extensively logged, and records of bygone giants are difficult to verify. The tallest specimen alive today, from southern Tasmania, is about 100 m (330 ft) high. But over a century ago, mountain ashes were often much bigger than this. In the 1870s, a living tree from Victoria was estimated to have reached 132 m (433 ft), while a decade earlier, a fallen mountain ash apparently measured over 145 m (476 ft) when the pieces of its broken trunk were added up. If it had been a building, rather than a tree, this monster would have been 44 storeys high.

In all the world's forests, nothing comes near this height today. However, giant trees keep growing, which means that the record increases, too. Mountain ashes are particularly speedy growers, so it is quite possible that one of them may eventually snatch back the title of Earth's tallest tree.

EXTREME TOP 10
TALLEST TREE SPECIES*

1 COAST REDWOOD
(CALIFORNIA, UNITED STATES)
115 M (377 FT)

2 MOUNTAIN ASH (TASMANIA, AUSTRALIA)
100 M (330 FT)

3 DOUGLAS FIR (OREGON, UNITED STATES)
99 M (325 FT)

4 SITKA SPRUCE (CALIFORNIA, UNITED STATES)
96 M (315 FT)

5 GIANT SEQUOIA (CALIFORNIA, UNITED STATES)
95 M (312 FT)

6 BLUE GUM (TASMANIA, AUSTRALIA)
91 M (299 FT)

7 MANNA GUM (TASMANIA, AUSTRALIA)
89 M (292 FT)

8 NOBLE FIR
(WASHINGTON STATE, UNITED STATES)
89 M (292 FT)

9 YELLOW MERANTI (SABAH, BORNEO)
88 M (289 FT)

10 ALPINE ASH (TASMANIA, AUSTRALIA)
88 M (289 FT)

Heights given relate to the tallest known example of the species. As trees are living, growing organisms, height records continually change. The figures for some pairs of species are equal due to rounding up.

FORESTS OF THE FAR NORTH

In the wild, eucalypts are nearly all found in Australasia or New Guinea, with just one species growing north of the Equator. Conifers are much more widespread – they grow on every continent except Antarctica, and they form immense forests in the far Northern Hemisphere. Here, the huge boreal forest makes up nearly a third of the world's tree cover. Named after Boreas, the Greek god of the north wind, it contains only a few dozen different kinds of tree, but it covers 15 million sq km (6 million sq miles) – far more than any other forest on Earth.

The boreal forest zone stretches right around Earth, from Scandinavia and Siberia to Alaska and Canada. In places, the forest is over 1500 km (900 miles) from its southern edge to its northern limit, where the climate becomes so severe that trees can no longer grow. Most boreal forest conifers are evergreen, but the hardiest ones are larches, which lose their leaves in autumn, and grow a new set every spring. Near the southern edge of the forest, the trees grow close

BOREAL FOREST
Alaska's boreal forest mostly comprises black spruces and white spruces, with a few other trees such as paper birches.

together, but further north, the forest opens out before finally fading away. In Russia, this transition zone is known as the taiga – a word that is sometimes used for the boreal forest as a whole.

The world's northernmost trees are a scattering of Dahurian larches located near the Siberian village of Khatanga, about 750 km (470 miles) north of the Arctic Circle. Here, winter temperatures can plunge to a glacial -50°C (-58°F), and the summer growing season is only a few weeks long. Beyond this point, the only woody plants are Arctic willows, which are specially adapted to life in the open tundra. Instead of growing upright, these ultra-hardy shrubs creep across the ground, forming springy mats that can be more than two centuries old.

BOREAL FOREST HUNTERS

Despite its bitterly cold winter climate, the boreal forest is full of animal life, from brown bears and wolves to insect grubs that develop inside trees. This forest is also the home of many species of mustelid – lithe, thickly furred mammals that include sables, martens, stoats and minks. All mustelids are hunters, and many can kill animals several times their own size. On land, the largest of them is the wolverine, a stocky predator that is shaped like a small bear, and legendary for its strength. Despite weighing less than

30 kg (65 lb), wolverines can kill animals as large as moose, and cold weather works to their advantage, because they often scavenge on dead remains. Their fur is covered with water-repellent oil that keeps it dry, stopping the hairs sticking together when the temperature drops far below freezing point.

Boreal forest birds include many summer visitors, but also some permanent residents that manage to find food all year round. One of the most striking is the great grey owl, a bird with a 1.5-m (5-ft) wingspan, and an enormous circular 'face' containing two staring yellow eyes. The owl's facial disc channels the faintest sounds into its deeply buried ears, allowing it to detect voles and other small mammals through up to 60 cm (24 in) of snow. Rather than searching for food on the wing, it watches and listens for prey from a favourite perch, before gliding down and punching its way through the snow to make a kill.

HEAVYWEIGHT CHAMPIONS

There are only about 650 kinds of conifer, compared to over 20,000 kinds of broadleaved tree. But despite being outnumbered, conifers hold an impressive clutch of records, including the title of the world's most massive single living thing. This particular record goes to California's giant sequoias, which grow in groves high up in the Sierra Nevada mountain range. The biggest specimens are over 3000 years old, and their thickest branches are so huge that they would make substantial trees in their own right.

Unlike coast redwoods – their distant relatives – giant sequoias have enormous tapering trunks, protected by spongy bark up to 90 cm (35 in) thick. The tallest are over 90 m (300 ft) high, which, combined with their exceptionally thick trunks and branches, gives them a colossal total weight. Excluding its root system, the largest giant sequoia – known as General Sherman – weighs over 2000 tonnes (2200 tons), which is over 10 times as much as an adult blue whale, and five times as much as a fully laden Boeing 747. Its wood volume is equivalent to 22 standard shipping

WOLVERINE

This boreal forest predator has many names. One, skunk bear, derives from its habit of marking its territory with pungent secretions from its anal glands.

GREAT GREY OWL

When conditions are optimal – there is plenty of food, and their habitat remains undisturbed – great grey owls can live for up to 10 years in the wild.

THE TREMBLING GIANT

Utah's Fishlake National Forest is home to The Trembling Giant, an extensive clonal colony of quaking aspen trees. The organism is also called Pando, which is Latin for 'I spread'.

CLONE ZONE

The world's heaviest organism is The Trembling Giant (also known as Pando) – an interconnected clump of quaking aspen trees in Utah. Including its roots, it is estimated to weigh about 6000 tonnes (6600 tons). The clump covers over 40 hectares (100 acres) and has over 47,000 trunks. It forms a single clone, meaning that all its parts are genetically identical, having grown from a single original tree. The Trembling Giant probably started life over 80,000 years ago – long before humans arrived in North America. Quaking aspens get their name from the way their leaves tremble in the breeze.

containers – something that would have attracted covetous glances in the late 1800s, when many of California's conifers fell under the axe. Fortunately, giant sequoias were protected by their size and their remote location, although some were cut down before the remaining trees were saved.

FRIENDLY FIRE

In the giant sequoia's mountain habitat, snow often lies on the ground for six months each year. Despite this, forest fires periodically sweep the sequoia groves. These fires kill many small trees and shrubs, but they actually help giant sequoias to thrive.

Giant sequoia bark is so thick that most forest fires do no damage to the living wood inside. Instead, fires clear away fallen branches and other debris, creating an ideal bed for the trees' tiny winged seeds. A mature giant sequoia can have over 10,000 cones, with more than 200 seeds in each, but instead of dropping straight away, the seeds often wait for years before fluttering to

the ground. That moment finally comes when the cones are heated by flames, which makes them open up their scales. The seeds land on a bed of fertile ash, and a tiny proportion of them produce young trees. To survive, they must lay down their own protective bark as fast as they can, before the next wildfire burns through the sequoia grove.

Once giant sequoias are mature, they are safely beyond many other dangers that menace smaller trees. Their bark and heartwood are rich in tannins – chemicals that protect their wood against insect and fungus attack. They are also so strong that high winds rarely harm them, and even lightning strikes seldom kill them outright, although they can destroy many metres of trunk. They continue growing into extreme old age, sometimes putting on a tonne of new wood each and every year.

BROADLEAVED FORESTS

Conifers are common in the far north and in mountains, but across the rest of the world, most forests comprise broadleaved trees. Unlike conifers, broadleaved trees are flowering plants, and they often use animals to pollinate their flowers and spread their seeds. Some kinds have seeds that are not much bigger than specks of dust, but the biggest seeds – produced by the coco de mer palm – weigh a colossal 18 kg (40 lb) each.

COCO DE MER SEED
Thought to resemble the female behind (especially after the husk has been removed), the coco de mer seed was long considered to have aphrodisiac powers. It is the largest and heaviest seed in the plant kingdom.

Broadleaved trees also hold the record for the biggest flower display. The talipot palm, from India and Sri Lanka, blooms just once, growing an enormous flower cluster that holds up to a quarter of a million blossoms. After flowering and forming its seeds, the tree then dies.

Palms grow mainly in warm places, but other species of broadleaved trees are found all over the globe. In temperate regions – such as eastern North America and western Europe – broadleaved trees are deciduous, shedding their leaves each autumn and growing a new set in spring. Before shedding their leaves, the trees shut down their chemical processes and then reabsorb the chlorophyll that makes the leaves green. As the green colour fades, it is often replaced by bright yellow, orange or red hues before the leaves finally die and fall to the ground.

TIME WARP

In many parts of the world, temperate broadleaved woodlands have been artificially managed for centuries, as sources of timber and other forest products. During the Age of Sail, hardwood or broadleaved timber was used for making warships – in the 1500s, for example, English carpenters used over 200 mature oak trunks to make King Henry VIII's warship *Mary Rose,* while in the 1700s, over 40 hectares (100 acres) of forest were used to construct Admiral Nelson's flagship,

▲

AMAZON RAINFOREST

Like a mirror reflecting the cloudy sky, the Ariau River is glassy as it flows gently through the Amazon rainforest in Brazil. The forest canopy is not tall, but very dense – an ideal habitat for protecting the thousands of bird and animal species that live here.

WHERE TO SEE
THE WORLD'S FATTEST
BROADLEAVED TREE

Measured at chest height, the world's fattest broadleaved tree is the Sunland Baobab, in Limpopo Province, South Africa. Its hollow trunk is over 33 m (108 ft) in circumference, and the tree is estimated to be at least 1000 years old. Incredibly, there is a 15-seat pub set up inside the tree's trunk!

HMS *Victory*. Hardwood timber was also used for building, and for producing all kinds of everyday necessities, from charcoal and cartwheels to chairs. As a result, few temperate broadleaved woodlands are exactly as they would have been in the wild.

However, there are some exceptions to this rule, which the tide of time seems to have passed by. One of them is Bialowieza Forest, a remnant of Europe's original wild forest, which straddles the border of Poland and Belarus. Originally preserved as a royal hunting ground, it is home to many animals that once roamed the European continent. Among them are wild boar, fallow deer and grey wolves, as well as the biggest free-roaming herd of European bison, a species that disappeared from the wild in the 1920s. Fortunately, several dozen European bison remained in zoos, and the species was slowly reintroduced. Today, Bialowieza Forest protects over 800 of these majestic animals, and many more live in captivity.

TREES IN THE TROPICS

Europe has about 500 kinds of indigenous or 'home-grown' trees. North America has about twice this number, while Australia has nearly 700 kinds of eucalypts, another 1000 kinds of acacia or wattle, as well as many other broadleaved species. It's an impressive total, but it trails far behind that of the remarkable Amazon rainforest – the largest tropical forest in the world. This huge evergreen blanket contains about 16,000 tree species, and, despite deforestation, it still has a mind-boggling total of nearly 400 billion individual trees.

Rainforests aren't the only forests in the tropics, because monsoon or seasonal forests are also found in warm parts of the world. In rainforests, it is hot and wet all year round, while monsoon forests get all their rainfall during the same few months each year. For humans, the rainforest climate can be irksome and

monotonous, but it is perfect for growing trees. The biggest trees – called emergents – seem to float like islands above the forest canopy, while the forest floor is often deep in shade. Here, slender saplings can wait for decades for a gap to open up overhead, giving them the light they need to reach the canopy themselves.

PASSENGERS AND PARASITES

Many rainforest plants and animals spend their entire lives in the canopy, high above the ground. Over half the world's orchids are tropical tree-dwellers, and so are many other plants, including bromeliads, mosses and ferns. Bromeliads are found only in the Americas, where they perch on branches, collecting pools of rainwater with their rosette of spiky leaves. In an area of forest the size of a football field, they can hold up to 25,000 litres (6600 gallons) of water – a huge treetop water source and habitat for insects and frogs that is topped up every time it rains.

In tropical rainforests, the fight for living space is intense, and some plants have evolved strange and sometimes sinister ways of getting the daylight that they need. Strangler fig seeds germinate high in the treetops, and then send slender roots all the way down to the ground. Once a young strangler fig has made contact with the soil, its growth speeds up, and its roots start to form a living jacket around its chosen host tree. The ill-fated host tree eventually dies and rots away, leaving a hollow-trunked strangler fig standing in its place.

The Swiss cheese plant, from Central and South America, germinates on the ground. Unlike most seedlings, it grows towards the darkest area around it, which guides it to the nearest tree. The plant then climbs upwards, until the light is bright enough for it to flower. However, if the tree is too short, the plant can change its mind. Its tip does a 180-degree turn, and heads back down again. Once it reaches the soil, it sets off to 'hunt' for another host tree, like a restless animal searching for its prey.

INSECT EMPIRES

Rainforests are home to a huge number of birds and mammals, but insects outnumber them by millions of times. The smallest species are only just visible to the naked eye, but the biggest are some of the most extreme in the insect world, measured by weight and body size. They include African Goliath beetles, which can weigh twice as much as a mouse, and male Hercules beetles from South America, which have enormous rhino-like 'horns' up to 9 cm (3½ in) in length. Birdwing butterflies, from Southeast Asia and northern Australia, have a record-breaking wingspan of up to 30 cm (12 in), while Chan's megastick – a species of stick insect from Borneo –

IT'S ABOUT TIME

The world's oldest individual trees are bristlecone pines from the White Mountains of California. They live at altitudes of up to 3000 m (10,000 ft), and grow extremely slowly, because they have to cope with cold temperatures, dry soil and icy winds. The oldest specimen discovered so far began its life over 5000 years ago.

HERCULES BEETLE
These fearsome-looking rainforest insects are well titled – like their strong namesake from classical mythology, some species can lift more than 800 times their own body weight.

has the greatest overall length, measuring up to 56 cm (22 in) with its legs stretched out along its sides. Rainforest stick insects lay some of the world's largest insect eggs. They can be bigger than peanuts, and are often dropped from trees onto the ground.

Rainforest insects also break records when they live together in family groups, or colonies. Army ants, from Central and South America, form roaming colonies containing hundreds of thousands of workers and soldiers, which stream across the forest floor. The column travels less than 20 m (65 ft) per hour, but the ants quickly smother and kill any animals that do not escape in time. African driver ants are even more ferocious: they have a similar roving lifestyle, but live in colonies containing up to 50 million insects, commanded by a single queen. Queen driver ants are some of the most prolific parents on Earth. When the colony comes to a temporary halt, the queen can lay up to 3 million eggs before the ants set off once more.

ARBOREAL ANIMAL

A three-toed sloth hangs from a tree branch, with her baby clinging to her belly, in Costa Rica's renowned Corcovado National Park, which protects a large section of lowland tropical rainforest. Famously slow-moving, three-toed sloths sleep for up to 20 hours each day.

North and South Poles

Remote, hostile and bitterly cold, the North and South Poles are the only two places in the world where the Sun rises and sets just once a year. The poles break all kinds of other records, too, but the differences between them are even stranger than the features that they share.

I F YOU ASK someone how many poles Earth has, their answer will almost certainly be wrong. The total isn't two, or four, or even six. Amazingly, the complete list comes to 10 or more. Some of Earth's poles are fixed in place, but many of them have a bizarre habit of wandering as time goes by.

First and foremost there are the two geographic poles, which are the traditional 'top' and 'bottom' of the globe. Explorers first reached them in the early twentieth century, after a number of daring – and sometimes fatal – expeditions in two of the world's most forbidding regions. The geographic poles are at opposite ends of the planet, and they are the only two points on the surface that lie exactly on Earth's axis of rotation. In other words, someone standing at either pole turns on the spot, while everyone else moves in a circle as the planet spins.

THE ENDS OF EARTH

The North Geographic Pole is in the heart of the Arctic Ocean – the smallest of the world's five oceans, and the only one that is almost completely ringed by land. The sea beneath it is about 4 km (2½ miles) deep, while floating ice covers its surface. Sea ice at the North Pole is up to 3 m (10 ft) thick, and it is kept on the move by ocean currents and the wind. In spring and autumn, when the wind is at its strongest, pieces of ice crash

?

EXTREME FACT
Antarctic skuas and snow petrels are the only wild animals that have been seen at the South Pole. Both of them normally live along Antarctica's frozen coast.

into each other with incredible force, either piling up into ridges or scraping past each other with an ear-splitting roar. During the early days of Arctic exploration, sailing ships were sometimes marooned in ice, and the sailors aboard would be exhausted by the 'Devil's Symphony' – their name for this constant and frightening barrage of sound.

The South Geographic Pole is very different, because it lies on the ice-covered plateau of Antarctica – the fifth-largest of the world's seven continents – and is located about 2800 m (9200 ft) above sea level. Antarctica's ice sheet is made from compressed snow, which is slowly sliding towards the continent's stormy coasts, propelled by its colossal weight. The ice's average thickness is about 2000 m (6500 ft) – or about six times the height of the Eiffel Tower – but the deepest areas are double this thickness, and contain ice that is over a million years old.

PEOPLE AT THE POLES

The North Pole has no full-time human inhabitants, although hundreds of scientists and intrepid travellers visit it each year. Most come by ship, some arrive on skis, some – amazingly – travel over the ice on mountain bikes and, occasionally, some surface aboard submarines. The South Pole receives fewer callers. However, unlike the North Pole, it is home to a permanent population of researchers who live and work at the Amundsen–Scott South Pole Station, the second-coldest address on Earth. Nearly all the South Pole's visitors stay only for the summer months, leaving a skeleton staff of scientists and technicians who manage the station through the darkness of the long polar winter.

Until 2006, the South Pole Station was supplied entirely by air from McMurdo Station, the largest base in Antarctica, and the world's southernmost port. Since then, an ice road has been opened that allows convoys to travel all the way to the pole. Special tractors complete the 1600-km (1000-mile) journey in about 40 days, skirting crevasses and pushing their way through 'snow dunes', or sastrugi, which are whipped into lines by the relentless Antarctic wind. These obstacles make this the slowest road on the planet, and the only one of its size that has no service stations.

EARTH'S 10 MAJOR POLES

NAME OF POLE	CURRENT LOCATION	CURRENT COORDINATES
North Geographic Pole	Arctic Ocean	90°N
North Magnetic Pole	Arctic Ocean	84.97°N 132.35°W
Northern Pole of Inaccessibility	Arctic Ocean	84.00°N 174.85°W
North Geomagnetic Pole	Arctic Ocean	80.08°N 72.21°W
Northern Pole of Cold	North-east Siberia	67.55°N 133.38°E
South Geographic Pole	Antarctica	90°S
Southern Pole of Inaccessibility	Antarctica	82.18°S 54.97°E
Southern Pole of Cold	Dome A, Antarctica	80.37°S 77.35°E
South Geomagnetic Pole	Antarctica	80.08°S 107.79°E
South Magnetic Pole	Southern Ocean	64.50°S 137.68°E

NORTH POLE
In 2011, scientists aboard the German research icebreaker RV Polarstern *visited the North Pole to investigate the state of the diminishing multiple-year sea ice in the Arctic Ocean.*

Close to the South Pole Station, a marker indicates the spot that is the southern end of the world. Despite its official-looking appearance, the marker is not completely accurate, because the ice sheet under the South Pole is sliding north-north-west at a rate of about 3 cm (1 in) per day. Once a year, in a special ceremony, the marker is moved to catch up. Left where it is, it would eventually reach the distant shores of the Weddell Sea – a journey that could take at least 100,000 years.

THE POLAR YEAR

The geographic poles are the only two places on Earth where all the world's time zones converge. In theory, a quick walk around the pole would take you through them all in quick succession, so in a handful of minutes, you could experience an entire 24-hour 'day'. In practice, the South Pole Station keeps to New Zealand time, as this is the departure point for most of the base's supplies.

The geographic poles are also the only places where the year is divided exactly in two, between a long summer day and a seemingly endless winter night. During the polar summer, the Sun stays above the horizon for six months, and it moves around in a circle, instead of rising and setting every day. As the summer wears on, the circle moves closer to the horizon, until the Sun finally grazes the ice and then drops out of sight. A long twilight follows – bright enough to read a paper – before the real darkness of the polar winter sets in. Then, nearly six months later, the process is reversed, as the first glimmers of the polar dawn appear low in the sky. As each day passes, the Sun climbs closer and closer to the horizon, until it bursts into view and the polar summer begins.

THE BIG CHILL

In the far north and south, summer and winter are relative words, because both poles can be excruciatingly cold. At the North Pole, air temperatures in summer barely climb above 0°C (32°F), while winter temperatures can drop to about -40°C (-40°F). Compared to this, the ocean beneath is relatively warm. It stays just above freezing point, which for sea water is a balmy -1.8°C (28.8°F). This huge store of heat limits the growth of sea ice, which is why it is rarely more than 5 m (16 ft) thick anywhere in the Arctic Ocean, even when the ice is several years old.

The South Pole's climate is much more extreme, because it is high up, and the sea is so far away. Even in the middle of summer, the thermometer never climbs above -12°C (10°F), and in midwinter, temperatures often drop to -60°C (-76°F), with a record low of -82.8°C (-117.0°F). Only one place in the world has registered temperatures lower than this – Vostok Station, near the centre of the East Antarctic Ice Sheet, which is about 1300 km (800 miles) from the pole itself. Vostok Station

GUIDING STARS OF THE POLAR REGIONS

Once every 23 hours and 56 minutes, the stars overhead circle around one of two fixed points, known as the North and South Celestial Poles. This happens because Earth is spinning, and not because the stars are actually on the move. Through a fortunate coincidence, a bright star called Polaris is almost directly above the North Pole, marking the position of the North Celestial Pole. For centuries, it has been used as a compass, showing which way true north lies. Its southern equivalent – a star called Sigma Octantis – is much fainter. It cannot be used for navigation, because it is barely visible to the naked eye.

◤ ANTARCTIC BLIZZARD

Visitors to Antarctica inevitably face one or more of the continent's harsh blizzards – where winds blast at around 160 km/h (100 mph), and visibility is often reduced to less than 1 m (3 ft).

◢ POLAR TWILIGHT

Emperor penguins gather together in the faint pinkish light of Antarctica's polar twilight. During this time of year, the sun is situated just a few degrees below the horizon.

is 650 m (2100 ft) higher than the South Pole Station, which gives it the edge in the record books. Here, the lowest temperature ever logged was -89.2°C (-128.6°F), during the winter of 1983. In 2010, a temperature of -93.2°C (-135.8°F) was recorded near here by satellite, although this is not officially recognised as a record as there are no ground measurements to back it up.

Another point on the ice sheet, called Dome A, is even higher, reaching just over 4000 m (13,100 ft). Average conditions here are slightly colder than at Vostok Station, which arguably makes this location – rather than Vostok Station – the world's chilliest place. However, even this is not the end of the story, because Ridge A, a remote crest about 100 km (60 miles) from Dome A, might be even colder. Here, or somewhere nearby on the ice sheet, winter temperatures could drop tantalisingly close to -100°C (-148°F), although no weather station has ever recorded this ultimate in polar extremes.

POLES ON THE MOVE

If you look at a detailed map of the Arctic or Antarctica, the North and South Poles aren't the only ones you'll find. Earth also has magnetic poles, which form part of its

magnetic field. Movements in the planet's molten iron core create the magnetic field, which wraps the whole world in invisible curves known as lines of force. At the North Magnetic Pole, the field points vertically downwards, and at the South Magnetic Pole, it points directly up.

Unlike the geographic poles, Earth's magnetic poles are constantly on the move. Every day, they pirouette in loops up to 80 km (50 miles) wide, and their average position – at the centre of the loops – keeps moving, too. These convoluted movements are due to changes in Earth's core, and also to changes in radiation from the Sun.

The North Magnetic Pole was first located in 1831, when it was on the Arctic coast of Canada, some 2000 km (1200 miles) from the 'true' North Pole. Since then, it has drifted north-west into the Arctic Ocean off Ellesmere Island, and is currently heading towards Siberia at a rate of about 40 km (25 miles) per year. Coincidentally, the South Magnetic Pole is heading north-west, too, although not so quickly. In the year 1900, it was on mainland Antarctica. It reached the coast in about 1970, and, like the North Magnetic Pole, it is now heading out to sea.

MAGNETIC FLIPS

Strangely, the two magnetic poles do not line up on opposite sides of Earth. Sometimes they wander slightly closer together, and sometimes further apart. On a scale of hundreds of thousands of years, something much more dramatic happens: Earth's magnetic field abruptly reverses, and the two magnetic poles change places. Telltale traces preserved in seabed lava show exactly when each of these 'flips' occurred.

The list of poles does not stop there, because Earth also has two geomagnetic poles, which do line up through Earth's centre point. Used mainly by astronomers, these poles show where compass needles would point if the planet's magnetic field was perfectly regular, like a bar magnet hanging in empty space. The North Geomagnetic Pole is currently off the northern coast of Greenland, and its southern equivalent is not far from Vostok Station, on Antarctica's featureless inland ice.

BEYOND THE POLES

Far away from the poles themselves, two natural boundaries mark the place where the polar worlds begin. One of them is the Arctic tree line – the zone where the boreal or northern forest gives way to treeless tundra. In the tundra, the top metre or two of soil usually thaws out in the summer, but beneath this the ground often stays frozen, in a layer known as permafrost.

In North America, permafrost extends to about 600 m (2000 ft) down, but in north-east Siberia, it reaches a record depth of nearly 1500 m (5000 ft). There are even patches of 'prehistoric' permafrost hidden deep down in countries such as Poland; these are relics from the end of the last ice age, around 12,000 years ago.

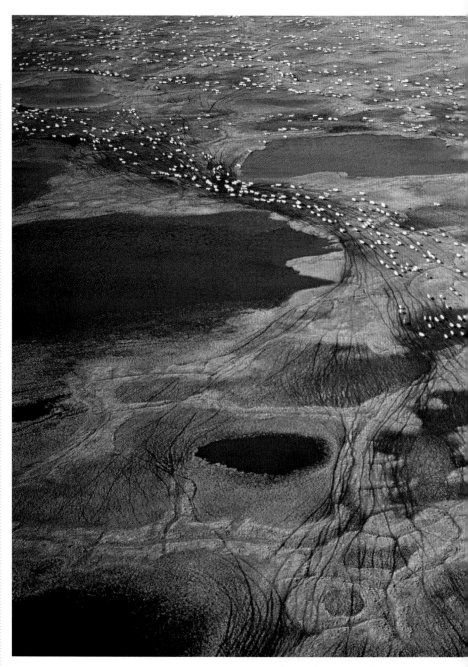

CARIBOU MIGRATION

In spring, up to half a million caribou – also known as reindeer – make the lengthy trek across the Alaskan tundra to their summer feeding grounds, travelling around 20–50 km (10–30 miles) per day.

🞀🞀
ARCTIC TREE LINE
Close to the Arctic Circle, the tree cover is sparse and stunted. Beyond the Arctic tree line, the air is too cold to support the growth of trees.

🞀🞀
MIGRATING SURFBIRDS
These stocky little birds travel to tundra regions in Alaska and the neighbouring Yukon territory in Canada to breed.

IT'S ABOUT TIME

The last reversal in Earth's magnetic field happened about 780,000 years ago. Based on past records, the next one could be due any time in the next few thousand years. During a magnetic 'flip', Earth's magnetic field drops to almost zero, reducing its protection against dangerous cosmic rays.

Permafrost stops water draining away, so the summer melt turns the tundra into a quagmire of boggy lakes and pools. It's hard going for humans, but a perfect habitat for some of the Arctic's animals. Vast numbers of mosquitoes breed in the shallow water, taking to the air in summer in enormous drifting clouds. Tundra ponds and coasts are also a prime habitat for migratory birds. Every year, hundreds of millions of geese, ducks and shorebirds come here to breed, after travelling from as far away as South America and Australia. In the constant daylight, these summer visitors feed around the clock, eating plants, insect larvae and a range of small animals along the shore.

Summer is a busy time for the Arctic's mammals, on land and at sea. Caribou give birth in early summer, sometimes travelling up to 2500 km (1500 miles) to reach their summer feeding grounds – a record migration for a mammal that lives on land. At sea, grey whales travel even further. Most of them breed in lagoons off the north-west coast of Mexico, before travelling north to Alaska and onwards as far as the Arctic's Chukchi Sea. The round trip measures up to 20,000 km (12,500 miles), and in the course of their 40-year life spans, grey whales can travel the equivalent of a return trip to the Moon.

COMING UP FOR AIR

By the time the Arctic summer ends, its migrants are long gone. Lemmings stay active beneath the snow, but at sea, most mammals – apart from the polar bear – face increasing problems from the growing sea ice. In some parts of the Arctic, whales and walruses congregate in areas of open water called polynias, which are kept ice-free by ocean currents or the wind. Some polynias are only a few kilometres across, but the largest are huge, and are in the same place year after year. The North Water Polynia, between Greenland and Canada's Ellesmere Island, is the Arctic's biggest, with a surface area the same size as South Carolina. Throughout the winter, it throngs with narwhals, beluga whales, walruses and seals.

Beyond these open-water havens, marine mammals can have problems getting air to breathe. The ringed

seal – which lives as far north as the pole – survives by using the claws on its front flippers to scrape away breathing holes in the ice. An adult ringed seal can maintain up to a dozen holes at once, each 2 m (7 ft) deep, but the colder the outside air becomes, the more time it has to spend stopping its lifelines freezing up.

Unfortunately for the seals, polar bears home in on seal breathing holes, and wait patiently for their owners to reappear. If a seal is lucky, it can break the surface unharmed, but if a polar bear is lurking nearby, the seal's blubber-wrapped body is grabbed and suddenly hauled out on the ice. A fat-rich meal like this will keep a polar bear going for at least a week.

THE SOUTHERN FRONTIER

In the far south, the polar world starts at the Antarctic Convergence, a zone where the cold Southern Ocean meets slightly warmer water further north. South of this boundary, the seas teem with penguins, seals and whales. There are no polar bears in the Antarctic, but in their place, leopard seals are formidable predators. Weighing up to 500 kg (1100 lb), they hunt fish, penguins and also other seals, and they have been known to attack human divers, although fatalities are very rare.

Unlike the Arctic, the Antarctic has very few land animals – the largest of them is a wingless midge that grows a mere 6 mm (¼ in) long. The region's plant life

EMPEROR PENGUINS

At about seven weeks of age, chicks stay together in a creche while their parents search for food; a few adults remain with them for protection.

RINGED SEAL

Before it comes to the surface, a ringed seal will often blow bubbles in their breathing hole to see if an alert – and hungry – polar bear is waiting above.

POLAR BEAR

An adult polar bear's paws measure around 30 cm (12 in) across; this large size helps when they are walking on snow or swimming in the ocean.

is also very sparse, and includes just two flowering species: Antarctic pearlwort and Antarctic hair grass. To make up for this, Antarctica's shores and sea ice teem with birds that get their food from the sea. Four of the world's 17 kinds of penguins breed here, either on rocky beaches or – in the case of the emperor penguin – on the ice, up to 80 km (50 miles) inland. Some penguin colonies contain over half a million birds, and ancient bones and eggshells show that the biggest have existed in the same place for thousands of years.

WINTER VIGIL

The emperor penguin is the only species that lays its single egg as the polar night begins. For nearly four months, the male cradles the egg on its feet, under a fold of skin. He keeps the egg at a steady temperature of about 34°C (93°F), an incredible achievement when the outside air temperature drops to -60°C (-76°F) for days at a time. When the chicks hatch, they huddle together in groups called creches, keeping slowly on the move so that each has a turn near the centre, out of the wind.

It may sound crazy, but there are advantages to this bizarre timetable. By the time the sea ice starts to melt, the chicks are almost as big as their parents, and they are ready to take up life in the waves. They have the whole of the polar summer to complete their development, in some of the richest fishing grounds in the world.

Islands and archipelagos

From outposts of continents to far-flung specks in tropical seas, islands have a character that is all their own. Many have been inhabited since the dawn of human history, but some of the most distant and inhospitable islands have seen fewer human visitors than the surface of the Moon.

I N DECEMBER 1821, the sailing ship *Emerald,* under the command of Captain William Elliot, observed the outline of an unknown island about 1400 km (870 miles) south-south-west of New Zealand. The position of the island was duly logged, and the island was described as 'very high, with peaked mountains'. Another ship later claimed to have sailed around it, although no landing place could be found. Emerald Island made its way into atlases and charts, and remained in print for over 150 years. But as subsequent expeditions discovered, Captain Elliot's island was a phantom – instead of craggy peaks, nothing was there except the vast emptiness of the open sea.

Phantom islands were common when pioneering navigators started making ocean charts. At one time, California was believed to be an island, and the North Atlantic was thought to contain a mysterious island known as Thule. Buss Island, supposedly on the edge of the Arctic, was even leased by the Hudson's Bay Company in 1675, giving it the right to any gold, silver or precious stones that could be found.

Today, satellite imagery means that islands are much better known, and the age of phantoms is long past. But even so, islands still include some of the remotest, most alluring and most inaccessible places on Earth.

ISLANDS AND CONTINENTS

Wherever you live, you are ultimately surrounded by the sea. However, that doesn't mean that you are on an island, because most of the world's land belongs to continents. Much bigger than islands, continents are made of rock called continental crust. This crust extends out to sea in shallow continental shelves, forming not only the seabed, but also creating continental islands, which are sometimes just a stone's throw from the shore.

Australia is usually classified as a continent, which leaves Greenland in the number one position as Earth's largest island. Nearly seven times bigger than the British Isles, it is smothered by an immense sheet of glacial ice up to 3 km (2 miles) deep, which weighs an estimated 2500 trillion tonnes (2800 trillion tons). Only the outer edges of Greenland are ice-free, but,

? EXTREME FACT

The largest uninhabited island in the world is Devon Island, in the Canadian Arctic. It is over 500 km (300 miles) long, and has winter temperatures that dip down to -50°C (-58°F).

◄ ROCK ISLANDS

Verdant jewels in the turquoise waters of the western Pacific Ocean, Palau's Rock Islands comprise 400 limestone islands as well as the world's largest number of marine lakes (bodies of sea water cut off from the ocean by land-based barriers).

COLOURFUL GREENLAND BUILDINGS
In Nuuk, the hue of a building originally symbolised its function: for example, red for commercial properties, yellow for hospitals. Today, the colour is simply an aesthetic choice.

even here, ice is never far away: fleets of icebergs troop majestically past the shore, heading north towards Baffin Island, before turning south again towards the North Atlantic's shipping lanes. In 1912, one of these icebergs famously sank the *Titanic* at latitude 41°N, which is almost level with New York City.

FURTHEST NORTH

Although humans first reached Greenland 5000 years ago, it is still the least densely populated country in the world. There are fewer than 60,000 people, a quarter of whom live in the capital city, Nuuk. Many native Greenlanders have never seen a tree, and in an island surrounded by bone-chilling water, 95 per cent do not know how to swim. Soccer is the country's national sport, but because the climate is so harsh, outdoor pitches are made from earth or sand instead of grass.

The southernmost point of Greenland lies well outside the Arctic Circle, while the northernmost point looks out over a small, low-lying island that is the most northerly permanent land on Earth. Called Kaffeklubben Island (or Inuit Qeqertaat), it was first visited by Western scientists in 1921. However, its position as record holder

is in dispute. In 1978, a survey team spotted the island of Oodaaq, a gravel bank even further north, and several other miniscule islets have also claimed the title, although most are temporary features, at the mercy of the waves. One thing is sure: if you step out over the winter sea ice, there is no more land between here and the North Geographic Pole, roughly 710 km (440 miles) away.

AMAZING ARCHIPELAGOS

Half a world away from icy Greenland, the Malay Archipelago is the largest collection of islands (by area) on the globe. Home to more than 350 million people, it lies between Southeast Asia and Australia, and contains at least 25,000 islands, divided up into seven different nation states. Few other archipelagos have such varied scenery: the biggest island, Borneo, has towering mountains as well as tropical swamps, while Sumatra and the Philippines have some of the most active volcanoes in the world.

Java, in the south of the archipelago, is home to more people than any other island on Earth. Over 130 million people live in its rapidly expanding cities, and on the island's green and fertile farms. Like many other islands in Southeast Asia, Java's steep hillsides are terraced for growing rice. Made of dried mud, these terraces need frequent maintenance, but some have been in continual use for more than 2000 years. Java and its neighbours are also home to some of the world's rarest wildlife. They include the prehistoric-looking Javan rhinoceros – one of the planet's most endangered mammals – and the ferocious komodo dragon, which at 3 m (10 ft) long is the largest lizard in the world. Despite their lumbering appearance, komodo dragons can catch prey as large as goats and deer. Adult dragons also have a cannibalistic streak, so, after hatching, their young spend most of their time in trees.

Sumatra's swamps are the habitat of a very different record breaker – the world's smallest known fish. Measuring as little as 8 mm (⅓ in) from head to tail,

◹ JAVANESE RICE TERRACES

Indonesia is the world's third-largest producer of rice. Large parts of Java are devoted to rice terraces, and many traditional Javanese homes include a shrine to the local goddess of rice, Dewi Sri.

▶ KOMODO DRAGON

Part of the monitor lizard family, these animals typically weigh 70–90 kg (150–200 lb) – as much as an average person. The largest known example tipped the scales at a massive 166 kg (366 lb).

DOUBLE AND TRIPLE ISLANDS

Like a stack of pancakes, some islands are located on other islands, which may also be on other islands themselves. The biggest double island, or island-on-an-island, is Samosir on Sumatra. Surrounded by Lake Toba, a volcanic crater lake, Samosir is both inhabited and farmed. The biggest triple island, or island-on-an-island-on-an-island, is thought to be an anonymous 1.6-ha (4-acre) patch of tundra in a lake on an island in a lake on Victoria Island, Nunavut, Canada, at coordinates 69.7928°N, 108.2411°W. With improvements in satellite imaging, it is almost certain that quadruple islands will be found, although none are yet officially catalogued.

it is one of the tiniest animals with a backbone, and one of the few that lives in the dark, acidic waters that percolate through rainforest peat.

ISLAND SWARMS

In terms of numbers, rather than absolute size, the world's biggest island group lies between Finland and Sweden, in a region called the Archipelago Sea. Officially, there are more than 50,000 islands on the Finnish side of the border, although the exact count will probably never be known. Seen from space, the islands look like a swarm of insects massed off the Finnish coast. Some are big enough for farming, but many more of them would fit into an average backyard.

Unlike the Malay Archipelago, few of the islands in the Archipelago Sea are over a handful of metres high. Their humpbacked shape is a clue to their origins: this part of the world was once covered by the Scandinavian ice sheet, which extended across most of northern Europe. At the end of the last ice age, when the ice sheet retreated, the rock beneath started to rise above sea level, having shed the ice's colossal weight. Today, this 'glacial rebound' is still continuing at a rate of up to 1 cm (⅖ inch) per year, creating yet more islands.

Because the Archipelago Sea is shallow, large ships have to follow specially marked shipping lanes that wind their way through the maze of islands and islets. Many of the larger islands are linked by bridges, but getting from island to island is easier in winter, because the sea often freezes over and cars can drive across the ice!

CORAL ISLANDS

In the Indian and Pacific Oceans, thousands of ring-shaped islands and archipelagos are scattered across the sea. Known as atolls, they are formed by coral reefs

Made up of almost 1200 coral islands spread out over an area of 90,000 sq km (35,000 sq miles), the Maldives is the world's lowest country – some 80 per cent of the land area is no more than 1 m (3 ft) above sea level.

perched on ancient volcanoes that have subsided under the water. Like a necklace, an atoll's islands surround a shallow lagoon. Some are only a few hundred metres across, but the largest are enormous: Kwajalein Atoll, in the Marshall Islands, is 283 km (176 miles) long, and encircles a lagoon that is twice the size of New York City. The Great Chagos Bank, in the Indian Ocean, is even bigger. It covers an area of over 12,600 sq km (4800 sq miles) – enough to swallow New York City 10 times over – although only a tiny amount of it is dry land.

Reef-building corals need warm water to grow, so atolls are rarely found outside the tropics. Most are very low-lying – the atolls that make up the Maldives, for example, have a high point of just 2.4 m (7⅘ ft), making this the flattest island nation on Earth. It's little wonder that Maldivians and other atoll-dwellers are particularly concerned by the prospect of rising sea levels brought about by climate change.

Uninhabited atolls often teem with nesting seabirds, and their lagoons are important breeding grounds for fish. The calm waters make for superb swimming, but danger lurks in the narrow channels that connect lagoons with the open sea. In some atolls – such as Kanton Island in the western Pacific – the tide races through the channels at up to 11 knots, which is equivalent to a fast run. Fish and turtles hurtle through the channels unharmed, but unwary swimmers risk being scraped against the coral and dragged out to sea.

EASTER ISLAND

Instead of lying close to continents, the world's most far-flung islands rise up from the depths of the seabed. Most of them were formed by submarine volcanoes, which are often still active today. Some oceanic islands are aligned in long sweeps called arcs, located above places where Earth's tectonic plates collide, but the most distant sit over hot spots – places of intense volcanic activity in Earth's crust that have persisted for millions of years.

Until the seventeenth century, Easter Island (or Rapa Nui), in the south-eastern Pacific Ocean, was the most remote inhabited island on the planet. It lies on a hot spot 3500 km (2200 miles) west of South America, and about 2100 km (1300 miles) from the closest human population on the tiny island of Pitcairn. Sailing aboard outrigger canoes, Polynesian navigators somehow found this isolated spot in the immensity of the world's biggest ocean. The date of their landfall is uncertain – it may have been as early as 700 AD – but the settlers flourished in their newly discovered home. The population eventually peaked at 15,000, an astonishing figure for an island less than 25 km (16 miles) in length.

Over the centuries, a complex culture developed, which left the island with its world-famous statues – an archaeological heritage equalled by few other

HOME ALONE

Easter Island's place in the record books lasted until 1643, when the first-known landing was made at Tristan da Cunha, currently the remotest inhabited island on Earth. The island was first spotted in 1506 by a Portuguese explorer, but over a century passed before the first humans set foot on its shores. It is just under 3400 km (2100 miles) from South America, in the South Atlantic, and the closest inhabited shoreline is the Cape of Good Hope, over 2800 km (1700 miles) to the east.

Like Easter Island, Tristan da Cunha was formed by volcanic eruptions. It is dominated by the symmetrical cone of Queen Mary's Peak, which is just over 2000 m (6600 ft) high. Today, its lower slopes are inhabited by about 250 people, who make a living by farming, fishing and marketing the island's stamps. The islanders share just eight surnames, and are nearly all descendants of settlers who arrived in the nineteenth century. Tristan da Cunha does not have enough level ground for an airstrip, so the only way to travel to the island is by ship.

Like a planet and its satellites, Tristan da Cunha is flanked by a small number of outlying islands, which form part of the same volcanic group. None of them are inhabited, although Nightingale Island provided a temporary refuge for Tristan da Cunha's entire population when Queen Mary's Peak suddenly erupted in 1961. With its sheer cliffs, nearby Inaccessible Island is perhaps

IT'S ABOUT TIME

LEMURS

The world's oldest island is Madagascar. Although it lies off the coast of Africa, it actually split off from India about 90 million years ago. About 90 per cent of Madagascar's native plants and animals are unique to this ancient island world.

places on Earth. The statues – properly known as moai – are carved out of tuff, which is a soft rock made from volcanic ash. The heaviest erected statue weighs over 74 tonnes (80 tons). Today, Easter Island has about 5000 permanent inhabitants, but each year over 10 times that number visit the island to see its mysterious statues.

the most forbidding. However, like Nightingale Island, it is a paradise for birds: albatrosses, shearwaters and penguins all breed on its slopes, or along its shore, and the world's smallest flightless bird – the Inaccessible Island rail – lives among the clumps of green ferns and tussock grass. Adult birds weigh about half as much as a chicken's egg, and are only about 17 cm (7 in) long.

NATURE'S ISLANDERS

The Inaccessible Island rail is an example of an endemic species – one that is found in a particular place, and nowhere else in the world. Remote islands have more of these irreplaceable plants and animals than anywhere else, because their wildlife has evolved on its own for millions of years. Endemic island animals and birds include giant tortoises from the Galápagos Islands, Madagascar's lemurs and New Zealand's kiwis.

Endemic plants are even more varied, and range from beautiful bird-pollinated shrubs in the Hawaiian Islands to the bizarre sack-of-potatoes tree, with its fat water-holding trunk, from the Indian Ocean island of Socotra. The island of New Caledonia has some of the world's tallest tree ferns, towering up to 30 m (100 ft) high, and it is also the home of the New Caledonian crow – one of the world's most intelligent animals, with tool-using skills even better than a chimpanzee's.

LOST AND FOUND

New Caledonian crows have adapted well to the arrival of humans in their island home. Unfortunately, many other endemic species have not been so lucky. Accidentally or deliberately, humans have introduced predatory mammals, such as cats and rats, which often decimate ground-nesting birds. In the past, sailors also released pigs and goats, which can lay waste to endemic plants. Over the centuries, thousands of endemic island species have become extinct, from the famous dodo of Mauritius, which died out in the seventeenth century, to the St Helena olive tree, which vanished forever in 2003.

However, not all the news is bad, because sometimes 'extinct' species have come back to life. The world's biggest stick insect – from Lord Howe Island, off the eastern coast of Australia – was thought to have died out in the early 1930s, depriving the world of a prehistoric-looking animal up to 15 cm (6 in) long. But in 1964, climbers found a single dead stick insect on Ball's Pyramid, a vertigo-inducing stack of volcanic rock about 20 km (12 miles) from Lord Howe Island itself. In 2001, a team of scientists scaled the sheer sides of Ball's Pyramid and found two dozen of the insects living on a damp ledge under some windswept shrubs. In 2003, four adults were taken off Ball's Pyramid, and, since then, thousands have been bred in zoos worldwide.

EXTREME TOP 10
WORLD'S LARGEST ISLANDS

1 GREENLAND (GREENLAND)
2,175,600 SQ KM (840,000 SQ MILES)

**2 NEW GUINEA
(INDONESIA, PAPUA NEW GUINEA)**
785,753 SQ KM (303,381 SQ MILES)

3 BORNEO (INDONESIA, MALAYSIA, BRUNEI)
748,168 SQ KM (288,869 SQ MILES)

4 MADAGASCAR (MADAGASCAR)
587,713 SQ KM (226,917 SQ MILES)

5 BAFFIN ISLAND (CANADA)
503,944 SQ KM (194,574 SQ MILES)

6 SUMATRA (INDONESIA)
443,066 SQ KM (171,069 SQ MILES)

7 HONSHU (JAPAN)
225,800 SQ KM (87,182 SQ MILES)

8 VICTORIA ISLAND (CANADA)
220,548 SQ KM (85,154 SQ MILES)

9 GREAT BRITAIN (UNITED KINGDOM)
209,331 SQ KM (80,823 SQ MILES)

10 ELLESMERE ISLAND (CANADA)
183,965 SQ KM (71,029 SQ MILES)

THE FINAL FRONTIER

Almost due south of Tristan da Cunha, by about 3200 km (2000 miles), storm-lashed Bouvet Island (or Bouvetøya) is the ultimate get-away-from-it-all destination, and the most isolated piece of land on Earth. Ringed by black volcanic cliffs and capped by glacial ice, it is also shrouded by cloud and pounded by relentless waves. It has no permanent inhabitants; the only visitors are scientists, climbers and amateur radio enthusiasts who have a taste for Earth's wildest extremes.

Bouvet Island was first spotted by its namesake – the French explorer Jean-Baptiste Charles Bouvet de Lozier – in 1739. Today, it belongs to Norway, after a party of Norwegian sailors and scientists spent several days ashore in 1927. Amazingly, Bouvet Island has its own country code domain for the Internet – .bv – but the suffix is owned by the Norwegian government and is not in current use. The nearest coastline to the island is Queen Maud Land in Antarctica, which is about 1700 km (1100 miles) to the south. When there are no ships in the area, the nearest humans are orbiting astronauts aboard the International Space Station, a mere 400 km (250 miles) above the island when it passes overhead.

TRISTAN DA CUNHA
A satellite image clearly shows Queen Mary's Peak, the top of the shield volcano that forms Tristan da Cunha. Edinburgh settlement lies on flat land at the north-west corner of the island.

CURIOUS PUFFINS
Located in the North Atlantic, Mykines – the westernmost isle of the Faroe Islands archipelago – is a haven for a wealth of seabirds, including Atlantic puffins. With their colourful beak – which is brightest during the breeding season – these birds have been dubbed 'sea parrots'.

EXTREME WATER

Earth's water is forever in a state of transition within the planet's hydrologic cycle. Moisture from the oceans evaporates, lingers in the atmosphere as water vapour or ice particles and ultimately falls from the sky as rain, hail or snow. It seeps into the soil, fills lakes and rivers, and creates snowfields and glaciers, before eventually returning to the oceans and continuing the cycle. As water moves, it helps shape Earth. Ocean currents drive the global climate. Mighty rivers and glaciers carve valleys. Rain and snow erode mountains. And the same water is thought to have been cycling in the same way for billions of years.

POWERFUL WAVES
*The North Shore of the Hawaiian island of Oahu offers experienced
surfers some of the largest waves in the world, especially during winter.*

ROUGH WATER
Drake Passage – located between the southernmost point of South America and the South Shetland Islands – is the often-turbulent meeting point of the Pacific, Atlantic and Southern Oceans.

EXTREME FACT
Because pressure increases with depth, by 100 kilopascals (14½ psi) for every 10 m (33 ft), the pressure in the deepest part of the ocean is more than 1000 times what it is at the ocean's surface.

Oceans and seas

There is a good reason why Earth is called 'the blue planet'. It is the only planet in the Solar System with oceans and seas; they cover 70 per cent of Earth's surface. From space, this huge expanse of salty water makes the planet appear predominantly blue.

A LL THIS WATER is actually contained within one enormous, interconnected world ocean. Geographically, however, there are most often considered to be five main oceans: the Pacific, Atlantic, Indian, Arctic and Southern Oceans. The latter includes the cold waters surrounding Antarctica, and it was the last to be officially defined – in the year 2000, by the International Hydrographic Organization.

MIND-BLOWING NUMBERS

By far the largest ocean, in terms of both area and volume, is the Pacific. It covers 165,250,000 sq km (63,800,000 sq miles), which is about a third of the entire surface area of the planet. The Atlantic Ocean is a distant second, with an area of 106,400,000 sq km (41,100,000 sq miles). Earth's smallest ocean is the Arctic, with an area of 14,000,000 sq km (5,400,000 sq miles).

The total volume of all the oceans is an estimated 1,335,000,000 cubic km (320,000,000 cubic miles). This represents about 96.5 per cent of all the water on Earth, and almost half of it – 660,000,000 cubic km (158,000,000 cubic miles) – is contained within the geographical boundaries of the Pacific Ocean. The eastern side of this vast body of water is bordered by Canada, the United States, Peru and Chile. Nations that lie along the western Pacific include Australia and China. In between, some of the island nations that sit entirely within the waters of the Pacific include the Philippines, Japan, Fiji and New Zealand.

OCEANS IN MOTION

A complex combination of factors creates persistent currents in the surface waters of oceans. These include wind, gravity, the rotation of Earth and the shifting temperature gradients between different latitudes and

depths in ocean waters. The fastest surface currents occur on the eastern boundaries of the continents, which, because they run along the western margins of the ocean basins, are known as western boundary currents. These flow north towards the Arctic in the Northern Hemisphere and south towards the Antarctic in the Southern Hemisphere. The two fastest-flowing boundary currents are the Gulf Stream in the Northern Hemisphere and the Agulhas Current in the Southern Hemisphere.

The Gulf Stream originates in the Gulf of Mexico near Florida, at the south-eastern end of the United States, and flows to the North Atlantic Ocean. It travels at an average speed of 6.4 km/h (4 mph), but reaches a maximum speed of 9 km/h (5³⁄₅ mph). The Agulhas Current begins off Mozambique, in south-eastern Africa, and flows south in the Indian Ocean at a slower average rate of up to 2.3 km/h (1²⁄₅ mph). But it reaches a top speed of about 9.3 km/h (5⁴⁄₅ mph) off South Africa's south-eastern coast.

The world's largest ocean current, transporting more water than any other, is the Antarctic Circumpolar Current. This travels 24,000 km (15,000 miles) eastwards around the continent of Antarctica, connecting en route with the Atlantic, Pacific and Indian Oceans. It moves 150 times the combined flow of all the world's rivers – up to 150 million cubic m (5300 million cubic ft) of water per second – and is considered to be one of the major drivers of Earth's climate. It is the only current that flows right around the planet, and it extends from the surface to depths of 2000–4000 m (6500–13,000 ft). It can be up to 2000 km (1200 miles) wide.

WONDERFUL WAVES

Along with tides and currents, waves are among the most noticeable of ocean movements. The biggest surface wave ever documented was generated by a tsunami. Most ocean surface waves, however, are created by winds, and when located in the open ocean they are often termed swells. These rise to become breakers when they approach shallow water, at reefs and beaches on the coasts of mainlands and islands.

The biggest open ocean wave ever recorded had a maximum height of 29.1 m (95²⁄₅ ft) from trough (low point) to crest (peak). It was reported in the year 2000 in water 250 km (160 miles) off the west coast of Scotland in the North Atlantic Ocean by instruments on board the British research vessel RRS *Discovery*. The 'significant wave height' – essentially an average measurement of the heights of waves creating the swell in the area at the time – was also the largest ever documented, at 18.5 m (60⁷⁄₁₀ ft).

SALINE EXPANSE

Sea water tastes salty because it contains the dissolved salts of a range of different chemical elements, most

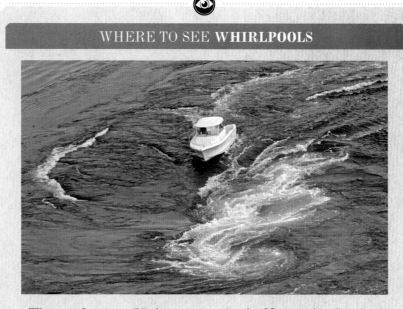

The maelstrom of Saltstraumen in the Norwegian Sea just off Norway produces the world's strongest 'whirlpools' – rapidly swirling vortices of water that are created here by tidal movements. It is most impressive at high tide, when whirlpools form that can be 10 m (33 ft) wide, 5 m (16 ft) deep and contain water moving at up to 40 km/h (25 mph).

HUGE WAVES
A brave surfer takes on one of the enormous waves at the offshore reef known as Dungeons near Cape Town, South Africa. Because of the fast-moving swells, surfers often use personal watercraft to tow them into the dangerous waves.

notably sodium and chloride. These salts also make sea water slightly denser than fresh water. On average, the total salt content across the surface water of all the oceans is 3.5 per cent, or 35 parts per thousand (ppt) – meaning that 1 litre (2 pints) of sea water contains approximately 35 g (1¹⁄₅ oz) of dissolved salts. Salinity, however, increases in tropical areas with very high evaporation rates. The saltiest open ocean water occurs in the Red Sea and Persian Gulf, where it can reach 40 ppt. The least salty open ocean water is in the Gulfs of Finland and Bothnia in the Baltic Sea, where freshwater flows from about 200 rivers can reduce salinity to just 8 ppt.

The Persian Gulf also contains the warmest ocean water found anywhere in the world – shallow surface temperatures often reach as high as 32–35°C (90–95°F). While normal fresh water freezes at sea level at 0°C (32°F), salt water freezes at -1.8°C (28.8°F) because of the salt content. Temperatures around this mark occur throughout the surface waters of the Southern Ocean in Antarctica during the winter months. The coldest deep-ocean water is Antarctic Bottom Water, which forms on the surface of the Weddell and Ross Seas on the Antarctic continental shelf and then sinks to the seabed, where its temperature ranges from 0 to -0.8°C (32 to 30.6°F). This chilled water flows northwards along the seabed and ultimately into most of the world's deep ocean basins.

BRYDE'S WHALE
Found throughout the warmer waters of the Pacific, Atlantic and Indian Oceans, Bryde's whales feed on plankton and crustaceans, as well as schooling fish such as anchovies, sardines, herring and mackerel – often clashing with birds that are after the same seafood meal.

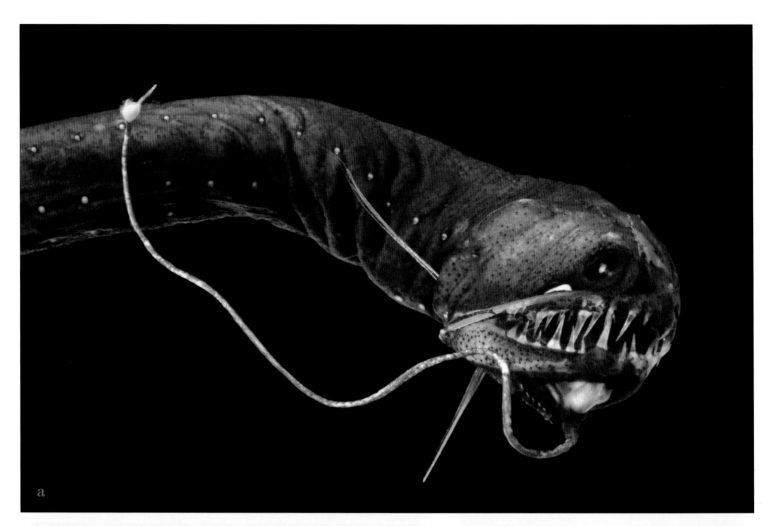

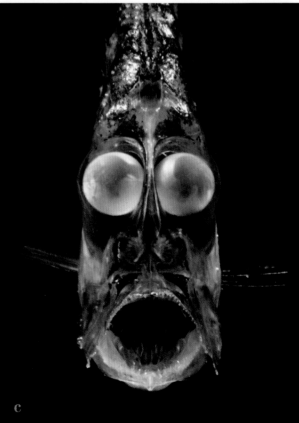

DEEP-SEA CREATURES

A wide range of odd-looking creatures is found in the mesopelagic zone, 200–1000 m (660–3300 ft) below the ocean's surface. (a) Scaleless black dragonfish is a bioluminescent predator. (b) Glass squid has a body covered in cartilaginous tubercles. (c) Hatchetfish is less than 4 cm (1⅗ in) in length.

LAST LIGHT

Most known life on Earth is ultimately fuelled by sunlight, which is converted by plants and some microorganisms into chemical energy during photosynthesis. The deepest point to which enough light can penetrate the oceans for photosynthesis to occur is about 200 m (660 ft), and it is at that point that the deep sea is most often considered to begin. Light in the red part of the spectrum is the first to disappear, failing to penetrate beyond a depth of about 100 m (330 ft). Because of this, many creatures surviving in the waters just below here are coloured red: it provides camouflage by making them seem invisible to the eyes of their predators.

No sunlight at all makes it past about 1000 m (3300 ft), where light in the blue part of the visible spectrum is the last to disappear. It is around this depth and near the seabed where a bizarre creature known as a blobfish is found. It was first brought up by trawl nets off south-eastern Australia in the early 2000s, and in 2013 it was dubbed 'Earth's ugliest creature' by the British-based Ugly Animal Preservation Society. Swim bladders would be useless at the pressures found where the blobfish lives, and so it has a body that is made primarily of jelly-like tissue. This is slightly less dense than the surrounding sea water, which helps the blobfish float just above the seabed, where it survives by sucking in passing food particles.

GOING DOWN

Earth's vast oceans contain our planet's largest and least-explored habitats, including huge expanses of seabed that are as inaccessible as outer space. Marine scientists estimated that by the second decade of the twenty-first century, less than 7 per cent of the seabed and other deep ocean regions had been explored.

Four times more people have walked on the Moon than have reached the deepest natural point on Earth. That site is in the Pacific Ocean – at the bottom of the world's deepest ocean trench, the Mariana Trench – and is known as Challenger Deep. In 2010, its depth was officially measured at 10,994 m (36,070 ft) by the US Center for Coastal and Ocean Mapping. If the world's highest land-based mountain, Mount Everest, were placed there, it would be topped by more than 2 km (1⅕ miles) of water.

Ocean trenches are the deepest parts of the ocean floor because they occur at subduction zones, where tectonic plates meet and one slides, very slowly, under another. In the case of the Mariana Trench, the Pacific Plate is slipping beneath the Philippine Sea Plate. The Mariana Trench is not merely a single deep-sea furrow, as its name implies, but a 2542-km (1580-mile) long series of mounts and valleys on the ocean floor – around 150 times bigger in area than Arizona's Grand Canyon. It is located just south of Japan and east of the Philippines

DEEP-DIVING MEN

In January 1960, Swiss oceanographer Jacques Piccard and US Navy officer and marine engineer Donald Walsh became the first people to reach Challenger Deep, travelling there together in a submersible called the *Trieste*. Problems with the vessel meant the pair only managed to spend 20 minutes on the seabed.

TRIESTE DUO
Measuring 18 m (59 ft) in length, the Trieste *submersible (above) comprised a spherical pressure capsule, for a crew of two, under large float chambers. Dr Andreas Rechnitzer (far left) headed the* Trieste *team, overseeing the record-breaking trip by Jacques Piccard (left) and Donald Walsh.*

Fifty-two years later, in March 2012, Canadian adventurer and movie director James Cameron mounted a successful expedition to Challenger Deep in the purpose-built submersible *Deepsea Challenger*. He became the third person to ever reach the site and the only person to make it solo. Cameron spent more than two hours at the bottom before a mechanical fault also forced him to return to the surface earlier than planned.

and Mariana Islands, which include the US territory of Guam. In 2009, the trench and its surrounding waters and submerged islands were proclaimed a Marine National Monument and its management assigned under the US National Wildlife Refuge System.

DEEP LIFE

Surprisingly, even deep-sea trenches support life. This is despite the sort of pressure that would be exerted beneath a 50-high stack of jumbo jets, and the complete absence of ambient light. In March 1995, an unmanned, remote-controlled Japanese submersible called *Kaiko* reached a depth of 10,911 m (35,797 ft) within Challenger Deep, returning with video evidence of a deep-sea cucumber, worm and crustacean, as well as sediment samples that contained hundreds of different species of single-celled organisms called foraminifera. Most were new to science, and biologists have speculated that these remote organisms may resemble Earth's earliest forms of life.

Other creatures that appear to abound in the deepest ocean waters are crustaceans known as amphipods – in particular, the species *Hirondellea gigas*, which is thought to live on minute particles of organic debris that sink down kilometres from the surface. There are at least 6000 species of amphipod on Earth, and many are no longer than 1 cm (²/₅ in). But *H. gigas*, a species

known to occur in Challenger Deep, is five times that size; the largest species, *Alicella gigantea*, which is four times bigger than *H. gigas*, is also found only at great depths.

In 2012, scientists using a remote-operated camera filmed a 'supergiant' specimen of *A. gigantea*, thought to measure 34 cm (13 in) long, at about 7 km (4⅓ miles) down in the Kermadec Trench off the Pacific Ocean island nation of New Zealand. The same scientific team also captured and brought to the surface a specimen that measured 28 cm (11 in) in length. This trend of deep-sea animals towards gigantism is a common zoological phenomenon, but no one is quite sure why it occurs.

UNIQUE BIOLOGY

In 1977, scientists from the US Scripps Institution of Oceanography made what turned out to be one of the most significant marine and biological discoveries of the twentieth century, near the Galápagos Islands. They were exploring more than 2 km (1 mile) below the surface along the East Pacific Rise – a mid-oceanic ridge, where tectonic plates diverge at great depths to create new seabed – and found the first-known hydrothermal vent, where water heated up to 340°C (640°F) spews rapidly out of Earth's crust. Despite the exceptionally high temperature, the sea water doesn't boil there because of the immense pressure. Immediately surrounding the vent was an extraordinarily diverse

assemblage of species not seen before. They are all part of a dynamic food chain based on bacteria and other microorganisms that consume various chemicals created when sea water mixes with hot magma from beneath Earth's crust.

During the early 1980s, scientists documented one particularly remarkable animal they called a Pompeii worm, which was thriving in huge numbers inside their own tubes around the Galápagos hydrothermal vents. It is now thought that a symbiotic relationship with bacteria that eat the chemicals in the vent water helps the Pompeii worms to survive their ultra high-temperature habitat. The worms secrete mucus upon which the bacteria feed, and the bacteria in turn appear to create a fleece-like insulation layer that protects the worms from the hot water.

Numerous deep-sea hydrothermal vents have since been discovered in the Atlantic, Indian and Southern Oceans, and two different types have been identified. 'Black smokers' create dark chimney-like structures, as zinc, iron and copper sulfide particles ejected with the water settle on the seabed; 'white smokers' are formed in a similar way, but from deposits of lighter-coloured barium, silicon and calcium minerals.

The deepest and hottest vents identified so far are located at the Beebe Vent Field, 4960 m (16,270 ft) down at the bottom of the Cayman Trench, in the Caribbean Sea off Jamaica and the Cayman Islands. Temperatures

≋
POMPEII WORM

A type of bristle worm, the Pompeii worm lives inside a thin tube on the side of a hydrothermal vent – the bottom of the tube can be as hot as 80°C (176°F).

⏶
DEEP-SEA AMPHIPOD

Species from the genus Lanceola *have been found as deep as 3000 m (10,000 ft) below the surface of the ocean.*

◪
SUBMARINE CANYON

Undersea canyons are water-filled highways for schools of fish, and often attract divers and nature photographers.

there have been measured at 450°C (842°F), hot enough to melt common metals such as lead, tin and zinc.

SUBMERGED VALLEYS

In addition to trenches, other significant ocean floor topographic features include submarine canyons, which are present on the edges of most of the continental slopes, where shallow waters give way to the deep sea. They are mostly steep-walled depressions very much like submerged versions of canyons formed on land by rivers. In fact, some may have once been connected to nearby land canyons. It is believed others may have originally been formed on land and become submerged during periods of sea-level rise.

The largest-known submarine canyon, and indeed the largest open canyon on Earth, is considered to be Zhemchug Canyon due to the size of its drainage area – 11,350 sq km (4380 sq miles) – and the huge volume of water it contains – 5800 cubic km (1400 cubic miles). This enormous canyon is located in the Bering Sea, which links the Arctic Ocean and northern Pacific Ocean, and it lies between the continents of Asia and North America. The head of the canyon is on the North American side of the Bering Sea, and its highest walls drop 2600 m (8500 ft) vertically to the seabed, making it considerably deeper than the land-based Grand Canyon, which is 1800 m (6000 ft) at its deepest.

CARIBBEAN SEA
English Harbour is situated on the southern coast of the island of Antigua. In the eighteenth century, it was used as a British naval base in the Caribbean because of its calm, protected waters.

To the south is Earth's longest submarine canyon – the Bering Canyon, which extends westwards from the continent of North America for an estimated 400 km (250 miles).

THE BIGGEST UNKNOWN

Submarine canyons are crucial sediment highways that transport eroded material and organic matter, including nutrients, from the continents out to the abyssal plains of the deep sea. Abyssal plains are flat or gently sloping sediment-rich expanses that form much of the seabed. They are initially created by the process of seabed spreading at mid-oceanic ridges and are consumed back into Earth at subduction zones.

From a size perspective alone, abyssal plains are one of the planet's most significant habitats, representing more than half of all Earth's surface – both terrestrial and aquatic. They are found mostly at depths of 3000–6000 m (10,000–20,000 ft), and were once considered to be desert-like habitats supporting very little life. But the Census of Diversity of Abyssal Marine Life – part of the decade-long international Census of Marine Life that was completed in 2010 – turned that perspective on its head when it found exceptionally high levels of biodiversity in abyssal plain sediment samples. Collected from seabeds in the Pacific, Atlantic, Indian and Southern Oceans, these sediments proved to be richly populated by many thousands of different species of bacteria,

TROPICAL FISH

Coral reefs are very colourful environments found in the warm seas and oceans of the world. In order to camouflage themselves, the fish that live in these habitats need to be brightly hued, too.

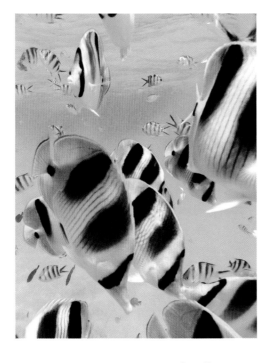

protozoans, worms, crustaceans and molluscs, most of which were new to science. It was just a taste of what biological sampling is expected to reveal in this realm in coming decades.

DEEP-SEA MINING PROSPECTS

There is another special feature of the abyssal plains that has not only caught the attention of researchers interested in biodiversity and geomorphology, but also those involved in big business – minerals. The ocean has been mined for natural gas and oil for decades, and large quantities of sand, gravel and minerals are already extracted from shallow marine areas. But deep-sea mining has only become a realistic prospect in the past decade thanks to advances in deep-sea robotic and sensor technologies.

Initial interest has been predominantly in metallic clusters called manganese nodules, which are also known as polymetallic nodules. These are found at 4000–5500 m (13,000–18,000 ft), and, in some areas, can cover 70 per cent of the seabed. They range from the size of sand grains to cabbages and are made mostly of manganese and iron, but there is also potential commercial interest in other minerals they contain at lower concentrations, including copper, nickel and cobalt. Manganese nodules are grown on the seabed by an interesting bacterial organism aptly known as *Metallogenium*. Starting as a tiny speck, these organisms coat their spider-like filaments with manganese and other metals extracted from the sea water; they grow steadily bigger, but at an extraordinarily slow rate.

It has also been discovered in recent years that hydrothermal vents are potentially rich sources of

EXTREME TOP 10
WORLD'S LARGEST SEAS

In geographical parlance, 'sea' is most often used to describe an area of ocean that is wholly or partly surrounded by land. According to that definition, these are the seas with the largest areas.

1 PHILIPPINE SEA
5,178,000 SQ KM (1,999,000 SQ MILES)

2 CORAL SEA
4,791,000 SQ KM (1,850,000 SQ MILES)

3 ARABIAN SEA
3,862,000 SQ KM (1,491,000 SQ MILES)

4 SOUTH CHINA SEA
3,685,000 SQ KM (1,423,000 SQ MILES)

5 WEDDELL SEA
2,800,000 SQ KM (1,081,000 SQ MILES)

6 CARIBBEAN SEA
2,754,000 SQ KM (1,063,000 SQ MILES)

7 MEDITERRANEAN SEA
2,510,000 SQ KM (969,000 SQ MILES)

8 TASMAN SEA
2,300,000 SQ KM (888,000 SQ MILES)

9 BERING SEA
2,292,000 SQ KM (885,000 SQ MILES)

10 BAY OF BENGAL
2,172,000 SQ KM (839,000 SQ MILES)

copper, silver and gold. These metals have been found in the seabed around these sites at a purity level of 10 per cent or higher.

The International Seabed Authority – a United Nations body set up in 1994 to manage mining interest in the deep sea – is now being inundated with inquiries about the abyssal plains and areas around hydrothermal vents. In 2000, it formalised regulations for the exploration of manganese nodules. And the following year it set out the rules for exploring another new seabed mining prospect – cobalt-rich crusts. The richest deposits of these are found in the Pacific Ocean, where it is believed that almost 2 per cent of the seabed could be covered by these crusts. That is thought to represent more than 6 million sq km (2.3 million sq miles) of cobalt-rich sediment – or around 1 billion tonnes (1.1 billion tons) of cobalt.

With deep-ocean mining emerging as an imminent commercial reality just as evidence is mounting of the unique biodiversity of abyssal plains and hydrothermal vents, the deep seabed could become one of the major environmental battlefields of the twenty-first century.

Tsunamis and 'king' tides

Horrific news of one of Earth's deadliest natural disasters rippled around the world on 26 December 2004.
A magnitude 9.3 earthquake off the coast of Sumatra had sent a vast amount of water across the Indian Ocean,
hitting coastlines on two continents and the islands between, and leaving behind a trail of death and destruction.

THE 2004 Indian Ocean Tsunami, as it became officially known, caused more deaths than any other tsunami in recorded history. In the weeks that followed the catastrophe, dead or missing people were reported from at least 11 countries, mostly in Asia but also along eastern Africa. Estimates of the final death toll range between 200,000 and 350,000 people.

Most of the casualties were in Indonesia, particularly the province of Aceh on the island of Sumatra. Other countries that suffered a large number of deaths as well as property damage were India, Thailand and Sri Lanka, while lives were lost also in Malaysia, Somalia and the Maldives. The global cost to property and infrastructure ultimately topped US$10 billion; the international humanitarian response to the tragedy was incredible, with US$14 billion raised to help the survivors rebuild their lives.

A PACIFIC CONCERN

Despite the Indian Ocean origin of what is often dubbed the Boxing Day Tsunami, the majority of tsunamis begin in the Pacific Ocean. Here, they are generated by seismic and volcanic activity in the geologically unstable region known as the Ring of Fire.

Japan – which sits over an area of particularly high seismic activity where four tectonic plates meet – has daily earthquake tremors and is regarded as the world's most tsunami-prone country. Although there is no question about the deadliest tsunami in history, lists of the top 10 worst tsunamis in history vary. Most, however, contain at least four that have struck Japan – in 1707, 1896, 1972 and 2011. The combined death toll for these four alone is estimated at more than 90,000 people.

With Japan being the most tsunami-beleaguered nation, it should come as no surprise that *tsunami* is a Japanese word, translating literally as 'harbour wave'. 'Seismic sea wave' is another term commonly applied to these destructive events.

ANATOMY OF A TSUNAMI

A tsunami is not a single wave, but a series known as a wave train. It is fundamentally a succession of huge

STAY SAFE

A sudden drop in the ocean level can occur just before a tsunami arrives, and this is a sign to move quickly to higher ground. So, too, is a loud roar, like a jet plane or train, coming from the ocean. If you are caught in a tsunami, grab a floating object and let the current carry you – never try to swim against the powerful wave.

2011 JAPANESE TSUNAMI

On 11 March 2011, a magnitude 9 earthquake struck off the north-eastern coast of Japan, sending an enormous tsunami hurtling towards the island nation. Around 25,000 people are thought to have perished during the catastrophe – most due to drowning – as the water surged up to 10 km (6 miles) inland, tossing aside houses and cars like unwanted toys.

ripples of energy created by the displacement of a large body of water. In more than 80 per cent of cases, the cause is undersea earthquakes.

Tsunamis travel under the water until they reach coastlines. Even when submerged, however, these waves have the same basic shape as waves found at the water's surface. They have high peaks (crests) and low points (troughs). And, when travelling through deep water, the distance between these – the wave height – is usually less than 1 m (3 ft) and often less than 30 cm (12 in). What these submarine waves lack in height, however, they make up for in length – and the distance from one crest or trough to the next can be as much as 500 km (300 miles). This long, low deep-water profile means the waves of a tsunami are undetectable from the ocean's surface, even though they may contain a huge amount of energy and be travelling at great speeds – more than 800 km/h (500 mph), which is as fast as a commercial jet.

It is not until a tsunami arrives at a coastline that the energy it contains transforms the wave train into a highly visible destructive force. Its speed of travel and wavelength both decrease as it enters shallow water, but the energy remains almost constant. And so, in a phenomenon known as 'shoaling', the decrease in wavelength and speed are countered by an increase in wave height. Coastal wave heights of around 10–40 m (30–130 ft) are common for major tsunamis, although

there were alarming reports from the 2004 Indian Ocean Tsunami of water surging 5 km (3 miles) inland on Sumatra after wave heights climbed to over 50 m (160 ft) at the coast. It might sound colossal when compared to normal coastal surf, but the biggest wave ever recorded – when a tsunami hit Alaska in 1958 – was more than 10 times taller.

The impacts of tsunamis are most often localised, occurring close to the event that created them. The devastating 2004 Indian Ocean catastrophe was, however, what is known as a 'teletsunami' – a relatively infrequent ocean-wide form of tsunami that travels 1000 km (600 miles) or more from its point of origin. Experts estimate that in the past two centuries there have been only about 20 of these, mostly in the Pacific Ocean. The 2004 tsunami travelled nearly 5000 km (3000 miles) from where it was created by an immense megathrust earthquake beneath the Indian Ocean north-west of the Indonesian island of Sumatra. Megathrust earthquakes occur where tectonic plates meet, and a large amount of energy is released as one plate is forced suddenly under the other during the geological process called subduction.

MULTIPLE CAUSES

Despite the underwater earthquake origins for most tsunamis, they can be generated by any phenomenon that causes a sudden displacement of a large amount of water. That includes explosive volcanic eruptions and landslides both above and below the water, glacial calving and even meteorite impacts.

In 1792, the eruption of Mount Unzen on the island of Kyushu was transformed into Japan's deadliest volcanic event in history after it generated a lethal localised tsunami. After months of spewing lava, and a series of earthquakes, Mount Unzen suffered a collapse on its eastern perimeter causing a landslide that spilled into the Ariake Sea and generated massive waves. Overall, about 15,000 people are believed to have lost their lives following the eruption of Mount Unzen, and most of these deaths were attributed to the tsunami that followed.

Almost a century later, Earth experienced an even more catastrophic tsunami, which was created by a volcanic eruption. It followed the 1883 explosion of the Indonesian volcanic island Krakatau; the blast was equivalent to 180 megatonnes (200 megatons) of TNT, and was four times more powerful than the biggest device ever detonated by people – the Russian nuclear weapon known as the Tsar Bomba. Although no one is thought to have been killed directly by the initial explosion, the 38-m (125-ft) high tsunami waves that it generated caused the death of more than 36,000 people, mostly on the islands of Sumatra and Java – more than any known tsunami produced by a volcanic eruption before or since.

1998 PAPUA NEW GUINEA TSUNAMI

Residents along the north coast were left with little more than a pile of debris when a tsunami struck on 17 July 1998. Whole villages were wiped out, with 500 people listed as missing.

UNDERWATER THREAT

During the late twentieth and early twenty-first centuries, advances in seabed mapping techniques and tsunami modelling science raised concerns about a source of these huge waves that had not previously received much attention – submarine landslides. A major turning point followed investigations into the 1998 tsunami that struck coastal villages around the town of Aitape on Papua New Guinea's north coast. Following a magnitude 7 earthquake, waves reaching 10–15 m (30–50 ft) in height struck the area, killing 2200 people, injuring 1000 and displacing 10 times more. Perplexed scientists found it difficult to correlate the size of the earthquake with a tsunami of such devastating impact. Subsequently, however, seabed mapping identified a submarine 'slump', or underwater landslide, in the area as the most likely cause of the killer tsunami waves.

Similarly, twenty-first-century research suggests a submarine landslide caused the 1908 tsunami that struck the Calabrian coast of southern Italy and the island of Sicily, although debate continues. This tsunami followed Europe's most powerful earthquake, a magnitude 7.2 event that hit below the Strait of Messina. Between the earthquake and tsunami, more than 100,000 lives were lost, and the dual catastrophe remains Europe's worst natural disaster on record.

What is the significance of new interest in underwater landslides as a possible source of tsunamis? They are the latest entry on what has become a frightening list of

THE BIGGEST BREAK

A huge tsunami in Alaska on 9 July 1958 created the tallest wave ever documented. It occurred when a magnitude 8 earthquake caused an estimated 30.6 million cubic m (1081 million cubic ft) of rubble to plummet more than 900 m (3000 ft) into the icy waters of Lituya Bay. This massive rock fall generated a localised tsunami with a wave height of 524 m (1720 ft), a measurement that was based on the elevation at which trees were ripped from the ground as the enormous wave hit the shoreline. There were some eyewitnesses, but the area is remote and sparsely populated so casualties were minimal. It is thought that the tsunami caused the death of just two people, who had been fishing in a boat that sank during the event and whose bodies were never found.

1908 ITALIAN TSUNAMI

Over 90 per cent of the buildings in the Sicilian city of Messina were destroyed by the earthquake and subsequent 12-m (39-ft) high tsunami that hit the region on 28 December 1908.

◄

LOW TIDE IN THE BAY OF FUNDY

The tides in Canada's Bay of Fundy are semidiurnal, meaning that there are two high tides and two low tides every day. When the tide goes out, some parts of the bay have little if any water at all, leaving boats such as these scallop draggers high and dry.

potential non-seismic origins for tsunamis – suggesting that these waves of water have a wider potential to cause devastation than previously thought.

WHEN WEATHER TURNS BAD

Another type of tsunami not generated by seismic activity is called a meteotsunami. This is weather-related, caused by meteorological phenomena known as atmospheric gravity waves, frontal passages and squall lines, all of which can cause large and rapid increases in air pressure. When these occur over large bodies of water they can, under certain conditions, create the same sort of tsunami waves generated by seismic activity, although they don't reach the same scale.

Meteotsunamis have been documented in coastal regions throughout the world, and they are known by different local names (for example, *abiki* in Japan, *rissaga* in Spain and *marrobbio* in Italy). They usually only have serious impacts when they are funnelled into shallow water in areas such as bays and coastal inlets. The largest waves associated with a meteotsunami struck Japan's Nagasaki Bay on 31 March 1979. The disaster occurred after waves generated in the East

China Sea to the west rose to about 5 m (16 ft) as they entered the bay, killing three people and causing widespread coastal damage.

It is not just ocean waters that can be affected by tsunamis – research has shown that there is proof of tsunamis hitting large lakes in the geological past, and that many lakes continue to have the potential to experience the phenomena on a deadly scale. In 2012, for example, University of Geneva researchers investigating geological evidence of a rockslide that caused a sixth-century tsunami on Lake Geneva, on the border of Switzerland and France, warned that it could happen again. Research also indicates that the great lakes of Africa and North America are also potential tsunami sites.

THE TIDAL RANGE

Historically, the term 'tidal wave' has been another name commonly used for tsunamis. It is, however, a misnomer, because these huge waves have nothing to do with tides, although their coastal impacts can be greatly exacerbated if they reach shorelines during times of high tides.

Tides are caused mostly by the gravitational attractive force of the Moon, which pulls large bodies of water towards it, creating rhythmic and regular rises and falls in Earth's oceans and seas. The gravitational pull of the Sun is, to a lesser extent, also involved. Certain topographic features, including the shape of coastal bays and inlets, significantly affect tide heights. And that is why the largest tides in the world occur at the funnel-shaped Bay of Fundy on the Atlantic coast between the Canadian provinces of Nova Scotia and New Brunswick. The biggest of the big occur at Minas Basin, an inlet on the eastern side of the bay, where the average range between high and low tides is about 12 m (39 ft). When conditions are right, however, the water level at high tide can rise by as much as 16 m (52 ft).

More than 100 billion tonnes (110 billion tons) of sea water is funnelled into and out of the bay on a twice

IT'S ABOUT TIME

Geological evidence in Chile, Antarctica and Australia suggests that Earth's climate was altered 2.5 million years ago after a 2-km (1⅕-mile) wide meteor hit the Pacific Ocean and generated tsunami waves more than 100 m (330 ft) high. Tsunamis like this, which occurred in the geological past (before written records), are known as palaeotsunamis.

daily basis as the tide rises and falls. Since 1984, Nova Scotia's Tidal Generating Station has been using this extraordinary force to create electricity, and it now produces enough to power about 6000 homes. Research, however, by the United States-based Electric Power Research Institute has shown that enough emission-free, renewable energy could be harnessed from the Bay of Fundy tidal phenomenon to supply at least 100,000 homes with all their power needs.

The biggest tides are known by oceanographers as macro tides, which by definition occur in areas with a tidal range of 4 m (13 ft) or above. Colloquially, however, these are often referred to as 'king' tides throughout the Pacific and particularly in Australia, where the tides in the country's far north-west reach enormous heights – the second highest in the world. These occur in King Sound, a large gulf near the town of Derby that, like the Bay of Fundy, is funnel-shaped. The biggest high tides there can reach a height of 11.8 m (38¾ ft), and they underpin a rare natural phenomenon known as a 'horizontal waterfall' – a frothing flow of tidal water squeezed between two narrowly spaced cliffs.

INLAND WAVE WALLS

In some areas with large tides and rivers that empty into the ocean, the relatively rare phenomenon known as a tidal bore can occur. This is a surge of water driven inland and upstream against a river's normal flow, creating waves that – unlike those of tsunamis – can be more accurately described as tidal waves.

The world's biggest tidal bore occurs on south-eastern China's Qiantang River, which flows into the East China Sea. Waves here can reach a height of around 9 m (30 ft) and travel at a speed of 40 km/h (25 mph). The tidal bore on the Qiantang River is at its largest between August and October each year. The International Qiantang River Tidal Bore Watching Festival is held each September, when the phenomenon reaches its peak around the eighteenth day of the eighth lunar month. In recent years, a nail-biting extreme surfing competition on the tidal bore has also been staged around the same time.

The most famous tidal bore, however, is arguably Brazil's pororoca, which begins where the mouth of the Amazon River meets the Atlantic Ocean. The tidal bore peaks at about 4 m (13 ft) around February and March, and travels as far as 800 km (500 miles) up the Amazon River. The word pororoca comes from the local Tupi Indian language, and it is an evocative term that describes the loud roar of the phenomenon as it makes its way up the Amazon. The sound precedes the wave by at least 30 minutes, and other signs that the phenomenon is approaching include birds suddenly taking off in fright.

The pororoca is also the focus of what is considered to be one of the world's most extreme and dangerous

surfing competitions. The Brazilian National Pororoca Surfing Championship has been held around March each year since 1999, and is based in the city of São Domingos do Capim.

DANGER AHEAD

Like other major tidal bores, the pace and power of the pororoca tend to stun, injure and even kill animals in its path, and because of this its peak is followed closely behind by predators and scavengers. On the Amazon, this includes piranhas, alligators and leopards, while opportunistic sharks and crocodiles have been reported swimming behind the tidal bore on the Styx River in north-eastern Australia.

Tidal bores should be treated with extreme caution and observed only from high points. They are far less predictable than tides, and their size and pace can be significantly increased by nearby storms. People have been killed by both the Qiantang and Amazon River tidal bores. And in 2013, more than 30 people were injured on the Qiantang River when a typhoon occurred nearby at around the same time as the tidal bore's peak.

HORIZONTAL WATERFALLS
Tidal water in Talbot Bay, northern Western Australia, rushes through two narrow gaps in the McLarty Range. Water can build up behind the smaller of the two gaps, creating a 4-m (13-ft) high cascade that is best viewed from the air.

'KING' TIDE, AUSTRALIA
During June 2007, New South Wales suffered through its worst storms in three decades. 'King' tides that occurred at the same time increased the size and ferocity of the storm surges that battered the state's coastline.

QIANTANG RIVER TIDAL BORE
On 31 August 2011, people were forced to run for their lives as waves from the tidal bore on the Qiantang River surged over a riverbank barrier in Hangzhou, China. More than 20 people were injured when they were knocked over by the waves.

COASTAL CLIFFS
The cliffs at Étretat in north-western France are renowned for their great beauty. Artists such as Claude Monet were drawn here to paint these natural wonders.

EXTREME FACT
The world's longest cross-sea bridge is the 42.5-km (26$^2/_5$-mile) Jiaozhou Bay Bridge that spans the East China Sea from the shores of the port city of Qingdao, in eastern China, to the coast of Huangdao District.

Coastlines and seashores

With so much of Earth covered by ocean, it is not surprising that most countries have a coastline. All but 44 of the 196 countries that existed in 2013 had at least one border along an ocean or sea. And most of the planet's people live near these coastlines and seashores.

A T ABOUT 80 people per square kilometre, the average population density for Earth's coasts is twice the global average. Almost half of the world's population – estimated at 7.2 billion in 2013 – live within 150 km (90 miles) of the coast. And the United Nations predicts that this proportion will rise to three-quarters by 2025, as the world's projected population leaps to more than 8 billion.

It is not just water views that have people the world over flocking to live near coasts. These places where land meets ocean are of immense economic significance. A quarter of all global primary production takes place in the coastal zone, and 90 per cent of the world's fish – a critical protein source for the planet's population – is either caught or farmed in coastal waters.

BIGGEST TO SMALLEST

Because a number of different methods are used to measure coastlines, lists of the nations with the longest coastlines can vary significantly. But all have Canada sitting in the number one position, with a coastline measuring 202,080 km (125,567 miles). That figure, however, does not take into account the coastlines of the 52,455 islands that lie within Canada's territories and provinces, which have a combined coastline length of 41,712 km (25,919 miles). Add that to Canada's total, and the country's coastline is an incredible 243,792 km (151,486 miles). It would take 33 years of walking 20 km (12 miles) a day to traverse all of this North American nation's massive coastline.

At the other end of the scale – and also undisputed – is the country with the shortest coastline: Monaco, a tiny principality in western Europe. Surrounded on three sides by France, its densely populated coastal edge lies along the Mediterranean Sea and has a total length of just 4.1 km (2½ miles).

The Indian Ocean island nation of the Maldives, which has just 644 km (400 miles) of coastline, is the world's lowest-lying country. It has no hills, but some sand dunes reach heights of 2.4 m (7⅘ ft) above sea level.

CANADIAN COAST
The 1100-km (700-mile) shoreline of picturesque Prince Edward Island forms part of Canada's extensive coastline.

CONFOUNDING COASTLINES

Measuring a coastline's length is no simple task. To begin with, they are geographically and geologically dynamic places that transform almost daily under the combined forces of wind and water. However, the most difficult aspect about measuring coastlines is that they are what are known mathematically as 'fractals' – curved shapes with lengths that change according to the scale at which they are measured. For this reason, in a phenomenon known as the 'coastal paradox', the official lengths of different countries' coastlines can vary enormously. Some cartographers will measure coasts as a series of straight lines on maps, while others will take into account the curve of every bay and inlet.

People live on just 10 per cent of the Maldives's 1192 coral islands, which on average lie between 1 m (3 ft) and 1.5 m (5 ft) above sea level.

MARINE SCULPTING

There is no universal definition of what constitutes a coastal region. On very small islands, coastal influences are ubiquitous. But, for mainlands and exceptionally large islands, most descriptions take in a strip that ranges in width from 60 to 200 km (40 to 125 miles) in both directions – out to sea and onto land. The habitats exposed to severe environmental extremes in these areas include sea cliffs, sand dunes and beaches.

The erosive forces of wind and water constantly batter sea cliffs, yet they are often endowed with diverse plant and animal communities. The most obvious residents are usually seabirds, and many of the world's sea cliffs support raucous breeding colonies of multiple species, partly because the extreme environment translates into protection from predators.

Often cited as the most spectacular in the world, the Kalaupapa Sea Cliffs are located on the Ho'olehua coast at the northern end of the small Hawaiian island of Molokai. They tower like colossal gatekeepers west of a former leper colony on the Kalaupapa Peninsula. Sufferers of leprosy, now known as Hansen's Disease, were quarantined here right up until the late twentieth century. The site is no longer required by law to be isolated, but it remains so by location. The cliffs rise to an unassailable 1010 m (3314 ft), and the wild swells of the northern Pacific Ocean provide containment for the peninsula's other three access points.

Molokai's extraordinary coastal monoliths are volcanic in origin; their horizontal layers of hard black basalt are telltale signs of ancient lava flows. They also bear the scars of recent landslips caused by erosion, and are coated with a veneer of stunted vegetation kept in check by trade winds that howl almost constantly at 16–30 km/h (10–19 mph).

Currently, the grand prize for the tallest sea cliff in the world goes to one in southern Greenland, known as Maujit Qaqarssuasia (or the 'Thumbnail'). First climbed in 2000, this glacier-eroded slab of granite drops 1560 m (5118 ft) in an almost-sheer fall into the turbulent sea below. Greenland's mighty sea cliffs are still little known, and it is possible that even bigger ones line its remote coastal fjords.

SENSATIONAL SAND

Although sand dunes in deserts can reach more than a kilometre in height, they are considerably lower in stature along the less stable environments of coastlines. The world's tallest coastal dune is Mount Tempest, a 285-m (935-ft) high sandhill on Moreton Island, about 40 km (25 miles) offshore from the eastern Australian

GREENLAND CLIFFS
The enormous cliffs of eastern Greenland tower over the Norwegian Sea. Many of these unnamed bluffs have yet to be measured, and may eventually claim the record for the tallest sea cliffs in the world.

MORETON ISLAND
The third-largest sand island in the world, Moreton Island, off the east coast of Australia, is home to two of the largest coastal sand dunes on the planet – Mount Tempest and Storm Mountain. Sand tobogganing is a popular sport here.

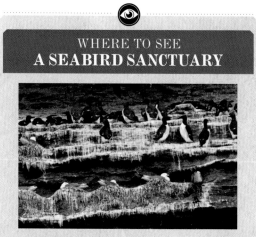

WHERE TO SEE
A SEABIRD SANCTUARY

The dramatic shale and sandstone Cliffs of Moher, in south-west Ireland, begin to reverberate from February onwards with the screeches of tens of thousands of nesting seabirds covering more than 20 different species, including guillemots and Atlantic puffins. As well as providing a secure nesting location, the cliffs overlook fertile fishing grounds in the North Atlantic Ocean.

city of Brisbane. Dunes are fundamentally piles of sand dumped by wind and waves, and to rise they need – as has occurred on Mount Tempest – for grains to first be captured by grasses and other low-lying vegetation. Without vegetation, sand spreads out in low formations such as beaches.

Praia do Cassino, near the city of Rio Grande on Brazil's southern coastline, is often awarded the title of the planet's longest beach. It is a picturesque 254 km (158 miles) of white sand that stretches northwards from near the Uruguayan border up to an artificial stone wall that extends into the water on the western edge of the South Atlantic Ocean. Often described as the world's 'longest uninterrupted' strip of natural sand, the beach at the seaside Bangladeshi town of Cox's Bazar measures 125 km (80 miles) in length. It is situated on the Bay of Bengal, at the north-eastern end of the Indian Ocean.

SEA CAVES

As impressive as long, seemingly infinite, stretches of sand can be, it takes rocks to show how the truly immense power of wind and water can mould a shoreline. Some of the most extreme geological examples of coastal erosive forces at their peak are evident in sea caves and blowholes, both of which begin with pounding breakers relentlessly smashing weak points at the base of coastal cliffs.

While inland caves most often form as a result of chemical processes, it is usually the sheer mechanical force of waves repeatedly hitting a rock surface at the same location that creates a sea cave. In a process that can take millennia, a hole develops from what starts as a mere depression and eventually becomes a space – filled with air, water or both – with its own entrance way and internal habitat that, ironically, become protected from the pounding surf.

Most exposed rocky shorelines are full of small underwater caves. But over time some can develop mammoth proportions. The world's largest sea cave is now said to be Rikoriko Cave on the Poor Knights Islands off the north-eastern coast of New Zealand, in the Pacific Ocean. The cave has a length of 130 m (427 ft) and width of 80 m (262 ft). It has a water depth of 26 m (85 ft), and the space from the water's surface to the ceiling measures a further 35 m (115 ft). Using a mix of 3D laser scanning technology and underwater hydrographic surveying techniques, the cave's total volume – both submerged and above water – has been calculated at 221,494 cubic m (7.8 million cubic ft). It is so large that it was the hiding place for a Japanese submarine that was undergoing repairs during World War II. Because of the cave's remarkable acoustics, it has also been used as a location for music performances.

Rikoriko Cave has only recently usurped the famous Sea Lion Caves, located on the Oregon coast in the United States, as the world's largest sea cave. But the US feature, which is a series of interconnected caves and caverns, still outdoes the New Zealand cave in terms of large wildlife. The site is a noisy breeding colony and haul-out location for both Steller and California sea lions, and it provides a perfect platform from which to view migrating grey whales.

EXPLOSIVE BLOWHOLES

As a sea cave expands laterally into the shoreline, the constant pressure of surging waves can erode vertical lines of weakness in the roof. When these finally break through to the surface, they can operate like release valves through which the ocean periodically surges – often in a loud and visually spectacular rush skywards. There are thousands of these phenomena, known as blowholes, along the world's coastlines, and many are tourist attractions. Often considered the largest in the world, Kiama's Big Blowhole on Australia's east coast can shoot water up to 25 m (82 ft) high. Among the most breathtaking examples are the Alofaaga Blowholes in the Samoan village of Taga. They have formed in what were originally lava tubes on a flat piece of volcanic rock, and at high tide they will reliably and repeatedly spray a rush of ocean water into the air that can reach more than 20 m (66 ft) high.

Blowholes are potentially perilous phenomena at which lives have been lost, so they should be viewed from a safe distance. The timing of blowholes is notoriously unpredictable, and many blow with enough power to knock adults off their feet. The surrounding rock surface is usually smooth and slippery, and it is possible to fall into large blowholes.

ARCHWAYS AND STACKS

On headlands with segments that run at right angles to the shoreline, natural rock archways can form as a result of wave action. Most begin as sea caves that are sculpted right through by severe erosion, and they ultimately take on an appearance reminiscent of Gothic architecture. The Green Bridge of Wales is one

ALOFAAGA BLOWHOLES

To demonstrate the power of these jets, locals often throw coconuts into these blowholes in Samoa – tourists are amazed by how high the coconuts fly! The blowholes are unfenced, so care must be taken at the site.

SEA LION CAVES

Once considered the largest sea cave in the world, the main chamber of Sea Lion Caves in Oregon is around 12 storeys in height. Algae and lichens paint the walls of the cave a vibrant emerald hue.

Submarine sinkholes found in a few coastal regions are evidence of erosion during the recent geological past. They are deep depressions that formed in limestone outcrops during ice ages, when sea levels were lower. The deepest – Dean's Blue Hole, in the Bahamas (pictured) – plunges downwards for 202 m (663 ft). The Great Blue Hole, off the coast of Belize, is the widest, with an entrance that spans 300 m (984 ft) across.

of the world's best-known examples. It is a spectacular limestone arch formation on the Pembrokeshire coast of southern Wales.

In geological terms, however, these archways do not survive very long, with the relentless forces that shape them in the first place eventually wearing them down to create stacks. These often near-vertical, gnarled stone formations that rise from the sea like ocean sentinels are also mostly transient geological formations. There is a dramatic series of limestone stacks, each up to 45 m (148 ft) tall, called the Twelve Apostles along the wild south-eastern coast of Australia. But they are located in a truly unforgiving location – called the Shipwreck Coast for good reason – and after the collapse in 2005 of one stack, known colloquially by locals as 'Judas', only eight remain standing.

The world's tallest stack is located about 1500 km (900 miles) north-east of the Twelve Apostles, roughly 20 km (12 miles) south-east of Lord Howe Island, in the Pacific Ocean. Called Ball's Pyramid, it rises, shaped like the tip of an ancient spear, to 562 m (1844 ft) above the water. The stack is the remains of a volcanic caldera, and it is believed to have formed 7 million years ago. In 1964, climbers found a huge stick insect there –

one of a tiny remnant population of the Lord Howe Island Phasmid, thought to have been extinct since the 1930s. At the time, it was acknowledged as the world's rarest insect. Some were later collected and put into an intensive captive-breeding program at Melbourne Zoo with great success. The species now appears to be safe from extinction.

TERRIBLE TIDES

The spray and noise of large breaking waves are clear signs of their power and potential danger. But the perils of a rising tide do not always evoke the same sense of urgency. Some tidal areas, however, deserve their fearsome reputations, and one of the most dangerous is Morecambe Bay, in north-west England – the site of the world's worst tidal tragedy in recent memory.

The shallow bay is funnel-shaped and experiences a large tidal range – the height difference between low and high tides – of up to 10.5 m (34½ ft). At low tide the water can recede more than 12 km (7 miles), exposing the biggest tidal flats in the United Kingdom – 310 sq km (120 sq miles) of sand and mud, rich with invertebrate life that each year attracts hundreds of thousands of wading birds. These flats contain extensive beds of cockles, a type of clam that is considered a culinary delicacy. In 2004, 23 illegal Chinese immigrants were collecting cockles here when, unable to read the warning signs written in English, they were caught by the rapidly rising tide and drowned.

CRITICAL HABITATS

Away from the most highly exposed areas where the fiercest forces of tides and coastal erosion reign, Earth's seashores and adjacent waters support some of the planet's most biodiverse and productive habitats: mangrove forests, seagrass meadows and coral reefs.

Mangrove forests are significant sites of marine productivity. They contain trees and shrubs adapted to cope with the high salt levels in the shallow tidal waters of tropical seashores. Mangrove forests line a quarter of the world's tropical coastlines and experience inundation and drying out on a daily basis because of the ebb and flow of tides. Since 1980, the area of mangrove forest worldwide has fallen by about 25 per cent to a 2013 estimate of 150,000 sq km (60,000 sq miles), 41 per cent of which is along the coastlines of just four countries: Indonesia, Brazil, Australia and Nigeria.

The largest-remaining uninterrupted tract of mangrove forest is the Sundarbans, a UNESCO World Heritage Site that spans 10,000 sq km (4000 sq miles) from south-west Bangladesh to south-east India. An immense tidal forest, it stretches for 266 km (165 miles) along the northern fringe of the Bay of Bengal, and up to 80 km (50 miles) inland. It is known particularly as the last wild habitat for a range of rare and threatened

TWELVE APOSTLES, AUSTRALIA

Despite the biblical name, there were only ever nine stacks within the Twelve Apostles group. Rubble is all that remains of the 'Judas' stack, which collapsed in 2005 partly due to fissures in the limestone rock.

MANGROVES IN THE SUNDARBANS

Wild deer is just one of 49 mammal species that frequent the Sundarbans in south-west Bangladesh and south-east India; the region also supports 315 species of birds. This habitat boasts 27 different types of mangroves, which is 40 per cent of the known species.

**INDONESIAN
CORAL REEF**

*Scuba divers and
snorkellers favour the
warm waters off the
coast of Sulawesi –
Indonesia's fourth-
largest island – for
their wide variety of
interesting coral reefs,
from steep walls to
colourful formations.*

**DUGONG IN
SEAGRASS**

*A dugong – also known
as a sea cow – and a
cleaner fish graze
together on a bed of
seagrass in the Red
Sea near Marsa Alam,
Egypt. Dugongs prefer
seagrasses that are
high in protein and
low in fibre.*

EXTREME TOP 10
LONGEST COASTLINES

1 **CANADA** 202,080 KM (125,567 MILES)

2 **INDONESIA** 54,716 KM (33,999 MILES)

3 **GREENLAND** 44,087 KM (27,394 MILES)

4 **RUSSIA** 37,653 KM (23,396 MILES)

5 **PHILIPPINES** 36,289 KM (22,549 MILES)

6 **JAPAN** 29,751 KM (18,486 MILES)

7 **AUSTRALIA** 25,760 KM (16,007 MILES)

8 **NORWAY** 25,148 KM (15,626 MILES)

9 **UNITED STATES** 19,924 KM (12,380 MILES)

10 **NEW ZEALAND** 15,134 KM (9,404 MILES)

animal species. This includes the Bengal tiger, estuarine crocodile, Indian python, Ganges River and Irrawaddy dolphins and river terrapin.

Mangroves provide physical protection for coastlines from damaging tropical storms, and they are crucial nursery grounds for a huge number of marine fish and invertebrate species. Mangroves also inundate the marine environment with such an immense level of nutrients that ultimately their influence trickles down to most of the life in Earth's oceans.

OCEAN PASTURES

Seagrasses are the only flowering plants that can live fully submerged in the oceans, but they are not really grasses. They are also not closely related to other marine plants, such as algae or seaweeds, but are in fact closer to lilies. Seagrasses can form large underwater meadows that stabilise marine sediments and provide food and habitat for a wide range of animals in tropical and temperate waters. Just 0.4 ha (1 acre) of seagrass produces over 9 tonnes (10 tons) of leaves per year and supports up to 40,000 fish and 50 million invertebrates.

But perhaps the most significant role for the oceans' seagrass beds in the twenty-first century – in the face of climate change due to elevated atmospheric carbon levels – is as a carbon sink. Studies show that seagrass beds remove from the atmosphere and store about 10 per cent of the world's annual global carbon emissions. Per hectare, they contain twice as much carbon as rainforests. The world's largest seagrass beds grow on the Saya de Malha Banks in the Indian Ocean, north-east of Madagascar. There are also huge seagrass meadows off the coasts of Florida and northern Australia.

DELICATE REEFS

For an estimated 25 per cent of marine creatures, home is a coral reef. Despite supporting such a staggering level of life, coral reefs – which are built upon and based around tiny invertebrate animals called polyps – are found in less than 1 per cent of Earth's oceans. That is just 284,300 sq km (109,800 sq miles) – an area less than half the size of France.

The soft-bodied polyps, most of which are no more than 6 mm (¼ in) wide, produce and sit within protective cup-shaped 'skeletons' made from calcium carbonate. It is these that survive long after the polyps have gone and accumulate over millennia to create reefs – providing the intricate architecture around, in and on which thousands of other species live. Most of the polyp species that build coral reefs need sunlight and warm water to do so, and for those reasons the biggest reefs are in shallow tropical coastal waters.

The world's single largest coral reef ecosystem is the Great Barrier Reef, which stretches for 2300 km (1400 miles) down the east coast of Australia in the Coral Sea of the western Pacific Ocean. It is made up of around 3000 individual reefs and is protected within the Great Barrier Reef Marine Park, which covers an area of about 344,400 sq km (133,000 sq miles) and includes 900 islands associated with the reef.

With almost 18 per cent of the world's reefs – 51,000 sq km (20,000 sq miles) – in its coastal waters, Indonesia has more coral reef habitat than any other country. Australia comes a very close second with just over 17 per cent – 49,000 sq km (19,000 sq miles). About a third of the world's coral reefs are located in an area spanning 5.7 million sq km (2.2 million sq miles) of the western Pacific Ocean, incorporating the nations of Indonesia, Malaysia, the Philippines, Papua New Guinea, Timor-Leste (East Timor) and the Solomon Islands. Dubbed the Coral Triangle, it is acknowledged as the world's most biodiverse marine area, akin to the Amazon Rainforest on land. Three-quarters of all known coral species occur here, as well as 3000 fish species – twice as many as anywhere else.

THE FUTURE OF COASTLINES

The pressure of population along the world's coastlines means that the habitats found here are some of Earth's most at-risk. Over 50 per cent of the planet's mangroves and 30 per cent of seagrass beds have disappeared in the last century. An estimated 60 per cent of coral reefs are now considered so degraded that they also risk disappearing from the planet. Most of these losses have, until recently, been due mainly to habitat destruction and pollution. But the biggest threats these habitats now face are due to global climate change, namely rising water temperatures and sea levels.

Not surprisingly, these threats are also the biggest now facing coastal human populations. At the current rate of warming, sea levels are predicted to rise across the planet by 50–140 cm (20–55 in) by 2100. And that will see several island nations – such as Kiribati and the Maldives – disappear or be rendered unliveable.

NILE DELTA
A worker harvests papyrus plants in the Nile delta near Cairo, Egypt. Since the time of the ancient Egyptians, papyrus has been used to make items such as paper, boats and mats.

Rivers and deltas

The planet's rivers function like a network of lifelines, distributing fresh water and nutrient-rich sediment as they course downhill, under the force of gravity, before ultimately connecting with the oceans and seas. But they can also be dangerous and unpredictable, with the capability to wreak havoc on a massive scale.

MOST AUTHORITIES list the longest river on Earth as the Nile, although this is still a matter of some debate, partly because no one is really sure exactly where the Nile begins. This point is likely to be, however, a stream just south of the Equator in eastern Africa's Great Lakes region, in either Burundi or its northern neighbour Rwanda. In Uganda, not far from its source, the Nile gathers water from Lake Victoria and, from there, eventually flows north as the White Nile. This is the longest of the two main tributaries of the Nile. It meets the other, the Blue Nile, in the Sudanese capital of Khartoum, after which it deviates for the first and only time from a south–north flow direction as it turns sharply to travel west for about 300 km (190 miles) at the Great Bend of the Nile.

From there the river is defined for the next 1850 km (1150 miles) by its passage through desert and a long series of shallow-water rapids known as the Cataracts of the Nile, created by deposits of rocks and boulders. Cataracts are technically large waterfalls, but none on the Nile really fits this description. They are, however, big enough to have made this section unnavigable for much of the time the river has been playing a significant role in human culture and history.

Ultimately, the Nile meanders for almost 6700 km (4200 miles) through at least 10 African nations. It forges a narrow yet fertile valley for approximately 800 km (500 miles) in southern Egypt, before eventually fanning out into one of the world's most famous deltas, in northern Egypt. It completes its journey to the ocean north of the Egyptian capital and Africa's largest city, Cairo, spilling into the south-eastern edge of the Mediterranean Sea.

EXTREME FACT

The ancient Greeks came up with the term 'delta' for the wetland areas that develop around river mouths, because they thought the regions looked like the triangular shape of the Greek letter *delta*.

AMAZON ANIMAL
Geoffroy's side-necked turtle is found in rivers, streams and lakes on the fringes of the Amazon Basin. It was named after Étienne Geoffroy Saint-Hilaire, a nineteenth-century French naturalist.

CONGO RIVER
Three young Congolese fishermen paddle their roughly hewn pirogue – a traditional dugout canoe often used as a fishing boat – across the Congo River, which shimmers like liquid gold as the sun sets.

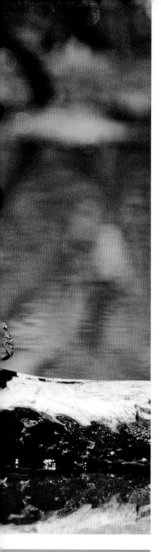

AMAZING RIVER

While the Amazon might not take the title of the world's longest river, it is exceptional in so many other ways. From its source in the Andes – not far from the Pacific Ocean on South America's west side – it flows east, traversing the continent for over 6400 km (3900 miles) to finally enter the Atlantic Ocean off the coast of Brazil. The river and its 15,000 tributaries and sub-tributaries pass through Peru, Bolivia, Ecuador, Venezuela and Colombia, creating the largest river basin in the world – 7,050,000 sq km (2,722,000 sq miles) in area.

This South American river is truly extraordinary on a global scale for the level of life it supports – 10 per cent of all known plant and animal species. The Amazon Basin has a range of important habitats that depend on the river meandering through it – from tropical savannas to cloud forests. But its largest proportion – 80 per cent – is covered by tropical rainforest. Estimated in 2013 to have an area of 5.5 million sq km (2.1 million sq miles), it is the largest remaining tract of tropical rainforest anywhere in the world – crucial not only for species diversity but also because it keeps between 90 and 140 billion tonnes (100 and 150 billion tons) of carbon locked out of the global atmosphere. Most of this is stored, of course, in the leaves and trunks of the trees; according to an extraordinary revelation from a decade-long analysis by 100 scientists published in 2013, there are almost 400 billion individual trees across 16,000 different species in the Amazon rainforest.

WIDE INFLUENCE

The marvellous Amazon is also usually considered to be the widest of the world's rivers, its banks separated by 1.6–56.3 km (1–35 miles) of water along its immense length. And when it's in flood, the Amazon's mouth can reach a staggering width of 325 km (202 miles). Here, at its peak, it discharges about 30 trillion litres (8 trillion gallons) of fresh water into the ocean each day – about 20 per cent of all Earth's water that runs off the land – diluting the salt concentration in the Atlantic for as far as 160 km (100 miles).

For much of the river's length, its waters travel at an average velocity of about 2.4 km/h (1½ mph) when it's not in flood. But the Amazon's massive volume is discharged from its mouth at the phenomenal average rate of about 209,000 cubic m/s (7,381,000 cubic ft/s), unmatched by any other river. Africa's second-longest river, the Congo – which rises in Zambia and flows for much of its length through the Democratic Republic of the Congo (formerly Zaire) – boasts the world's second-highest average discharge rate, although at 41,200 cubic m/s (1,455,000 cubic ft/s) it doesn't even get close to that of the Amazon.

The Congo is, however, deeper than the Amazon. Its bed plunges in some sections to more than 220 m

(720 ft) below the surface, deeper than any river. Almost as impressive is the depth of 200 m (660 ft) reached in parts of the Yangtze, the world's next deepest and Asia's longest river.

LIFE AND DEATH

With a length of 5464 km (3395 miles), the Yellow River (also known as Huang He) is Asia's third-longest river. But what sets this watercourse in northern China apart is hinted at in its name. The reason it is yellow is because of its enormous sediment load – higher than that of any other river. Each year it transports an average of 1800 million tonnes (2000 million tons) of sediment, almost 10 per cent of the total world average of 20,000 million tonnes (22,000 million tons). This sediment load comes from a fine-grained and wind-blown deposit of clay-like soil known as loess, which occurs near the Yellow River's origins and spills from the river to create fertile flood plains along its length. Historically, the villages and towns that flourished thanks to the agricultural production that could take place on these plains – possibly as far back as 5000 BC – have been critical to the development of the nation. It's why the Yellow River is revered as the 'cradle of Chinese civilisation'.

It has also, however, been the source of immense tragedy. Most rivers have the capacity to flood – but the Yellow River has the worst history for flooding of any of the world's rivers. It's been breaking its banks repeatedly on a huge and deadly scale for many hundreds of years, ironically due in part to the heavy sediment load that's the source of so much life. In modern times, the most destructive of the Yellow River's floods occurred

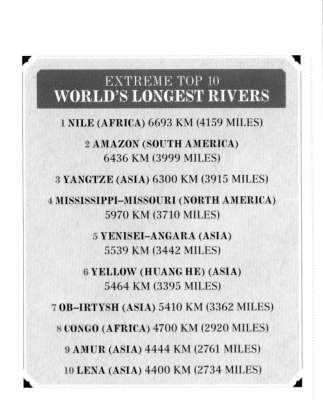
in 1931 and is considered to be the deadliest natural disaster of the twentieth century. Up to 3.7 million people are estimated to have died during the flood or from the disease and famine that it triggered.

WILD RIDES

Most rivers and streams begin as trickles from rain or melting snow in a landscape's highest areas. They always run downhill – regardless of what direction that may be – under the force of gravity, gaining momentum and collecting sediment and debris along the way. As they build in size they can scour the landscape, carving ever-wider and deeper paths before them.

In their early stages, rivers are particularly prone to the phenomenon known as rapids. These often result because various forms of bedrock at a river's base erode at different rates according to how hard they are, leading to softer rock breaking away while stones and boulders of harder rock remain to obstruct the water's flow. Rapids can be associated with waves, swirling whirlpools, dangerous obstacles and ultimately waterfalls. The standardised International Scale of River Difficulty assigns class ratings to rivers with rapids to indicate their level of navigability, from the safe Class I to the dangerous Class VI, which usually indicates that a river is impossible to travel on in any sort of craft. That doesn't, however, stop people trying.

Western Africa's Congo River has a reputation for being one of the world's most challenging waterways, with many V- and VI-class stretches. It boasts three particularly ominous sets of rapids. The first, a 120-km (75-mile) segment dubbed the Gates of Hell, is virtually unnavigable in parts. Then there is a 100-km (60-mile)

YELLOW RIVER (HUANG HE)

The Chinese city of Lanzhou is located on the upper reaches of the Yellow River (Huang He), not far from the source of the river: the Bayan Har Mountains.

stretch that includes the seven cataracts of the Boyoma Falls (previously called Stanley Falls) on the Upper Congo. Near the end, in the Lower Congo, there's a long series of rapids and cataracts that include Livingstone Falls. This drops down 270 m (900 ft) along a distance of 350 km (220 miles) and also includes the rapids of Inga Falls, the site of two hydroelectric dams.

ASIAN THRILLS

For river kayaking and rafting extremists, Tibet's Yarlung Tsangpo River is most often regarded as the ultimate paddle. Known as the 'Everest of Rivers' because of its challenging nature, it occurs at the highest elevation – 4000 m (13,000 ft) – of any of the world's major rivers. It's a truly spectacular 2840-km (1765-mile) long watercourse that emerges from near Mount Kailash in Tibet and flows east across the Tibetan Plateau, before making a sharp turn to pass through one of its wildest sections, the 250-km (150-mile) long Yarlung Tsangpo Grand Canyon, sculpted from hard granite over millions of years by the erosive force of the river. The river drops 2700 m (9000 ft) in altitude along the length of the canyon, and it begins the descent with a notorious set of rapids where lives have been lost. In 2002, American filmmaker and extreme kayaker Scott Lindgren became the first person to successfully descend the river past this section.

While the Yarlung Tsangpo Grand Canyon is quite deep, it is only the world's third-deepest river canyon. The Indus Gorge in Pakistan, carved by Asia's mighty Indus River, is regarded as Earth's deepest canyon. It is up to 7000 m (23,000 ft) deep where it passes Nanga Parbat, the world's ninth-highest mountain.

SUBTERRANEAN FLOWS

Not all rivers flow above ground. Some begin beneath the surface and remain there for much or all of their length. The longest known of these was discovered in 2007, winding through a landscape of limestone for

YARLUNG TSANGPO RIVER

A fearless kayaker is dwarfed by the enormous boulders and turbulent water in a formidable section of rapids on the Yarlung Tsangpo River in Tibet.

153 km (95 miles) beneath the Yucatán Peninsula in south-eastern Mexico. The river is part of a large subterranean cave system that extends beneath the tropical jungles of the peninsula, where several other shorter subterranean rivers have also been identified.

Until the Mexico discovery, an underground river that runs for 8.2 km (5 miles), also through limestone, about 76 km (47 miles) north-west of the city of Puerto Princesa in the Philippines, was the longest-known subterranean river. This flows directly into the Pacific Ocean and is considered so unusual on a world scale that it's been protected since 1999 within a World Heritage Area.

In 2011, Brazilian scientists announced to the world a discovery that, at first, sounded as if it would make the subterranean rivers in Mexico and the Philippines pale into insignificance. Following analysis of information gathered from hundreds of wells left by petrochemical exploration boreholes dug across the Amazon region during the 1970s and 1980s, they had identified a new salty 'river' about the same length as the Amazon, but located 4000 m (13,000 ft) beneath it. Named the Rio Hamza, after the lead researcher on the team that discovered it, the newly identified watercourse travels below the Andes and then eastwards to the Atlantic Ocean, mirroring the flow of the Amazon. Its movement, however, is substantially slower than the Amazon, and it seeps – rather than flows – along at a comparative trickle of 3900 cubic m/s (138,000 cubic ft/s). The geological world remains divided as to whether the Rio Hamza truly fits the traditional description of a river.

There may also be revelations emerging within the next few years about another mighty subterranean river – this time in Vietnam. A cave located during the 1990s near the Laos–Vietnam border – and formed more than 2 million years ago by an underground river – was recently acknowledged as the world's largest cave passage. Hang Son Doong – or Mountain River Cave – is 150 m (500 ft) wide and 5 km (3 miles) long, and was opened to the public for the first time in 2013. A fast-flowing subterranean river is known to continue through the cave, but it's yet to be fully explored and measured.

COPYING NATURE

Humans have emulated rivers as transport systems for centuries through the construction of canals. The longest of these artificial rivers is the Grand Canal in northern China, which is also known as the Beijing–Hangzhou Canal because of the two cities that it links. Almost 1800 km (1200 miles) in length, it was built from the fifth century onwards as a trade and communication route between China's north and south, and it continues to be used today.

Despite the length and antiquity of the Grand Canal, two others are perhaps better known internationally – the Panama and Suez Canals. Completed in 1914 to provide a fast and safe shipping link between the Atlantic and Pacific Oceans, the Panama Canal is just 77 km (48 miles) long. An estimated 14,000 ships travel though it each year. The Suez, which connects the Mediterranean and Red Seas at the eastern end of the Nile delta in Egypt, was built to expedite shipping trade between Europe and Asia. It was opened in 1869 and is 193 km (120 miles) long.

There are, of course, whole cities based on canals. These artificial rivers are, for example, the lifeblood of Venice, in north-eastern Italy; Amsterdam, capital of the Netherlands; Hoi An, on the central coast of Vietnam; Bruges, in Belgium; and Thailand's capital, Bangkok. In the United States, however, there is a city with a greater length of navigable canals than anywhere else in the world – Cape Coral in Florida. Located on the Gulf of Mexico, it has been built on 640 km (400 miles) of canals, many of which are frequented by alligators.

OFF COURSE

Not all rivers head towards the oceans, and not all rivers are always full of water. On the world's most arid inhabited continent, Australia, rivers often run dry. Over a large proportion of the continent for much of the year – sometimes all of the year – evaporation exceeds rainfall, which is one reason why Australia's rivers have the world's highest natural flow variability.

PANAMA CANAL
The Miraflores Locks are one of three lock systems situated along the Panama Canal. A popular visitors' centre on the site features an observation deck as well as fascinating exhibits about the history of the canal.

GRAND CANAL, VENICE
The Italian city of Venice boasts more than 150 canals, the largest of which is the 4-km (2½-mile) long, reverse S-shaped Grand Canal. Only four bridges cross the Grand Canal; gondolas also take people from one side to the other.

It means that there are many rivers, particularly in the continent's sun-baked interior, that sporadically gush with floodwaters after spending years being nothing more than a long, sandy hollow in a parched landscape. One of the best-known examples is the Todd River, the bed of which is straddled by the central Australian town of Alice Springs on the edge of the Simpson Desert. The ephemeral 272-km (169-mile) long Todd floods every few years, after which it spends several years contracting down to a series of evaporating waterholes in the sand, eventually becoming nothing more than a dry riverbed.

The Mojave River, in California's Mojave Desert, behaves in a similar way, although, when it does flow, much of its water travels beneath the ground. Its surface channels flow sporadically, and when they do they head in the direction of, and terminate in, the desert – away from the ocean. For this reason, and because much of its flow is beneath the surface, it is sometimes referred to as an 'upside-down' and 'backwards-flowing' river.

GOING BACKWARDS

Another river with a reputation for 'flowing backwards' is the Bosut, which passes through Croatia and Serbia. Its water usually proceeds to the north-east, but the flow is known to move extremely slowly – when strong winds blow, its direction of flow appears to flip and the water travels in the opposite direction.

In August 2012, a similar phenomenon occurred on the Mississippi River because of the strong onshore winds and storm surge that accompanied Hurricane Isaac as it hit the coastline of Louisiana on the Gulf of Mexico. Sensors in the river detected the water flowing upstream, for almost 24 hours at the height of the storm, at a rate of 5200 cubic m/s (184,000 cubic ft/s).

REACHING THE END

Many rivers come to their end at coastal estuaries, where fresh and salt water mix to create expanses of briny water in protected areas. They are biological and geological transition zones, where rivers come under the influence of tides, and ocean waters are sheltered. Because of this, they are usually full of invertebrate life, which in turn often attracts large numbers and varieties of bird life. The planet's largest estuary is the Gulf of St Lawrence in south-eastern Canada, on the North Atlantic Ocean. It incorporates several straits, bays and small islands, and covers an area of about 236,000 sq km (91,000 sq miles).

Deltas form on estuaries when rivers reach them while they are still carrying a lot of sediment, and the conditions are right for the sediment to be deposited. This nutrient-rich material can accumulate over millennia to create some of the planet's most fertile land. From a biological perspective, deltas are areas of enormous species diversity; fish and waterbirds are particularly

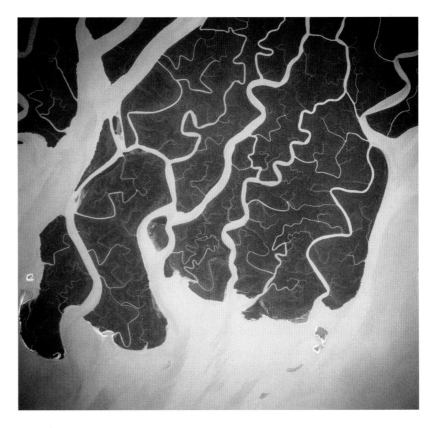

GANGES DELTA
The sinuous streams and rivers that form the Ganges delta (also known as the Bengal delta) are clearly seen in this photograph taken from the Space Shuttle Atlantis.

DRY TODD RIVER
For over 50 years, the annual Henley-on-Todd Regatta in Central Australia has seen crews running their 'boats' down the dry riverbed. In 1993 the river flooded, cancelling the event.

PEARL RIVER DELTA
In the last 35 years, Shenzhen – China's first completely planned city – has grown from a rural village to become the industrial centre of the Pearl River delta.

abundant here. Habitats range from terrestrial to aquatic and marine, and life is constantly shaped by interplays between fresh- and salt-water conditions.

The world's deltas are also of immense significance for people. Some of the world's largest and most culturally influential cities have developed and continue to grow around large river deltas. For example, the Nile delta underpinned agricultural, economic and cultural development in ancient Egypt, and it continues to be Egypt's most densely populated area.

MIGHTY DELTAS

Today in China, nine huge cities are presently in the process of merging into one giant mega-city around the fertile Pearl River delta, where three major rivers meet and flow into the South China Sea. The region remained a sparsely populated rural area until the 1970s, but it is predicted that by 2030 a city of more than 60 million people – far bigger than any city elsewhere – will emerge in this area, and it will be a key driver of both the Chinese and global economy in the twenty-first century.

The world's largest delta is the Ganges delta in Bangladesh and India, where three huge rivers meet: the Ganges, Brahmaputra and Meghna. An area of significant agricultural production, it covers more than 105,000 sq km (41,000 sq miles) at the northern edge of the Bay of Bengal. More than 125 million people now live on the Ganges delta, and its population density of about 1200 people per sq km (3100 people per sq mile) makes it one of the world's most heavily populated areas.

Waterfalls and cascades

There are tens of thousands of locations across Earth where rivers and streams drop downwards suddenly to form the geological phenomenon known as waterfalls. These are mostly created by the erosive force of water, usually over millennia, and are found from the poles to the tropics and on every continent.

IFFERENCES IN the strength and depth of bedrock making up a river's bed mean it will be eroded at different rates by the water travelling above. Softer rocks eventually wash away, while harder bedrock remains a barrier and sets up the vertical drop that ultimately transforms churning rapids into falling water.

The erosion that creates waterfalls in the first place continues so that they are in a constant state of change. Geologists estimate that Niagara Falls – North America's largest waterfall by volume, and arguably the world's best-known waterfall – has receded by up to 1.5 m (5 ft) per year during at least the last five centuries. Niagara's current annual rate of erosion has been reduced to about 30 cm (12 in) because much of its volume is diverted for the creation of hydroelectric power.

WHEN SIZE MATTERS

Water plunges downwards in an uninterrupted free fall for almost a kilometre from the sandstone precipice that tops the South American force of nature officially named Kerepakupai Merú, but better known as Angel Falls. While there are no uniformly accepted criteria that define a waterfall's starting or finishing points, consensus among experts is that this spectacular Venezuelan waterfall is the world's tallest on land, with a total estimated height of 979 m (3212 ft) – including the longest continuous waterfall drop on Earth, an estimated 807 m (2648 ft).

It's said that the plunge from the top of Angel Falls is so great that, in the intense tropical heat, the water vaporises by the end of its fall, spraying out in a mist before it hits the bottom. These falls are fed by the Gauja River and emerge from the table-topped Mount Auyantepui above the dense jungles of the Canaima National Park. The first outsider to see this spectacular natural phenomenon and the person credited with its discovery was an American adventurer named Jimmie Angel, who first sighted the falls from the air while on a 1933 reconnaissance flight in search of indicator signs for gold deposits.

The adventurer returned for a closer look at the falls in 1937, when he landed his monoplane at the top.

❓

EXTREME FACT
Waterfalls that drop directly into oceans are rare. The 12-m (40-ft) high Alamere Falls, on California's Pacific coast, is one of the very few that does.

⏵⏵

ANGEL FALLS
Known to the Spanish-speaking inhabitants of Venezuela as Salto Ángel, this waterfall is so high that it is often shrouded in clouds. On clear days, however, visitors are often left speechless by the sheer beauty of the world's tallest land-based waterfall.

Unfortunately, the plane was damaged during landing and became bogged, so Angel was forced to make the 18-km (11-mile) trek out on foot; the plane remained on site for another three decades. The falls were later named after Angel, who reportedly had his ashes scattered there after his death in the late 1950s. Surrounded by dense jungle, the falls remain hard to reach and are still most easily viewed from a light aircraft.

WIDTH AND VOLUME

Height isn't the only measurement used to define the world's record-breaking waterfalls. Khone Falls – known also as Khone Phapheng Falls – located on the Mekong River in Laos is a series of falls each less than 21 m (69 ft) in height, but which together span a breadth of 10 km (6 miles) – wider than any other falls in the world. During the monsoon season, the Mekong River floods because of exceptionally high rainfall in its catchment, and Khone Falls becomes so swamped by water that it almost disappears from view.

WHEN NIAGARA RAN DRY

In mid-1969, a US Army engineering team held back the Niagara River with a temporary 183-m (600-ft) dam, using 27,000 tonnes (30,000 tons) of rock to halt Niagara Falls' US flow. There had been concerns that huge rubble piles at Niagara's base resulting from 1931 and 1954 rockslides needed to be removed. That proved too cost-prohibitive. But while the falls' base was exposed, the opportunity was taken to survey the site, as well as to bolster and strengthen faults in the hope of delaying erosion on the American side. The temporary dam was blown up after several months, and 170,000 cubic m (6 million cubic ft) of water suddenly returned to thunder every minute over the US side of the falls.

The other size-defining feature of waterfalls is volume. On average, water rushes through the Khone Falls at a rate of 11,000 cubic m/s (390,000 cubic ft/s), making it the world's fifth largest waterfall by volume. But it has recorded a maximum – almost unrivalled – flow rate of 49,000 cubic m/s (1,700,000 cubic ft/s) in peak flood. In general, however, Inga Falls, on the Congo River in the Democratic Republic of the Congo, is considered the largest waterfall by average volume. Even with almost a third of the river's flow diverted for the creation of hydroelectricity, the estimated volume of water flowing over the falls is 25,800 cubic m/s (910,000 cubic ft/s) – approximately the same volume per second as 10 Olympic-size swimming pools!

OVERALL WINNER

The epithet of 'largest waterfall in the world', however, most often goes to Africa's Victoria Falls, based on a combined total height of 108 m (354 ft) and average width of 1708 m (5604 ft). Renowned as one of the world's most spectacular waterfalls, this massive natural water feature tumbles over a wall of basalt on the Zambezi River and straddles the border of Zambia and Zimbabwe. UNESCO, the international body that oversees World Heritage Sites, refers to the falls as 'the largest curtain of falling water in the world'. Mist and spray rise up to 500 m (1600 ft) above the top of this curtain and can be seen from at least 30 km (20 miles) away. This has given rise to the local name for the falls, Mosi-oa-Tunya, which translates roughly to 'the smoke that thunders'. The splash zone here creates its own unique and fragile riverine rainforest ecosystem that contains plants and animals that don't survive in the drier savanna habitat through which the Zambezi River flows north and south of the falls.

Victoria Falls was famously first documented outside of Africa, in 1855, by the Scottish missionary and explorer David Livingstone, after he had travelled down the Zambezi in a canoe to look for the 'smoke that thunders' that he'd heard about from local tribespeople. He named the falls Victoria after the reigning British monarch at the time.

CASCADING COLOUR

Some waterfalls are considered remarkable for the pretty or unusual colour of their water. Among the most astounding is the aptly named Blood Falls that flows out from a hyper-saline pool of water trapped within the Taylor Glacier in East Antarctica. The five-storey-high waterfall discharges a constant stream of cherry-red water, so rich with iron – due partly, it's thought, to the activity of the communities of sulfur- and iron-eating bacteria it contains – that it literally rusts on contact with oxygen. The temperature in the falls reaches as low as -10°C (14°F), but the water

HUKOU WATERFALL
As China's second-largest falls (after the famous Huangguoshu Waterfall), Hukou Waterfall attracts more than 100,000 tourists per year.

VICTORIA FALLS
As it has 'exceptional geomorphological features', Victoria Falls, in Africa, has been protected since 1989 as a UNESCO World Heritage Site.

PLITVICE LAKES FALLS
In addition to the stunning falls, visitors to this site in Croatia may also see one or more of the 126 bird species that call the area home.

remains unfrozen and flowing because it is so salty. British geographer Thomas Griffith Taylor discovered these unusual falls in 1911 while on a mapping expedition in the region.

With a far less gruesome – but equally dramatic – appearance, central Croatia's Plitvice Lakes falls feature beautiful turquoise tones. Here, the unique green–blue colouration is a result of mineral run-off from the surrounding Dinaric Alps, and it contributes to the reputation of these falls as being among the most picturesque on the planet. Altogether, there are 16 waterfalls – the highest of which is 70 m (230 ft) tall – and they are separated by natural barriers of travertine that have been formed by the activity of algae coupled with water flowing over deposits of chalk and limestone for several millennia.

The intensely yellow tones of China's Hukou Waterfall are also due to run-off from the land. The waterfall is the largest situated on the famous Yellow River (also known as Huang He), which gets its Western name from the distinctive colour of its heavy sediment load of clay-like soil from the dusty Loess Plateau. The Yellow River is famous for its destructive and deadly floods, and in the rainy season the falls here almost double in width to about 50 m (160 ft). The name Hukou means 'mouth of a kettle' and describes the bubbling appearance of the falls as they tumble over a 20-m (65-ft) drop.

BEAR FEAST
Each July, brown bears converge on Brooks Falls in Alaska's Katmai National Park & Preserve, waiting for salmon to make their way up the river towards their spawning grounds. As the fish leap over the waterfall, the bears often snatch them out of mid-air with their mouth.

PURE BEAUTY

When it comes to the subjective quality of natural beauty, the stunning Iguazú Falls on the Argentina–Brazil border invariably tops most lists of the world's best waterfalls. The site boasts 200-plus individual drops of varying heights and widths that together span several kilometres to create a tropical spectacle of loud and misty energy that is widely regarded as one of Earth's great natural wonders. Contributing to the breathtaking appearance of the falls is the lush subtropical forest that surrounds the site, where more than 2000 different plant species have been documented – including many that occur nowhere else. These forests are home to an equally diverse array of animals, including jaguars, ocelots, tapirs and howler monkeys.

Another of the world's tumbling water features that regularly makes lists of the most scenic waterfalls is Baatara Gorge Waterfall, in the Middle Eastern republic of Lebanon. Also known as the Balaa Gorge Waterfall, it drops 255 m (837 ft) through several eroded tiers of horizontal rock to finally plunge into a limestone cave. It's a popular and easily accessed site frequented by cave enthusiasts from around the world.

WATERFALL-CLIMBING FISH

Pacific salmon are famous for swimming upstream from the ocean to return to their freshwater birthplaces to spawn, leaping up and over any small waterfalls they encounter in their travels. While these energetic and well-documented migrations are remarkable enough, there are lesser-known fish capable of even more extraordinary ascents of waterfalls.

The Nopoli rock-climbing goby is found on all the islands of Hawaii, but nowhere else in the world. It's

BAATARA GORGE WATERFALL

Only discovered in 1952, this unusual waterfall in Lebanon is at its best at the end of winter when snowmelt boosts the volume of water cascading into the Jurassic limestone cavern below the surface.

IGUAZÚ FALLS

The spray that constantly arises from the tumbling water at Iguazú Falls, on the Argentina–Brazil border, completely soaks the surrounding landscape, which encourages the growth of a verdant subtropical forest.

EXTREME TOP 10
WORLD'S TALLEST LAND-BASED WATERFALLS

1 ANGEL FALLS (VENEZUELA)
979 M (3212 FT)

2 TUGELA FALLS (SOUTH AFRICA)
948 M (3110 FT)

3 THREE SISTERS FALLS (PERU)
914 M (3000 FT)

4 OLO'UPENA FALLS (UNITED STATES)
900 M (2953 FT)

5 YUMBILLA FALLS (PERU)
896 M (2938 FT)

6 VINNUFOSSEN (NORWAY)
865 M (2837 FT)

7 SKORGEFOSSEN (NORWAY)
864 M (2835 FT)

8 PU'UKA'OKU FALLS (UNITED STATES)
840 M (2756 FT)*

9 JAMES BRUCE FALLS (CANADA)
840 M (2755 FT)*

10 BROWNE FALLS (NEW ZEALAND)
836 M (2744 FT)

The metre figures are equal due to rounding up.

a species that lives in the ocean when young, where it feeds on tiny plants floating in the plankton. But these fish are born in freshwater streams, which they return to once they mature into 18-cm (7-in) long adults. Just before making the journey, their mouths transform into suckers, which are vital for processing the new diet that they'll survive on as adults – algae scraped from the surface of rocks in their freshwater home streams. Recently, however, scientists have discovered that these mouth suckers have another critical role. By acting as remarkably strong suction caps, they enable the fish to climb up the slippery, turbulent walls of waterfalls, where they have been documented scaling record heights of up to 100 m (330 ft).

Considerably smaller – reaching lengths of just a few centimetres – is the even less well-known waterfall-climbing cave fish. As its common name suggests, it is capable of climbing walls that are wet with fast-flowing water. This is a blind fish that is found only in limestone cave systems in Thailand. It uses its highly adapted fins to grasp rocks and climb upwards for short distances.

UNDERWATER TUMULT

While there's little argument about the impressive scale of Angel, Inga, Victoria and all the other large waterfalls based on land, the water feature that truly

Mauritius has many eye-catching cascades – among them Chamarel Waterfall, the country's highest – but none is as impressive as the 'waterfall' that appears to flow beneath its warm coastal waters.

earns the title of Earth's biggest waterfall is also the one that's hardest to see. Deep in the icy waters of the North Atlantic Ocean, in the Denmark Strait between Greenland and Iceland, is a waterfall of such mammoth proportions that its land-based rivals look almost like trickles in comparison.

Here at the mighty Denmark Strait Cataract, colder, denser waters from the Greenland Sea steadily build up behind shallow continental shelves that act like a seabed 'dam'. The cold waters eventually spill over this natural impediment and plunge downwards for some 3500 m (11,500 ft) – a distance that's more than three times the height of Venezuela's Angel Falls – into the slightly warmer waters of the Irminger Sea, flowing at a rate of 5 million cubic m/s (175 million cubic ft/s) in the process. Scientists say that the volume of this submerged cataract is an incomprehensible thousand times bigger than the combined volume of all the waterfalls found on land.

Back up on the ocean's surface, at the south-western end of the island of Mauritius in the Indian Ocean, east of Africa, is a sight that appears from the air to rival what's hidden deep in the Denmark Strait. Mauritius is one of several islands along the southern end of an elevated area known as the Mascarene Plateau, which was created by relatively recent seabed spreading.

Waters around the islands here mostly drop down to no deeper than 150 m (490 ft). Off the plateau, however, they suddenly plunge thousands of metres. Lighter-coloured sand carried by currents from the nearby islands swirl off the plateau and into the darker ocean depths. Viewed from above, it appears to be a huge waterfall in the middle of the ocean. Although spectacular, it is, in fact, no more than a trick of light, colour and movement in a tropical sea – one of Earth's renowned mirages.

A TIDAL EFFECT

Another remarkable marine 'waterfall' effect occurs in the Buccaneer Archipelago in the Indian Ocean off north-west Western Australia. Here in Talbot Bay, where the tidal range is one of the highest in the world, a curious phenomenon known as a 'horizontal waterfall' occurs each day as the tides change. Described as one of the great wonders of the natural world, it isn't, of course, a waterfall – but it looks like one when viewed from any elevated vantage point. The effect occurs as intense tidal currents attempt to enter and leave the bay via two narrow coastal gorges. Water builds up behind the gorges with each transition between low and high tides, and

the amazing waterfall effect is created as this banked-up water is forced to rush through the narrow gorges as the tide changes.

A large tidal range is also responsible for the strange phenomenon known as the Reversing Falls on the St John River in the Canadian province of New Brunswick. The river empties into the Bay of Fundy – noted for having the world's biggest tidal range. When the tide is high, it can push water back up the river so that it 'rolls' against a series of underwater ledges to create backward-flowing rapids.

LOST FALLS

All over Earth there are several remnants and signs of once-great cascades and cataracts that are no longer touched by water because of geological change or human interference. In central Washington State, on the western side of the United States, there is an ancient riverbed known as the Grand Coulee, and at its heart lies one of North America's great natural wonders – a scalloped, 5.6-km (3½-mile) wide ledge of basalt perched over a 122-m (400-ft) drop. It is known as the Dry Falls Cataract, because water doesn't flow here and probably hasn't for thousands of years, as indicated by vegetation along the basalt precipice.

IT'S ABOUT TIME

The 10,000-year-old, 30-m (100-ft) high Mackinac Waterfall was discovered in 2007 submerged but perfectly preserved beneath the waters of Lake Huron, one of North America's five Great Lakes. The top of the falls begins 34 m (110 ft) beneath the water's surface, and it would have once been the eastward outflow point for Lake Michigan.

But when it did, it must have been a massive force of nature that could have matched and possibly outdone any of the modern land-based falls. At five times the width of Niagara Falls, it's certainly the biggest waterfall ever to have flowed in North America, and it's thought that it might also have rivalled the water-carrying capacities of some of the other modern greats.

Both the Grand Coulee and its falls were created in a period of catastrophic flooding that occurred on an unimaginable scale thousands of years ago during the last glacial retreat, when a massive wall of water travelling at 105 km/h (65 mph) rushed down the river and over the falls. Glacial flooding is thought to have kept the flow gushing for several thousand years.

GONE FOREVER

The planet lost another of its great waterfalls far more recently. One of the largest of the modern waterfalls by volume, the Guaíra Falls of the upper Paraná River on the Brazil–Paraguay border disappeared when they were flooded in 1982 during the construction of the Itaipu Dam hydroelectric project; the rocks that created the falls were later destroyed to prevent them from being a navigation hazard. The falls had an estimated mean annual flow rate of 13,300 cubic m/s (470,000 cubic ft/s), certainly enough to make it one of the largest waterfalls by volume. But at full force during a flood, it was believed to have reached a flow rate of some 50,000 cubic m/s (1,750,000 cubic ft/s). It's said that the crashing noise of the falls could be heard from more than 30 km (20 miles) away, and that – as for the exposed tops of all the great waterfalls of the tropics and subtropics – sunlight playing on the splashing mist created permanent rainbows.

Guaíra comprised 18 falls, with a total drop of 114 m (375 ft). These were formed as the Paraná River crossed the Maracaju Mountains and was forced through narrow canyons, where its width was abruptly reduced by more than three-quarters – from 381 m (1250 ft) to 61 m (200 ft). The region's new dam now covers an area of 1350 sq km (520 sq miles), and over 14,000 megawatts of energy can be created via a series of obstructions and spillways along almost 8 km (5 miles) of the Paraná River. It's an elaborate complex that has now become one of the world's largest hydroelectric plants.

FROZEN FALLS

It's hard to imagine that with all the tumbling energetic momentum that defines waterfalls, they can freeze still and solid when river temperatures get low enough. Like most other fresh water at sea level, waterfalls will begin to freeze once their water temperature drops to 0°C (32°F). They don't freeze as quickly as still water, but they will freeze. As their temperature falls, the water molecules slow and eventually begin sticking together to form tiny solid discs known as frazil ice. Then, in the same way that snowflakes grow, water molecules will begin clumping together so that even water flowing in a free fall can become frozen. Small and often unnamed cascades and waterfalls tend to be the most likely to freeze over, but any waterfall will eventually come to an icy standstill given the right conditions.

Frozen waterfalls are being seen increasingly as ever-evolving challenges in the extreme sport of ice-climbing. Because waterfall ice forms from running water, it tends to present mountaineers and rock climbers with a different kind of climbing trial to that found when tackling alpine ice, which forms from compacted snow. Also adding to their attraction for extreme ice-climbing specialists, frozen waterfalls are less permanent and predictable than alpine ice.

THE FANG

This frozen waterfall in Colorado only used to form once every five years. But a rope has been hung down the waterfall to give ice crystals something to cling to, so it now freezes more often.

THE WONDER

Climbing the frozen Bridal Veil Falls in Colorado is fraught with danger – as well as the threat from avalanches, this icy demon can send large, sharp icicles hurtling down onto unsuspecting climbers.

When frozen in winter, Colorado's 111-m (365-ft) high Bridal Veil Falls – first scaled as a frozen waterfall in the 1970s – continues to be regarded as one of the most technically challenging ice-climbs in North America. The names of waterfalls as frozen attractions used by ice-climbers are often different to what they are called when they are flowing in the summer months. In the winter this one is known simply as The Wonder.

An imposing feature known to extreme ice-climbing enthusiasts as The Fang is also located in Colorado. It's a huge pillar of ice that looks like a massive straight white canine, and it only forms during exceptionally cold winters at a waterfall in the town of Vail. At its peak, The Fang towers more than 50 m (165 ft) in height from an 8-m (26-ft) wide base.

In North America, the Canadian Rockies feature many and varied waterfalls that provide fantastic ice-climbing sites for all skill levels. The best places in the United States to find frozen falls are Colorado and Wyoming, as well as the high altitudes of California. In Europe, Norway is the centre of frozen waterfall climbing, with the town of Rjukan regarded as the country's key area. There is an ice-climbing festival held here each February.

Lakes and reservoirs

In south-eastern Siberia, close to the geographical heart of the Asian continent and a long way from the nearest coast, lies the planet's deepest lake. So revered is it for the extraordinary range of life it supports, Lake Baikal is variously referred to as the 'Galápagos of Russia', 'Sacred Sea' and 'Pearl of Siberia'.

T HE REMARKABLE Lake Baikal is an enormous natural basin where the water plunges to a depth of 1637 m (5371 ft). It holds 20 per cent of the planet's unfrozen fresh water – 23,000 cubic km (5500 cubic miles) of liquid. No other single reservoir on Earth – natural or artificial – contains more fresh water. But it's just one of 17 natural lakes worldwide that each covers an area that is bigger than 10,000 sq km (4000 sq miles).

UNIQUE LAKES

Lake Baikal is often compared to the Galápagos Islands because of its extensive and mostly unique biodiversity. Formed about 25 million years ago, it is Earth's oldest lake; its unusual suite of plants and animals reflects its evolution in isolation across that vast period of time. So far, the animal species count for the lake is at least 1340, more than half of which are found nowhere else on the planet. The most iconic of these is the Baikal seal, the planet's only exclusively freshwater seal, which is also known as the nerpa. No one is quite sure how seals first reached Lake Baikal – perhaps via an ancient sea link to the Arctic Ocean – but this species is now endemic to the lake.

As big as Lake Baikal is, it's not the largest lake on Earth. The world's largest inland body of water is full of briny – not fresh – water: the Caspian Sea, which, despite its name, is certainly a lake by definition. (The accepted geological definition of a lake is simply that it is a 'large' standing body of water surrounded by land.) Bordered by Russia, Azerbaijan, Iran, Turkmenistan and Kazakhstan, the Caspian Sea covers 371,000 sq km (143,000 sq miles), an area slightly larger than the size of Germany. It's the only lake in the world with a surface area bigger than 100,000 sq km (40,000 sq miles), so it's not surprising that it was widely considered to be a sea in ancient times.

? EXTREME FACT
The largest lake on an island is Nettilling Lake on Canada's Baffin Island. It covers an area of 5542 sq km (2140 sq miles).

▸ PEARL OF SIBERIA
The rocky coastline of Olkhon Island – the largest island located in Lake Baikal, and the world's fourth-largest island within a lake – offers visitors a tranquil view of Lake Baikal's deep blue waters.

SALT SOURCE

The Caspian Sea's water is brackish, with an average salt level of 12 parts per thousand (ppt), about a third that of normal sea water. The saltiness is partly a legacy of its origins as a gulf on the ancient Paratethys Sea, a large but shallow body of ocean water bordered by Africa, Europe and Asia. The Caspian Sea gradually became landlocked from about 5.5 million years ago, as tectonic forces shifted the surrounding continents. It has remained salty because its waters are contained in a closed endorheic basin – it has no outflow and only loses water through evaporation and seepage.

Just as for Lake Baikal, long isolation has meant that the Caspian Sea has many unique species that don't occur anywhere else, including the critically endangered Caspian Sea sturgeon. This long-lived, slow-growing creature is thought to have been the largest freshwater fish that ever lived, reaching staggering lengths of up to 6 m (20 ft). But specimens of this size are no longer seen. The species has been over-exploited to near extinction because its unfertilised eggs form the much-desired delicacy known as black caviar.

From the largest body of inland salt water to the saltiest: Earth's most saline natural body of water is at the other end of the planet – Antarctica's Lake Don Juan. Also known as Don Juan Pond, it was discovered in 1961 and is estimated, based on 2011 calculations, to have a volume of 3000 cubic m (106,000 cubic ft). Scientists speculate that if water exists on Mars, it's likely to be similar to what's in Earth's Lake Don Juan, where the saline content is about 40 per cent – up to 12 times as salty as normal sea water. It's this high salinity that stops the water in the lake from freezing in an environment where the surface temperature in winter can plummet to -50°C (-58°F).

INTRODUCING THE GREATS

The Caspian Sea's mammoth volume of 78,200 cubic km (18,800 cubic miles) represents about one-third of Earth's non-ocean surface water. The next largest lake in terms of area – North America's Lake Superior – is less than a quarter of the size of the Caspian Sea. Unlike the Caspian Sea, however, it contains fresh water. Lake Superior is one of North America's five Great Lakes; the others are Lakes Michigan, Huron, Erie and Ontario. Although they are considered separate lakes, they are actually interconnected and together represent the largest freshwater system on Earth, containing 84 per cent of North America's surface fresh water and about 21 per cent of the world's. All straddle the United States–Canada border, except for Lake Michigan, which is situated entirely within the United States. With an area of 57,800 sq km (22,300 sq miles), Lake Michigan is the largest lake to be contained entirely within just one country. North America's Great Lakes

all ultimately drain via Lake Ontario into the Atlantic Ocean. On a world scale, these lakes are very young indeed – they formed just 12,000 years ago during Earth's last glacial retreat.

Africa, too, has a group of standing water bodies known as Great Lakes, which span three separate catchment areas in the eastern and central parts of the continent. There are usually considered to be seven in the group – Lakes Victoria, Tanganyika, Malawi, Turkana, Albert, Kivu and Edward – and most have their own claims to fame.

Lake Victoria is renowned as the world's second-largest freshwater lake by area after Lake Superior. In terms of freshwater volume and depth, Lake Tanganyika – at 18,900 cubic km (4500 cubic miles) in volume and 1470 m (4820 ft) in depth – is beaten only by Lake Baikal. Lake Malawi (also called Lake Nyasa), which boasts more than 1000 fish species, is known for having the world's highest level of freshwater fish diversity. And Lake Turkana (formerly Lake Rudolf) covers an area of 6405 sq km (2473 sq miles); protected within a World Heritage Area, it is the world's largest permanent desert lake. Despite being surrounded by

---

EXTREME TOP 10
WORLD'S LARGEST LAKES*

1 CASPIAN SEA (AZERBAIJAN, IRAN, KAZAKHSTAN, RUSSIA, TURKMENISTAN)
371,000 SQ KM (143,000 SQ MILES)

2 LAKE SUPERIOR (CANADA, UNITED STATES)
82,100 SQ KM (31,700 SQ MILES)

3 LAKE VICTORIA (KENYA, TANZANIA, UGANDA)
69,500 SQ KM (26,800 SQ MILES)

4 LAKE HURON (CANADA, UNITED STATES)
59,600 SQ KM (23,000 SQ MILES)

5 LAKE MICHIGAN (UNITED STATES)
57,800 SQ KM (22,300 SQ MILES)

6 LAKE TANGANYIKA (BURUNDI, DEMOCRATIC REPUBLIC OF THE CONGO, TANZANIA, ZAMBIA)
32,900 SQ KM (12,700 SQ MILES)

7 LAKE BAIKAL (RUSSIA)
31,500 SQ KM (12,200 SQ MILES)

8 GREAT BEAR LAKE (CANADA)
31,200 SQ KM (12,000 SQ MILES)

9 LAKE NYASA (MALAWI, MOZAMBIQUE, TANZANIA)
29,600 SQ KM (11,400 SQ MILES)

10 GREAT SLAVE LAKE (CANADA)
28,600 SQ KM (11,000 SQ MILES)

*By surface area

LAKE DON JUAN
Located at the western end of Wright Valley – part of Antarctica's famous McMurdo Dry Valleys – hyper-saline Lake Don Juan was named after Don Roe and John Hickey, the two helicopter pilots who discovered it.

LAKE VICTORIA
Two young Kenyan boys paddle a brightly painted canoe near Dunga Beach, which is situated on the north-eastern shore of Lake Victoria. The nearby city of Kisumu is one of the lake's main ports.

a lunar-like landscape, the lake abounds with life: most noticeably Nile crocodiles, hippopotamuses and huge numbers of waterbirds – both resident and migrating – including the iconic greater flamingo.

ALKALINE LAKES

Lake Turkana is also the world's largest alkaline lake: it has a pH of about 9.4 because of high levels of sodium and bicarbonate ions in its water, leached from volcanic rocks in its catchment. This mineral content colours its waters bright jade green. Also known as soda lakes, alkaline lakes occur all over the world, and Africa has at least a dozen more. In Tanzania's Lake Natron, pH levels can reach higher than 10 thanks to an accumulation of dissolved ions from minerals that flow into the lake from surrounding hills. Despite their seeming toxicity, many alkaline lakes support a range of specially adapted ecosystems based on algae or microorganisms that not only survive but thrive in their unique waters.

North of Lake Natron, Lake Magadi is so alkaline that almost nothing lives in it. Lake Magadi receives

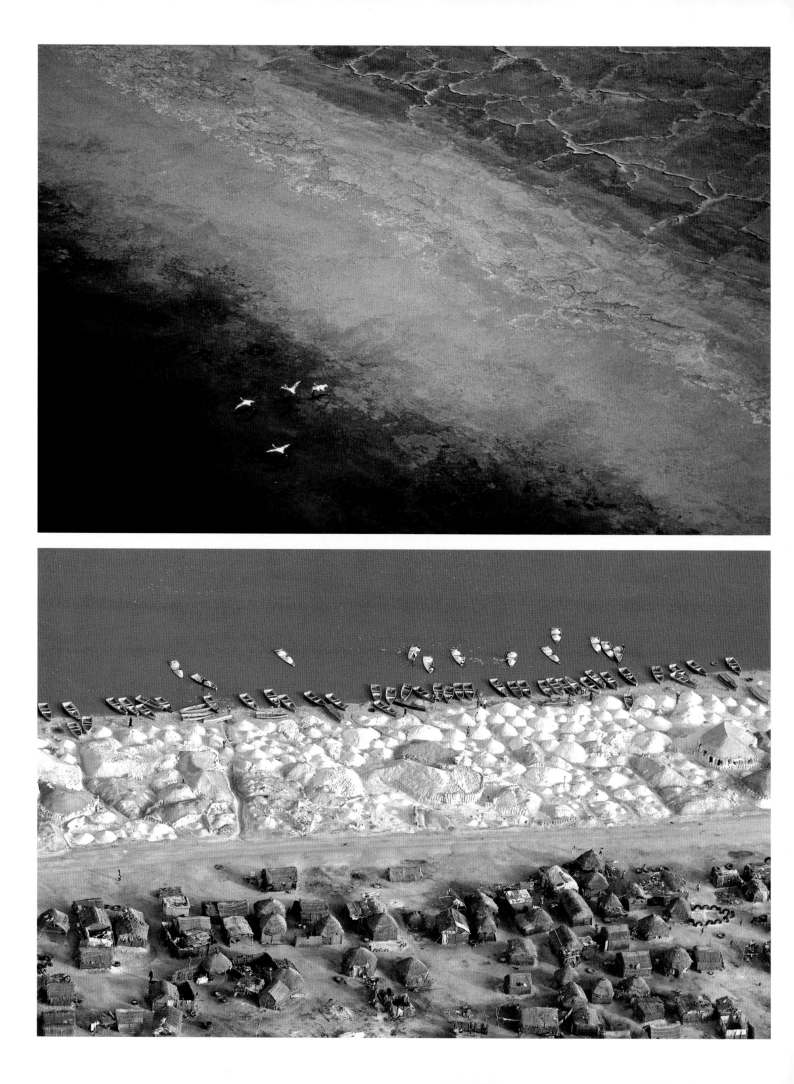

WHERE TO SEE
FLAMINGOS

When conditions are right, huge colonies of flamingos breed at Africa's Lake Natron. The lake's harsh alkaline environment discourages most large predators, while perennial springs in the area provide fresh water for flamingo chicks. Adults feed on the specially adapted microorganisms high in red pigments that thrive in the alkaline waters, and this turns the flamingos' feathers pink. Well-fed flamingos are bright pink, but when food is scarce their feathers can become pale pink or even white.

some minor water flow from monsoonal rains, but it is fed mainly by hot volcanic springs located around its edges that bubble with water heavily impregnated by calcium carbonate. For much of the year, Lake Magadi is covered by only a very thin layer of water that evaporates during the dry season to expose a layer of a mineral called 'trona', which is extremely high in sodium carbonate. The lake is one of the most extreme aquatic habitats on Earth, and almost no multicellular organisms can live here – with the exception of one remarkable and well-studied little fish species. The Lake Magadi tilapia survives low oxygen and high temperatures in small lagoons around the edge of the lake. During the dry season, however, the outskirts of the lake ripple with birds such as flamingos, pelicans, spoonbills and herons, which feed on small animals living in freshwater streams that trickle into the lake.

COLOUR AND CLARITY

Also located in Africa is a lake famous for having a hue that is not traditionally associated with aquatic environments – bright pink. Located in Senegal, Lake Retba (known also as Lac Rose) is coloured milky pink by high concentrations of a salt-loving microalgae called *Dunaliella salina*. This organism produces large amounts of the red pigment beta-carotene in response to its extreme habitat. During the wet season the lake's colour pales as the waters are diluted. But in the dry season – from November to June – its waters can intensify to almost blood red as concentrations of *D. salina* bloom.

On the considerably colder South Island of New Zealand, in the Pacific Ocean, Lakes Pukaki, Ohau and Tekapo are fed by glacial melt-water that gives them an intense blue colour. The lakes are located

LAKE MAGADI
Four lesser flamingos fly over soda flats at the edge of Kenya's Lake Magadi. During prehistoric times, Lake Magadi was much larger – subsuming the nearby Lake Natron – and it contained fresh water.

LAKE RETBA
Salt is gathered by hand from the bed of Lake Retba in Senegal and brought back to shore, where it is stored in piles before being used or sold. Salt collectors protect their skin with shea butter before entering the water.

not far from the country's highest mountain – Aoraki/Mount Cook – and their fantastic colour is due to the way suspended fine silt or glacial 'rock flour' in their waters diffracts sunlight. This fine particulate matter is ground from rocks by huge glaciers as they forge their way across the countryside, carving and shaping the land as they go.

New Zealand also boasts the lake with the clearest water, according to the results of a 2011 study by water-research scientists. Visibility in Blue Lake (also known as Rotomairewhenua in the local Maori language) is 70–80 m (230–260 ft), the highest recorded for any lake. Amazingly, the upper reading is the same as the clarity for distilled water. The lake is in Nelson Lakes National Park in the northern part of New Zealand's Southern Alps, and it is believed to be so clear because all the particulate matter is filtered out of its water during its underground flow from nearby Lake Constance.

While Blue Lake is renowned for what is missing from its waters, the freshwater Lake Kivu, another of Africa's Great Lakes, is famous for the hazardous gas that saturates its waters. Lake Kivu, which lies between the Democratic Republic of the Congo and Rwanda, is one of only three 'exploding lakes' known in the world. The others are Lakes Nyos and Monoun, both in the western African nation of Cameroon.

LAKES THAT KILL

Lake Nyos has the tragic status as the world's deadliest lake. Drowning, of course, is always a prospect on any body of water, but that's not what has earned Lake Nyos its grim reputation. It is a crater lake – formed in the caldera of a dormant volcano. On 21 August 1986, following reports of low rumblings heard around the lake, a rare type of natural disaster known as a 'limnic eruption' occurred when Lake Nyos released a cloud of carbon dioxide gas, which reached up to 100 m (330 ft) high. It suffocated to death about 1700 people and thousands of animals in villages as far away as 25 km (16 miles).

The only other similar documented event occurred at Lake Monoun, about 100 km (60 miles) south-east of Lake Nyos, two years previously when a cloud of carbon dioxide erupted from the lake, killing 37 people. These rare but deadly eruptions are thought to occur after a toxic gas – such as carbon dioxide – saturates the waters of a lake to the point where excess gas erupts into the surrounding air. One theory is that the gas is produced by magma beneath the lake. Another is that decomposing organic matter is the source of the carbon dioxide. In Lake Kivu, a second gas – methane – is also present.

HIDDEN LAKES

Not all lakes are obvious or permanent. The largest ephemeral lake in the world is Kati Thanda–Lake Eyre, near the centre of the Australian continent. This large depression in a parched landscape was first observed by Europeans in 1840, but it was not known to be a lake until its first filling on record, more than a century later, in 1949. At 15 m (49 ft) below sea level, the lake is the lowest point in Australia and at the end of a vast drainage system that covers about 16 per cent of the continent – 1.2 million sq km (460,000 sq miles).

The lake has only completely filled three times in the last 150 years, but even in dry seasons it usually contains some traces of water. Most of the time, Kati Thanda–Lake Eyre is largely an extensive saltpan 144 km (89 miles) long and 77 km (48 miles) wide, created by thousands of years of floodwater evaporation. When it floods, the lake becomes a massive breeding ground for hundreds of thousands of waterbirds, such as pelicans and silver gulls, which are more often seen on coastlines thousands of kilometres away. These birds thrive on the invertebrate life that survives in a dormant state during long periods of desiccation in the lake's sediments or is transported in floodwaters that arrive from far away.

There are, however, even more remote and seemingly inhospitable lake environments that are biologically productive. In 2013, scientists reported on signs of life found within Lake Vostok, the largest of hundreds of underground lakes in Antarctica, and the largest underground lake known on Earth. The fresh water of Lake Vostok, which has an estimated volume of 5400 cubic km (1300 cubic miles) and average depth of around 400 m (1300 ft), has been sealed away beneath almost 4 km (2½ miles) of ice for millions of years. Analysis of DNA samples from the lake has revealed, however, that it contains not only bacteria but also more complex multicellular animals.

KATI THANDA–LAKE EYRE

The Warburton River is responsible for around 65 per cent of the water that makes its way to this central Australian lake, channelled from floodwaters some 1000 km (600 miles) away in Queensland.

LAKE KARIBA

Bleached limbs of dead trees reach up gracefully from the serene surface of Lake Kariba, on the border of Zimbabwe and Zambia, one of the only signs that this is an artificial reservoir created by the flooding of the Kariba Gorge.

RIVER RELICS

One of southern Asia's biggest lakes, Kabar Taal in north-eastern India, is a waterhole left as a legacy by an ancient river. Lying north of the modern Ganges River and covering 63 sq km (24 sq miles), it's a lake of national significance with extraordinary biodiversity: it is home to 41 fish species and 163 different birds, including 57 migratory species. Kabar Taal is an oxbow lake, created when the main stream of a meandering river cuts a shorter path through the landscape, and sediment blocks the ends of the original river loop to form a curved lake. Many of the world's oxbow lakes are crescent-shaped. But some, such as the famous billabongs of Australia, are rounder remnant waterholes left in ancient riverbeds.

STORAGE CAPACITY

Humans have been making their own lakes in the form of reservoirs since the early days of agriculture thousands of years ago. The largest in terms of volume is Lake Kariba on the border of the African nations of Zambia and Zimbabwe. It holds 185 cubic km (44 cubic miles) of water, covers an area of about 5400 sq km (2100 sq miles) and was created in the late 1950s by damming the Zambezi River. Lake Kariba is located within the East African Rift, a developing tectonic plate boundary where the African Plate is thought to be slowly diverging into two plates. It's a seismically active area, but before Lake Kariba was built earthquake activity was classed as very low in the region around the potential reservoir. There was a sudden increase in seismic activity – including about 20 magnitude 5 earthquakes – as Lake Kariba was filled, because of pressure from the weight of the water (a phenomenon known as Reservoir-Induced Seismicity).

In terms of surface area, the world's largest reservoir is the 8500-sq-km (3300-sq-mile) Lake Volta in the western African nation of Ghana. It was created by the construction of the Akosombo Dam on the Volta River, a hydroelectric project that was completed in 1965. Almost 80,000 people needed to be relocated to create the huge Lake Volta.

The deepest reservoir on Earth is Parker Dam on the Colorado River in Arizona. It was a remarkable feat of construction for the mid-1930s, when engineers looking for the bedrock they needed to support the dam wall were forced to dig well below the original riverbed. The result is the deepest dam on earth – 98 m (320 ft), of which 72 m (236 ft) lies below the original riverbed.

KAKADU WETLAND
Paperbark trees emerge from the tranquil surface of Yellow Water Lagoon, one of the prettiest wetland areas in Australia's Kakadu National Park.

EXTREME FACT
Australia has 65 sites protected under the Ramsar Convention, including two of the country's largest wetlands: Kakadu National Park in the Northern Territory, and Coongie Lakes in South Australia.

Swamps and other wetlands

Wetlands have been a hot topic of conversation on the Gulf Coast of the United States – and, indeed, the world over – since Hurricane Katrina hit the area in 2005, with devastating consequences. The careless clearing of wetland habitats in the decades prior to the killer storm was partly to blame for the severity of Katrina's impact.

R ESTORATION OF marshlands is now being seen as a way of buffering the area against future violent weather. This growing perspective of wetlands as valuable landscapes is vastly different to the view that prevailed for much of the twentieth century: that Earth's naturally flooded lands were worthless habitats. No other environments have suffered as much deliberate devastation as wetlands. These waterlogged realms – where aquatic and terrestrial habitats come together – include swamps, fens, bogs, peatlands, marshlands and flooded forests. They once covered about 12 per cent of the planet's land area. But so many have been drained, filled and raised that they now cover less than 6 per cent – a global area of about 5.7 million sq km (2.2 million sq miles).

Wetlands are found on all the continents except Antarctica, and across all climates. More than half of the world's wetlands are in subtropical or tropical regions, including some of the world's largest continuous areas of swamps. But they're also found in seemingly lifeless frozen wastelands near the Arctic Circle. As well as acting as physical protection against wild weather, Earth's wetlands function like environmental sponges to mitigate floodwaters. And, perhaps most importantly on a planet with a shortage of clean drinking water, they act as natural filtration systems that cleanse water of impurities before it is returned to watertables and continues through the planet's hydrologic cycle.

WET AND WILD

Swamps are vegetated wetlands, and the largest of these – in fact, the world's largest wetland of any sort – is the Pantanal, located near the centre of the South American continent. This vast interconnected system of flood plains and marshlands covers over 150,000 sq km (58,000 sq miles) where the borders of Brazil, Bolivia and Paraguay meet. It's bigger than England, covers an area more than 10 times larger than North America's

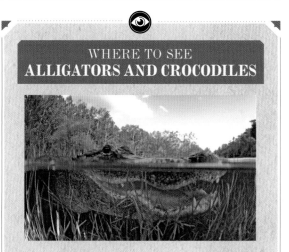

WHERE TO SEE
ALLIGATORS AND CROCODILES

The only place on Earth where alligators and crocodiles can be seen living side by side is in the Florida Everglades, where fresh water and salt water mix. The American alligator (pictured) is at the southern end of its range here, while the American crocodile is at its most northern. Both are native to the United States.

famous Florida Everglades and is considered to have the greatest concentration of animal life in both North and South America – higher even than the Amazon rainforest.

The main reason for the region having such a high number and range of animal species is because the Pantanal's vegetation is a complex mix of moisture-loving plants from surrounding areas of tropical rainforest, savanna and woodlands. With more than 650 different species of birds – including the largest of all parrots by length, the stunningly blue hyacinth macaw – the Pantanal is widely regarded by both amateur and professional ornithologists as one of the best places on Earth for birdwatching.

The area also boasts 150 mammal species, including the endangered giant otter and the world's largest-remaining jaguar population. It has significant numbers of ocelots, pumas, maned wolves, Brazilian tapirs, giant anteaters and capybaras – the world's biggest rodent. There are more than 50 reptile species, including the Yacare caiman, a relative of alligators; the yellow anaconda, a water-loving snake that can grow longer than 4 m (13 ft); and the green iguana. The Pantanal also has about 270 species of fish and a staggering diversity of insects, including more than 1130 butterfly species.

SAFE HAVENS

Despite the Pantanal's enormous size and international reputation, it faces ongoing threats including gold and diamond mining, deforestation and cattle ranching. The key protective mechanism for wetlands throughout the world like the Pantanal is the intergovernmental Convention on Wetlands of International Importance – better known as the Ramsar Convention, after the Iranian city of Ramsar where it was first adopted in 1971 as part of a global strategy. The convention, which aims at ensuring the 'conservation and wise use' of wetlands, is the only international treaty that targets a particular type of environment – recognition of the significance of wetlands to the planet. While wetlands are extraordinary havens for biodiversity, it is their role as natural filters for the world's water that has seen interest in their protection transcend cultural, geographical and political boundaries.

It is an indication of just how significant this is now considered to be on the world stage that, as of December 2013, 85 per cent of all countries were signatories to the convention, which listed 2170 wetland sites of international importance covering a total area of 2,070,454 sq km (799,407 sq miles). The largest single site on that list – and the world's largest protected wetland located within a single county – is the Ngiri-Tumba-Maindombe wetland, which covers 65,696 sq km (25,365 sq miles) east of the Congo River in equatorial Africa's Congo Basin. A large part of this vast wetland area, around the Lake Tumba region, is flooded forest.

Like the Pantanal, the Ngiri-Tumba-Maindombe contains one of the world's highest concentrations of biodiversity and protects a remarkable suite of animals. These include rare forest elephants, buffaloes, leopards, crocodiles and hippopotamuses, as well as 150 different fish species and, like so many wetland areas, a vast variety of birds. But, biodiversity aside, Ngiri-Tumba-Maindombe is also protected because it is seen as having a crucial role in maintaining and controlling a clean supply of fresh water to the people living in this part of Africa, where a tropical monsoonal climate prevails. The vegetation of the now-protected wetlands mitigates and absorbs water during the rainy season, helping to protect downstream communities from flooding.

PRESERVED DECAY

In temperate and cold areas, bogs are among the most significant types of wetlands. They are usually associated with dense coverings of sphagnum, a type of moss with large cells that absorb and retain huge amounts of moisture. And they are generally places where almost all the water comes from precipitation in the form of either snow or rain. This lack of a moving water supply means that bog soils are normally low in nutrients and oxygen. The nutrient paucity often makes bogs hotbeds of diversity for carnivorous plants, such as sundews and Venus flytraps, which snare insects as a food source.

The lack of oxygen also means that many bacteria living in waterlogged bog soil respire by using sulfur compounds in the plant material as a source of oxygen. The process often results in the production of hydrogen sulfide gas, which makes bogs and some other wetlands smell of 'rotten eggs'.

Much of the largest swamp system in the Northern Hemisphere, the Great Vasyugan Mire, is a bog. And although it looks from afar to be a vast under-vegetated wasteland, it has huge importance on a world scale. The mire lies close to the Arctic Circle, covering an area of 55,000 sq km (21,000 sq miles) in south-western Siberia. Dead plants accumulate here – as they do on other bogs – as a material called peat, which forms layers up to

CAPYBARAS

HYACINTH MACAW

OCELOT

LIFE IN THE PANTANAL

Animal and bird sanctuaries within the Pantanal protect a wide range of creatures, from the palm nut-eating hyacinth macaw and the mostly nocturnal ocelot to the highly social capybara and the gregarious giant otter, the world's noisiest otter species.

GIANT OTTER

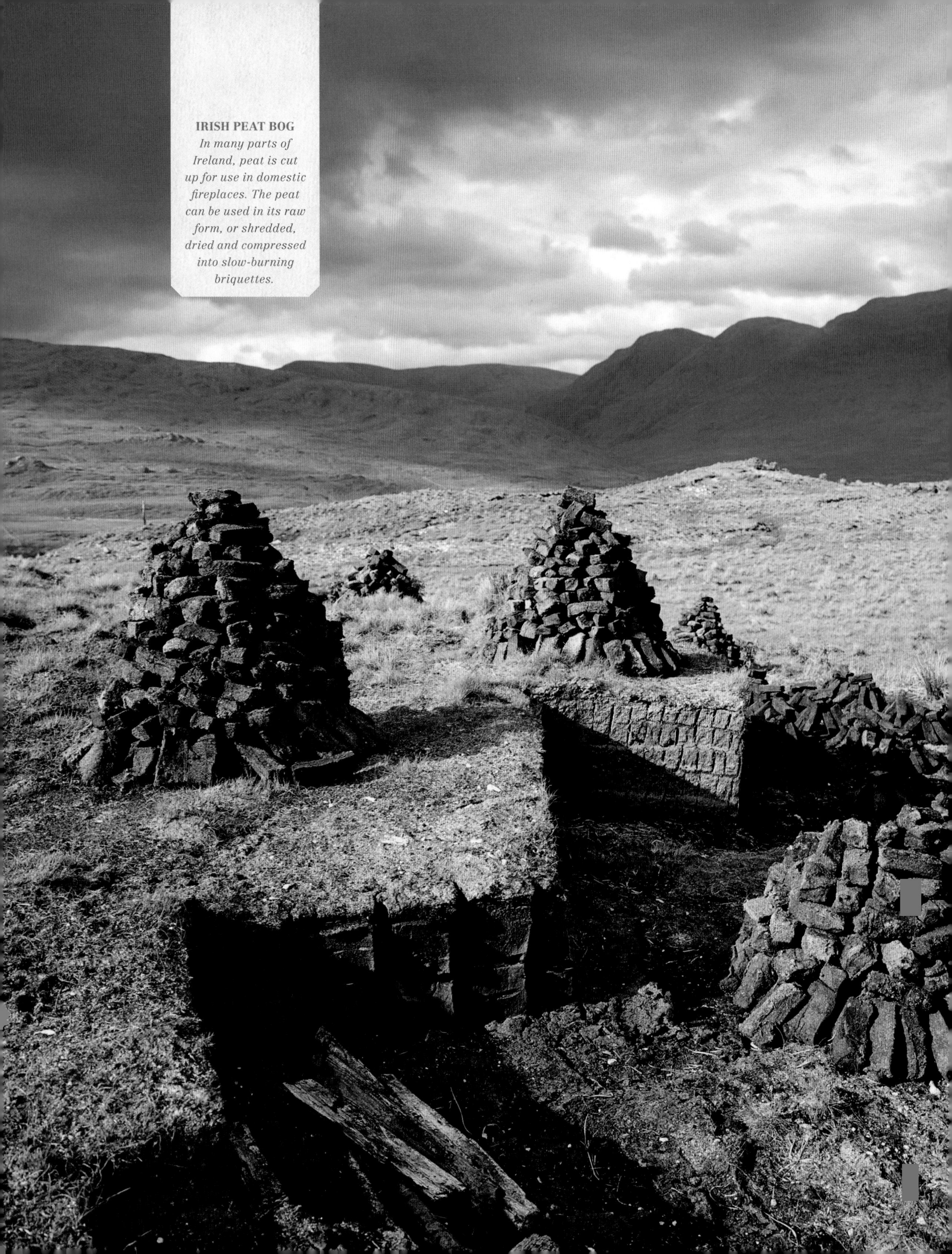

IRISH PEAT BOG
In many parts of Ireland, peat is cut up for use in domestic fireplaces. The peat can be used in its raw form, or shredded, dried and compressed into slow-burning briquettes.

CARNIVOROUS PLANTS

North Carolina's Green Swamp is renowned for its Venus flytraps. When insects touch hairs in the 'mouth' of these plants, the opening snaps shut – trapping the insects.

BOG BODY

Tollund Man was found in a peat bog on the Danish section of the Jutland Peninsula in 1950. Radiocarbon dating showed that he died between 375 and 210 BC.

4 m (13 ft) deep. The Great Vasyugan Mire accounts for about 2 per cent of the world's peat bogs, including the planet's largest area of frozen peat bog. According to a number of recent studies, this huge deposit of frozen organic material has begun thawing for the first time in 11,000 years. It's a phenomenon that has alarmed scientists around the world because of the potential consequences it will have for the world's climate.

CLIMATIC IMPACT

Plants rot considerably slower on peat bogs than they grow. Decay proceeds very slowly due to the low oxygen levels and also because the high level of vegetation makes the surrounding soil acidic – conditions that hamper the bacteria and fungi usually responsible for decomposition in other environments. Rotting is curbed even further, almost halted, by freezing. And so what these conditions do is keep much of the carbon contained in the dead vegetation locked away and out of Earth's atmosphere. Thawing, however, allows the decay process to restart and the carbon contained in the vegetation to be released, much of it in the form of the gas methane.

Earth's peat bogs play a vital role in the global climate by keeping around 455 billion tonnes (502 billion tons) of carbon locked away, gradually releasing just 45 million tonnes (50 million tons) annually into the atmosphere as methane. That figure could escalate if the Great Vasyugan Mire continues to thaw, accelerating climate change.

BOG BODIES

Because decomposition rates are impeded in peat bogs, it means that not only does plant matter in them break down very slowly, but also any animal material. And that includes the bodies of humans.

Since the 1700s, the remains of hundreds of people have been uncovered from bogs, mostly in cold parts of northern Europe. They've been in various states of decomposition and from a variety of times in recent history, although most date from between 800 BC and 200 AD. The oldest so far is Koelbjerg Woman. She was discovered in Denmark in 1941 and is known only from a well-preserved skull and other bones. Studies of the remains have identified that she died about 8000 BC and was no more than 25 years of age at the time of her death.

While bogs rich in lime with a high pH tend to preserve bodies only as bones, others have the physical and chemical environments that preserve soft tissues. They release chemicals that leach calcium from bodies, leaving the flesh of bog bodies to be preserved like tanned hide. Some of these bodies are so well preserved that it is possible to see how they died and also gain other remarkable details about historical humans.

One of the most complete bog bodies so far found is that of a man uncovered in 1952 in the village of Grauballe in Denmark. Grauballe Man lived more than 2000 years ago, but his remains still had a full head of hair and sunken leather skin. He had met a violent end with his throat slashed from ear to ear, and his last meal had included pork and a porridge of barley and other seeds and herbs.

Another body, of a man found in 1904 in a peat pit on the Bourtanger Moor in the Netherlands, also clearly shows a violent death. Intestines protrude through a stab wound on the right side of his body. He's thought to have met his grisly end, along with a companion who was found with him, sometime between 160 BC and 220 AD.

TREED BOGS

On the coastal plain of the United States' eastern side, along the Atlantic Ocean, there is a rare and unique forested bog habitat known as the pocosins. These ultra-moist landscapes covered in evergreen shrubs and trees are found mostly in the state of North Carolina.

They are upland habitats that are a long way from streams and other flowing water sources, so that – like other bogs – all their moisture comes from rain and snow. They are based on a soft and soggy soil that is a mix of peat and sand, is low in nutrients and oxygen and is highly acidic. Unlike other bogs, however, pocosins occasionally dry out and suffer from periodic wildfires. Most stands experience a major fire every 10 to 20 years, and so there is also a lot of charcoal in the soil. Pocosins range in size from small ½-hectare (1-acre) pockets to boggy forests of several thousand hectares.

The habitat was extensively drained and converted for agriculture during the 1960s and 1970s, but its perpetually damp status deterred a lot of potential development. Although half of the pocosin habitat in the United States has gone, there is still about 3600 sq km

---

STAY SAFE
If you get caught in quicksand:
✦ Don't struggle wildly.
✦ If you are stuck, lean backward onto the sand to spread your body weight across as large a surface area as possible.
✦ Use slow, angled movements to get to the edge and pull yourself out.
✦ Be assured that your body will float because it is less dense than the sediment–water mix.

(1400 sq miles) that remain undisturbed. This has become a vital refuge for a range of mammal and bird species from temperate Northern Hemisphere regions, including the iconic American black bear and the endangered red-cockaded woodpecker as well as salamanders, frogs and moisture-loving reptiles.

WEIRD 'WETLANDS'

At a few bog-like locations in the world, the most obvious liquid lying at or near the surface of the soil is not water but a considerably thicker, more viscous material: tar. This low-grade crude oil substance is a sticky form of natural asphalt that's proved capable of trapping animals and preserving their fossils. The most famous and best-studied site is the La Brea Tar Pits in the Californian city of Los Angeles. The asphalt still seeps to the surface here, and the pits are now located right in the middle of town.

The now-protected site is used extensively for education and research. As a result, these remarkably gooey pits have offered up one of the world's richest collections of Pleistocene vertebrate fossils. These include 59 mammal species and 135 bird species that slipped into the pits and died up to 40,000 years ago. Altogether, more than 3 million specimens have been found at the 9-hectare (23-acre) site, including sabre-toothed cats, mammoths and giant jaguars. Most of the fossils are of predators; scientists believe that each time the site trapped a struggling animal, it became surrounded by predators approaching for the kill and they, in turn, became caught in the tar.

The world's largest tar pit is Pitch Lake, in the village of La Brea on the Caribbean island of Trinidad. It's about 40 hectares (100 acres) in area, up to 76 m (250 ft) in depth and holds about 9 million tonnes (10 million tons) of asphalt. People occasionally swim in the lake's emulsion of water, gas, bitumen and mineral matter, believing it to be therapeutic. And every now and then an ancient relic, such as a prehistoric tree trunk, rises to the surface and then disappears again.

CRAZY QUICKSAND

Deadly quicksand that is capable of sucking captured people and animals under the surface is a Hollywood exaggeration. Quicksand is a phenomenon of simple physics known as a 'colloid hydrogel', which occurs when sediment becomes waterlogged. The water reduces the friction between individual sand grains, so that they can no longer support weight, and the sediment can become difficult to move through. While quicksand can occur anywhere, it is most often seen on riverbanks, beaches, marshes and lake shorelines or near underground springs.

The world's most infamous quicksand location is Morecambe Bay in north-western England. Numerous warning signs alert unsuspecting visitors to the bay's potentially treacherous sandy mudflats. But every so often someone gets caught and needs rescue services to free them before they become swamped by rapidly rising tidal water. Travellers are also warned to be careful of quicksand while travelling through shallow wetland areas on the edge of the Rub' al Khali desert on the Arabian Peninsula.

WETLAND REFUGE
Okavango Delta – also known as Okavango Swamp – is a wetland oasis within the arid north-western corner of Botswana. It attracts a multitude of animals and birds in search of food and water, including the plains zebra, red lechwe, hippopotamus, African fish eagle and lilac-breasted roller.

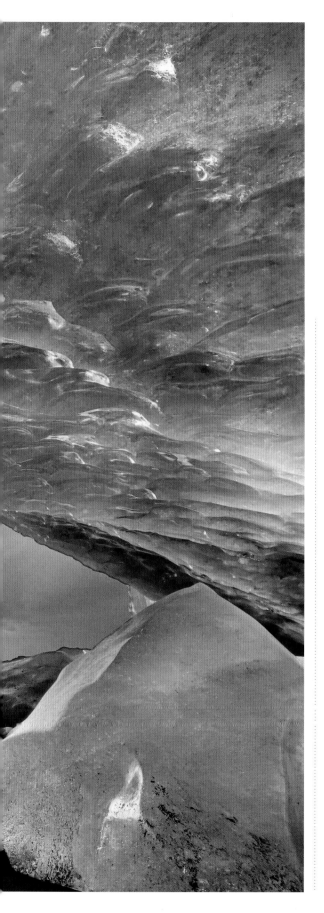

Glaciers and sea ice

Vast glaciers have carved and moulded Earth's landscape as they have advanced and retreated in 40,000- to 100,000-year cycles for at least the past 2.5 million years. With just a few exceptions, these massive ice blocks are presently melting at unprecedented rates, which has led to an average sea-level rise of almost 20 cm (8 in) since 1870.

THERE ARE ABOUT 171,000 glaciers across the planet, and between them they hold around 70 per cent of Earth's fresh water – almost 30 million cubic km (more than 7 million cubic miles). If the ice in all of them were to melt, the oceans around the world would rise by about 70 m (230 ft).

The largest glaciers are ice sheets that cover an area of more than 50,000 sq km (19,000 sq miles). Earth presently has two ice sheets – on Greenland and Antarctica – and between them they contain 99 per cent of Earth's freshwater ice. Each of these is so heavy that, in a geological phenomenon called isostatic depression, they are bending the continental crust beneath them.

About 10 per cent of Earth's land area is covered by glacial ice, most of which is contained in these two ice sheets. Up until 20,000 years ago, however, 32 per cent of Earth's land area was covered by glaciers.

POLAR EXPANSES

The Antarctic Ice Sheet is the largest of Earth's enduring continental glaciers, covering an area of 14 million sq km (5.4 million sq miles) – larger than any single country except Russia – and featuring a maximum thickness of 4776 m (15,669 ft). The Greenland Ice Sheet is much smaller than its Southern Hemisphere counterpart, covering an area of 1.7 million sq km (656,000 sq miles) – almost 80 per cent of Greenland's terrestrial area. Recent research has shown, however, that the Greenland Ice Sheet is now melting at a rate not seen since records began, six times faster during the first decade of the twenty-first century than in the previous decade.

It's estimated that the Greenland Ice Sheet began forming at least 100,000 years ago. But that's a mere drop in the ocean of time compared to the oldest glacial ice discovered on Earth so far. Ice from an ancient alpine glacier buried beneath rubble in Antarctica's Beacon Valley is thought to be 8 million years old. Beacon Valley

? EXTREME FACT
As glacial ice becomes denser due to pressure from accumulating snow, it appears blue because it reflects mostly blue light and absorbs the other colours.

◄ STUNNING GLACIER
Iceland's Fjallsjökull is an outlet glacier – a river of ice that flows from an ice sheet, ice cap or ice field, with exposed bedrock on either side. It features breathtaking ice caves that are popular with photographers.

IT'S ABOUT TIME

At the peak of the last glacial period, which extended from 110,000 to 12,000 years ago, the massive Laurentide Ice Sheet covered much of Canada and the United States, while the vast Weichselian Ice Sheet cloaked large parts of northern Europe. And the 480,000-sq-km (185,000-sq-mile) Patagonian Ice Sheet extended from the Andes into parts of present-day Argentina and right down across Chile.

is one of the McMurdo Dry Valleys, a desert-like series of snow-free depressions in Antarctica, and the continent's largest iceless region. In 2007, researchers extracted bacteria from the 8-million-year-old ice and grew them in a laboratory, prompting concerns about the outcome when ancient bacteria and viruses trapped in glacial ice are released as the retreat of Earth's glaciers continues.

The other main type of continental glacier is called an ice cap, and it covers an area less than 50,000 sq km (19,000 sq miles). The largest glacier in Europe is an ice cap – the Severny Island Ice Cap, covering an area of 20,000 sq km (7700 sq miles) on Severny Island off the north coast of Russia. Vast areas of interconnected ice caps and other glaciers are known as ice fields. The world's biggest outside of the poles covers 21,980 sq km (8490 sq miles) of Kluane National Park and Reserve in the Yukon in western Canada. In the vast sameness of the ice-field landscape, exposed mountain peaks known as nunataks that rise higher than elsewhere in these areas provide much-needed reference points.

ICE MOVES

The massive bodies of dense ice that most people think of as glaciers are the slow-moving frozen rivers of snow and compacted ice called alpine glaciers. These occur on all continents except Australia, and across all latitudes – even the tropics. They form above the snowline – the altitude at which there is year-round snow – growing bigger when winter snowfall exceeds summer melting and shrinking when the situation is reversed.

They gradually travel downhill, impelled by the sheer weight of the ice they contain under the force of gravity. And they move faster at the top than they do at the base because of the restrictive forces of friction at play as they grind against rocks and sediment in the surrounding landscape.

The expression 'to move at glacial speed' stems from the fact that most alpine glaciers travel at such a slow pace that their movement is undetectable without sophisticated and sensitive measuring equipment or the use of time-lapse photography. The heavier and warmer they are, the faster they move, but, on average, glaciers travel at a rate of about 60 m (200 ft) a year.

⌐
**KLUANE
NATIONAL PARK**
*From the air, 56-km
(35-mile) long Donjek
Glacier in Canada's
Kluane National
Park has the classic
appearance of an
ice river as it slides
between the pristine
peaks of a majestic
mountain wilderness.*

⌐
HUBBARD GLACIER
*In 1986, Alaska's
Hubbard Glacier –
the world's largest
non-polar tidewater
glacier – blocked the
entrance to Russell
Fjord, forming a lake.
A few months later
the dam collapsed,
and water burst out
of the fjord.*

⌐
FLOATING ICEBERG
*As demonstrated by
this small iceberg –
which calved from
Greenland's renowned
Jakobshavn Glacier
before floating off
into Disko Bay –
about 90 per cent of
an iceberg's mass lies
below the surface of
the ocean or sea.*

Another fascinating feature about glacial movement is that it is not always consistent for individual glaciers. Sometimes they can move at a relative sprint for short bursts. Alaska's Hubbard Glacier, for example, had a two-month surge forward in 1986 during which it covered 10 m (33 ft) a day.

The glacial speed record, however, goes to Greenland's Jakobshavn Glacier, known locally as Sermeq Kujalleq. Already famous as the world's fastest-moving glacier, in the spring of 2003 it moved at a comparative gallop when it travelled at the extraordinary equivalent of 12,600 m (41,300 ft) per year.

BIG BLOCKS

It's thought that the iceberg that tragically sank the *Titanic* in 1912 in the North Atlantic Ocean may have originally come from the Jakobshavn Glacier, which is the source of about 10 per cent of all icebergs in the waters around Greenland. Alaska's Hubbard Glacier is also known for releasing ocean-going icebergs. It's a type of alpine glacier called a tidewater glacier, which flows to the sea. By the loud and violent process known as calving, end pieces of ice break free and float off into the ocean, where they become shipping hazards.

The largest icebergs, however, come from the ice shelves surrounding Antarctica. Ice shelves are thick slabs of ice that stretch from the land over nearby water, and are formed by ice sheets and other glaciers flowing onto the surface of the ocean. The Ross Ice Shelf is the world's largest; it flows out over the Ross Sea, which is part of the Southern Ocean.

Early in 2000, the Ross Ice Shelf calved the biggest iceberg on record, a massive ice block named B-15 with an area of around 10,600 sq km (4100 sq miles) – bigger than the island of Cyprus. Pieces of the iceberg survived for more than a decade, and at least one small remaining section – known as B-15J – was captured in a satellite image in late 2011 still afloat in the Southern Ocean.

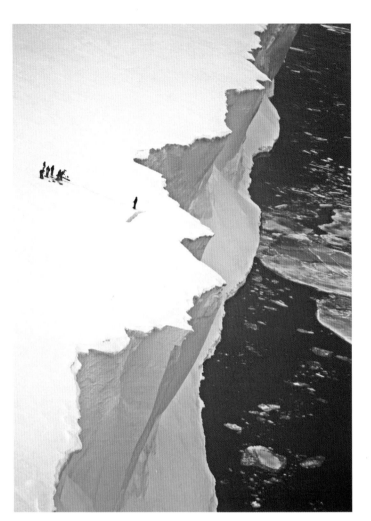

GROWTH AND DECLINE

Hubbard Glacier was first mapped in 1895, and it has been observed ever since to be thickening and advancing towards the Gulf of Alaska. It is one of the exceptions in the modern glacial world, where thinning and retreating have been the trend for much of the last century.

Another rare exception is Argentina's Perito Moreno Glacier, located in Los Glaciares National Park within the province of Santa Cruz. It is one of 48 South American glaciers fed in the Andes by the Southern Patagonian Ice Field, which is the larger of two remnant ice fields left after the decline of the Patagonian Ice Sheet. It is also the world's third-largest reserve of fresh water after the Antarctic and Greenland Ice Sheets. The 30-km (19-mile) long Perito Moreno Glacier is one of only three glaciers in Patagonia known to be growing, thanks to increased snowfall near the start of the glacier and strong, cold winds that have maintained low temperatures.

While it's not unexpected that glaciers in tropical climates would be suffering on a warming planet, many of the glaciers showing the largest proportionate losses are in Earth's mid-latitude mountain ranges, including the Alps and Andes. Some of the largest glaciers that have receded during the past 30 years are New Zealand's Tasman Glacier; Iceland's Vatnajökull; glaciers on Mount Kilimanjaro, in Tanzania; and the planet's largest alpine glacier – Antarctica's Lambert Glacier.

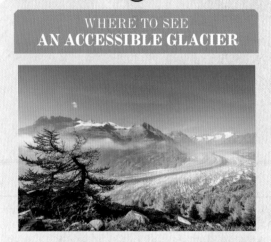

ENORMOUS ICE RIVERS

Lambert Glacier spans about 100 km (60 miles) at its widest point, is about 400 km (250 miles) long and is estimated to be 2500 m (8200 ft) deep at its centre. It is a truly massive river of slowly moving ice covering about 1 million sq km (386,000 sq miles) near the northern edge of the Antarctic continent. It was first identified in 1952 by an American geographer, John Roscoe, who originally named it Baker Three Glacier. It was, however, later renamed by a team from the Australian National Antarctic Research Expeditions after Bruce Lambert, the then Australian Director of National Mapping.

Some glaciers that travel down steep valleys to meet flat plains create a distinctive river-delta effect at their terminal end. They are a particular type of alpine glacier known as a piedmont glacier. The largest of these in the world is Alaska's Malaspina Glacier, which spills out across 5000 sq km (2000 sq miles) of coastal plain.

ICE SCULPTING

The sheer size and solid nature of glaciers gives them formidable powers of erosion, even if they don't move with a lot of pace. Many of the planet's larger landscape features were forged during Earth's last glacial period. Moraines are among the most widespread of these. They are deposits of sediment and rock that build up in front,

beneath and to the sides of glaciers, which remain long after the glaciers have retreated from an area.

Undulating plains and small hills are ubiquitous moraine features worldwide, but they often become hidden in time by vegetation. The US state of Illinois, for example, which is largely thought of as very flat, is actually a landscape of subtle hills and depressions created by moraines left behind by the Laurentide Ice Sheet between 25,000 and 14,000 years ago. Large, broad ridges running across the state's north-east are visible from space and have been identified as terminal moraines, pushed up by the snouts of advancing glaciers thousands of years ago.

Many of the largest moraine areas across the world are important natural filters for ground water. This has been the major rationale for the protection of Oak Ridges Moraine, in the Canadian province of Ontario. This moraine, left behind about 12,000 years ago by retreating glaciers, covers an area of 1900 sq km (730 sq miles) and is 330 m (1080 ft) at its deepest. Sand and gravel deposits across the moraine function like a massive sponge, absorbing water from rain and snow and storing it in underground aquifers before releasing it to the headwaters of dozens of rivers and streams in the area.

The northern Italian town of Ivrea is well known for being surrounded by a dramatic moraine landscape of hills and plains, which was shaped through successive

MALASPINA GLACIER

A number of alpine glaciers travel along valleys and then flow out onto a flat coastal plain to form the unique lobe-like shape of Alaska's Malaspina Glacier. The glacial ice does not reach the nearby Gulf of Alaska.

periods of glaciation over the last million years. Perhaps the most renowned feature is the extended arched area of hills known as the Morainic Amphitheatre of Ivrea, which was created by the Balteo Glacier that flowed through the area between 130,000 and 10,000 years ago, when much of Europe was still covered by the Weichselian Ice Sheet. The Balteo Glacier was 3 km (2 miles) wide, at least 600 m (2000 ft) deep and stretched through the Alps for more than 100 km (60 miles).

VALLEYS AND LAKES

Valleys carved by glaciers – known as glacial troughs – are frequently U-shaped, and these are found in all of the world's mountainous areas that have been exposed to glaciers. The wide, flat-bottomed Jollie River Valley in New Zealand's Southern Alps and the 13-km (8-mile) long Yosemite Valley in the United States are both textbook examples. The largest glacial trough on the planet, however, is a work in progress – the enormous depression that's still being enlarged by the world's biggest alpine glacier, Antarctica's Lambert Glacier.

Much of the landscape of north-western England's famously beautiful Lake District was sculpted by glacial movements between 25,000 and 10,000 years ago, after the area was previously formed by volcanic eruptions. The region is characterised by deep U-shaped glacial valleys, now flooded by rivers; lake basins that were gouged out by glaciers and later filled with cold glacial melt-water; and narrow, steep-sided, sharp ridges known as arêtes, formed by adjacent glaciers pushing past each other.

Glacial movements also created North America's Great Lakes as well as the region surrounding them. More than 20,000 years ago the area was covered by the great Laurentide Ice Sheet, which – with a maximum thickness of up to 3200 m (10,500 ft) – was so heavy that it gouged out the basins of what are today known as the Great Lakes. The lakes were filled by melt-water from the ice sheet as it retreated.

Chains of smaller water-filled depressions called paternoster lakes are a characteristic series of water bodies that form in glacial valleys as ice retreats and melts. The picturesque Emerald and Dream Lakes in Colorado on the western edge of North America's Great Plains are a classic example of this geological feature.

GLACIAL BIOLOGY

Once thought to be devoid of life, glaciers are now known to harbour a wide range of tiny cold-tolerant animals and microplants. This includes 100 different species of snow algae. One that's very common is called *Chlamydomonas nivalis,* which produces a red pigment and can bloom to create a glacial phenomenon known as red snow or 'watermelon snow'.

ARCTIC LOSS

The lives of polar bears are intimately linked to the natural fluctuations of Arctic sea ice. Polar bears have an almost exclusive diet of seals; although they can swim, polar bears aren't good enough at it to be able to hunt for seals in the water. So they rely on hunting at the edge of the Arctic sea ice, where they can use their formidable skills as a terrestrial predator to snatch seals as they swim close to the shore or haul out onto the frozen sea surface. In summer, when there is little sea ice, polar bears survive on fat reserves. If Arctic sea ice continues to decline, so will the hunting grounds available to polar bears.

These tiny plants sustain communities of small, cold-loving, invertebrate extremophiles such as rotifers, tardigrades (water bears), ice worms, glacial midges and stoneflies. Also common are snow fleas, which are not really fleas but tiny animals called springtails that jump about on glaciers worldwide. Some self-contained colonies of tiny plants and animals live in cryoconite holes – water-filled cylindrical melt-holes reported on the surface of glaciers in many parts of the world.

FROZEN SEA

During the Southern Hemisphere's winter, up to 12 per cent of the combined surface area of the world's oceans is covered by frozen sea water – floating sea ice. It comes and goes with the seasons, but at its maximum it can overlie an area equivalent in size to that covered by tundra or deserts.

The biggest expanse of sea ice occurs in the Southern Ocean, and in 2013 it grew to its largest extent since satellite records began in the late 1970s. NASA satellite data showed that winter sea-ice cover around Antarctica reached a record 19.47 million sq km (7.52 million sq miles) in 2013, slightly higher than the previous winter, which at 19.44 million sq km (7.51 million sq miles) had also been a record. According to NASA's calculations, the Antarctic sea-ice cover is growing by 1.5 per cent every decade. Why should this happen during an unprecedented period of global warming? Scientists are at a loss to explain this anomaly, but they believe an increase in wild rainy and snowy weather on the Southern Ocean could be involved.

The recent expansion of Antarctic winter sea ice is in marked contrast to the disturbing trend occurring at the other end of the planet. The area of sea-ice cover in 2013 in the Arctic Ocean was 18 per cent below the 1981–2010 mean average.

ARCTIC SEA ICE
A polar bear looks out over the rapidly thinning sea ice off the coast of the Norwegian island of Nordaustlandet. When the sea ice melts, polar bears must give up hunting and come ashore until it freezes again; this is happening earlier and earlier every year thanks to a warming Arctic.

EXTREME AIR AND WEATHER

We live at the bottom of an ocean of air:
the atmosphere. The interaction between the Sun,
the air and Earth's water gives us extraordinary
extremes of weather – from droughts, floods
and blizzards to thunderstorms, cyclones and
tornadoes. More subtly, sunlight interacts with
water droplets and ice crystals suspended in
the atmosphere to produce a range of stunning
and intriguing optical effects – and electrically
charged particles from the Sun stream down
to Earth, creating the dazzling beauty of the
auroras. Without the atmosphere, none of
this – and none of us – would be possible.

SUNSET AND SUNBEAMS
*When the Sun is low in the sky, behind a bank of clouds, crepuscular rays
radiate through gaps in the clouds to add an ethereal glow to the sky.*

Lightning and thunder

Myths about thunderstorms are commonplace in many cultures. In Norse mythology, for example, the god Thor produces lightning and thunder by striking an anvil with his hammer. Although modern science has provided explanations for these phenomena, the tremendous power unleashed by thunderstorms still fills people with fear and wonder.

USING DATA collected by dedicated instruments on board satellites as well as on the ground, meteorologists have worked out that around 2000 thunderstorms are raging at any one time. These storms produce a few dozen lightning flashes every second – more than a billion every year. Thunderstorms happen all over the globe, apart from the regions around the North and South Poles, and rarely over oceans. They are more common in some parts of the world than others.

While preparing maps of the distribution of lightning flashes worldwide in 2004, a team of NASA scientists inadvertently brought fame to the village of Kifuka in the Democratic Republic of the Congo. The team determined that an area close to that village receives nearly 160 lightning strikes per square kilometre (about 400 per square mile) per year – more frequent than anywhere else in the world, and over 100 times the average.

LIGHTNING DOES STRIKE TWICE

Meteorologically speaking, the well-known and often repeated idiom 'lightning never strikes twice' is not at all true. Lightning tends to strike the highest objects on whatever landscape happens to be right under a thunderstorm; for many hundreds of years, religious buildings were the tallest structures on the landscape, and were regularly struck by lightning. In eighteenth-century France, a review of death records gathered between 1753 and 1786 revealed that lightning conducting down ropes from belltowers killed 103 bellringers across the country during that period alone. As a result, in 1787 the French government banned the practice of ringing church bells to warn of approaching thunderstorms. The spire of St Peter's Basilica, in Vatican City, is taller than most buildings around it, and is often hit. On the day Pope Benedict XVI announced his resignation in February 2013, two powerful flashes of lightning struck the basilica within minutes of each other.

PARIS'S EIFFEL TOWER
As the tallest structure in Paris – and constructed largely from wrought iron – the iconic Eiffel Tower has been a magnet for lightning since its erection in 1889.

Today, most cities have buildings that are much taller than churches, mosques, temples and pagodas. Toronto's CN Tower, one of the world's tallest man-made structures, is struck an average of 75 times every year, and the all-metal Eiffel Tower in Paris receives around 100 strikes per year. Television broadcast towers are also particular targets. The actual number of strikes a structure receives depends not only on its height, but also on the frequency of lightning in that region. The world's tallest building, the Burj Khalifa in Dubai, does get struck, but not often, as it is in a part of the world where thunderstorms are very rare.

Objects don't have to be on the ground to receive a lightning strike. Airline industry estimates suggest that large commercial airliners each receive at least one strike a year on average, as they fly through or near storm clouds. Fortunately, the combination of an aluminium fuselage and carefully designed safety features nearly always protects the aeroplanes and their passengers. In 1969, the rocket carrying NASA's

LIGHTNING
Hot and humid summers in Hong Kong occasionally bring thunderstorms to the region, complete with powerful lightning bolts that zigzag all the way down to Victoria Harbour.

VOLCANIC LIGHTNING
In 2010, the dark and ominous ash cloud over the erupting Eyjafjallajökull volcano in Iceland was illuminated by lightning caused by electrical discharges within the ash cloud.

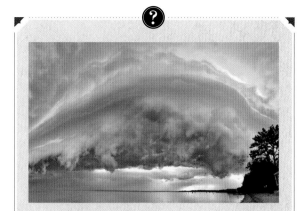

EXTREME FACT

Bulbous mammatus clouds (from the Greek word for breasts) and rolling arcus clouds (pictured) are sometimes seen at the base of a cumulonimbus cloud; undulating pileus clouds (from the Greek for cap) often adorn the top.

Apollo 12 mission received two strikes a second or so apart, as it pushed its way up through a thundercloud on its way to the Moon. The strikes knocked out the craft's instruments, which had to be rebooted quickly.

THE INGREDIENTS OF A STORM

Thunder never happens without lightning. The sound of thunder is a sonic boom – a shock wave formed by the rapid expansion of air as it is instantly heated to around 30,000°C (54,000°F) by lightning passing through it; in comparison, the temperature of the Sun's surface is just 5500°C (10,000°F). Lightning carries electric currents of tens of thousands of amperes; electric currents in domestic wiring are just a few amperes. The total amount of energy released in an average flash of lightning is about the same as all the electrical energy used by a typical family home in a 10-day period. No wonder lightning can be so destructive – and thunder so loud.

A typical thunderclap produced by lightning normally has a 'sound pressure level' of 120 dB (decibels) – about the same as a jet aircraft taking off nearby. The light of a lightning flash reaches you almost instantaneously, while the sound travels at a relative crawl, 340 m/s (1120 ft/s). So the sound from a lightning flash a kilometre away will take three seconds to reach you (about five seconds for a mile) – counting the time interval between the flash and the bang is a handy way of estimating how far away that last lightning flash hit.

A lightning flash is just a very large electric spark, or 'discharge'. The crucial ingredient required to cook up lightning is a separation of electric charges. In the atmosphere, this can happen wherever there is a strong current of rising warm air: an updraught. So, lightning

is sometimes observed during volcanic eruptions, above forest fires and even in nuclear explosions. But almost all lightning is produced in thunderstorms – and the most important aspect of a thunderstorm is the thundercloud, or, to give it its official name, cumulonimbus. Clouds are normally classified as either low-, middle- or high-altitude, but towering cumulonimbus clouds straddle all three levels. Their flat base is as low as 2000 m (6500 ft) above the ground, and the top typically stretches up to 12,000 m (39,000 ft) – but sometimes as high as 20,000 m (65,000 ft), or just under two and a half times the height of Mount Everest. A cloud that size weighs the same as several thousand jumbo jets.

Sometimes, especially along a weather front (which is the boundary between two different air masses), thunderclouds join up into an organised array called a mesoscale convective system. These huge entities are around 100 km (60 miles) wide, and are accompanied by dark, ominous shelf clouds. These extended storms bring high winds and frequent lightning as they move across the landscape.

INSIDE A THUNDERCLOUD

Cumulonimbus clouds form over ground that has been heated by the Sun. Warm, moist air rising from the ground creates a strong updraught; water vapour condenses as it rises, forming the water droplets and ice crystals that make up the cloud. At the very top, the updraught spills out into a distinct anvil shape. When ice crystals at the top of the cloud become too big to stay up, they fall through the cloud, creating a down draught. In the resulting maelstrom of rising and falling air, the descending particles of water and ice collide with similar particles rising up through the cloud. During these collisions, the particles become electrically charged; extra electrons (negatively charged) are carried down to the bottom of the cloud. The exact process remains a mystery, despite a range of sophisticated theories – but the result is an extremely strong electric field within and around the cloud.

The strong electric field inside a thundercloud is often enough to create a huge discharge of electricity inside the cloud, or between the base of one cloud and the top of another. Cloud to cloud and inter cloud lightning accounts for about three-quarters of all lightning flashes.

The enormous outpouring of water through and out of a thundercloud in the main part of the storm tends to equalise the charges in that part of the cloud – so most lightning strikes occur before or after the main part of the storm. Sometimes, lightning can strike long before a storm even reaches an area – where the sky may not even be cloudy. These 'bolts from the blue' are almost always 'positive lightning', initiated from the positively charged cloud top. The longest-ever recorded horizontal distance between cloud and strike is 190 km (120 miles), which occurred near Dallas, Texas, in 2001.

ULURU LIGHTNING
Despite being located near the arid centre of Australia, Uluru (also known as Ayers Rock) does experience some storms. From October to February, strong and dusty winds often herald the appearance of dark thunderclouds and dazzling lightning over the world's largest monolith.

▲
LAKE MARACAIBO

In Venezuela, the Catatumbo Lightning (Relámpago del Catatumbo) – better known as the Beacon of Maracaibo – is the most sustained and predictable lightning storm in the world. It lasts for several hours, with about five lightning flashes every minute.

DOWN TO THE GROUND

The most spectacular and destructive lightning is cloud-to-ground lightning. The process begins with a barely visible bulge of negative charge emerging from the base of the cloud. The bulge becomes an extended tube, which quickly pushes through the air in steps of around 50 m (160 ft). This 'stepped leader' branches out, as if searching for a way to connect with the ground and relieve the pressure created by the excess of electrons in the base of the cloud.

When any branch of the stepped leader comes within a few tens of metres from the ground – about the height of a ten-storey building – it exerts a strong effect on objects on the ground, which respond by sending up positively charged 'streamers' of ionised air. If one of the positive streamers makes contact with a branch of the stepped leader, a channel is formed along which an enormous electric current (the return stroke) can flow, allowing huge amounts of electric charge to drain from the cloud. It is the return stroke that creates the intense heat, the flash of light and the thunder.

DANGER! LIGHTNING!

Thunder is just a very loud noise; the risks of thunder from a nearby lightning strike are limited to temporary hearing loss. The real threats in a thunderstorm come

THE BEACON OF MARACAIBO

On around 150 nights every year, powerful cloud-to-cloud lightning illuminates the sky above where the Catatumbo River drains into Lake Maracaibo, in Venezuela. The spectacular display can often be seen 200 km (125 miles) away. For centuries it helped sailors in the Gulf of Venezuela and the Caribbean Sea to find their way, earning it the nickname 'The Beacon of Maracaibo'.

from the lightning – and the dangers are numerous. For example, lightning can cause spikes in domestic electricity supplies that ruin electronic equipment. A direct strike to the electrical distribution system can damage powerlines and transformers, and lead to a temporary power cut. Fortunately, pylons and substations are fitted with lightning arresters that direct any excess current to earth, and domestic surge protectors work in a similar way.

Lightning kills around 24,000 people worldwide each year, and injures around 10 times as many. Those who spend a lot of time outdoors are most at risk of being hit – particularly out in the open, away

from tall structures that would otherwise take the strike. Golfers, agricultural workers and park rangers are among the most frequent victims. American park ranger Roy Sullivan was struck by lightning seven times between the years 1942 and 1977, and managed to survive. Visitors to New York City's Jacob Riis Park in 1938 were less lucky: three people were killed there by a lightning flash, almost one year after three others died in exactly the same spot.

In 1998, a daily newspaper in Kinshasa, the capital of the Democratic Republic of the Congo, reported that an entire visiting football team had been killed by a lightning strike, while the home team were completely unscathed. The sensational report is likely to have been exaggerated, but in the same week a similar incident was captured on film. Lightning struck a football pitch in Johannesburg, South Africa, causing most of the players to drop to the ground immediately, writhing in pain. Fortunately, no one was killed in that incident.

DON'T TAKE COVER UNDER A TREE

When lightning strikes a tree, powerful electric currents pass down through the trunk. The sap immediately vaporises, blowing the trunk apart with a terrifying explosive force. This is the main reason why standing under a tree in a thunderstorm is not a good idea. You could also be a victim of 'side splash' – in which current

CLOUD TO GROUND

Thunderstorms drench the Grand Canyon with much-needed rain, but they also irradiate the area with dangerous lightning. Experts advise visitors to stay clear of the canyon rim and rocky outcrops when lightning is present.

LIGHTNING DAMAGE

The physical power of lightning goes beyond just electrocution – this modern church in Georgia, in the United States, was literally ripped in two when a lightning bolt struck the belltower and then quickly travelled to the ground.

from an electrified tree jumps to nearby objects. Cows are at particular risk. In 2004, a single strike killed 31 cows that were sheltering under a tree in Jutland, Denmark; in 2005, 68 cows were killed in the same circumstance in New South Wales, Australia; and in 2008, 53 sheltering cows were killed in the same way in Katosi, Uganda. Trees also sometimes catch fire; around one-third of all wildfires are caused by lightning.

Rather than finding shelter under a tree, the best way to stay safe before, during and after a thunderstorm is simply to stay indoors. Larger buildings are fitted with lightning rods (also known as lightning conductors), and electrical wiring running throughout a smaller building will normally act like a 'cage', protecting those inside and draining the electric current to earth. If you are not near an accessible building, climbing into a car is certainly better than staying out in the open: again, the car's metal body acts like a cage that will protect you from electric shock.

MADE BY LIGHTNING

As well as creating awe and wonder, and putting people and their property at risk, lightning has some other, less well-known effects. One of the most important is 'fixing' nitrogen. All living things need compounds of nitrogen to survive: nitrogen is an essential element in all proteins and DNA, for example. Nitrogen gas makes up around three-quarters of the atmosphere. But animals and plants cannot use it in this form; they depend on nitrogen-fixing bacteria – and lightning – to produce nitrogen compounds they can use. As it

heats the air, lightning causes a reaction between the two main components of the atmosphere: oxygen and nitrogen. The resulting nitrogen oxides then dissolve in rain and falls to the ground. Lightning is responsible for approximately 8 per cent of the biologically available nitrogen on planet Earth.

As a by-product of generating nitrogen oxides, lightning produces another important gas: ozone. The name 'ozone' is derived from *ozein,* a Greek word meaning 'to smell'; the scientist who discovered ozone, German–Swiss chemist Christian Friedrich Schönbein, first identified it as a smelly gas produced by thunderstorms. Since most lightning flashes take place at high level, within or between thunderclouds, the majority of the ozone produced does not contribute to ground-level ozone pollution. Instead, most of it ends up high in the atmosphere, some of it adding to the ozone layer, which gives life on Earth important protection against harmful ultraviolet radiation.

When a bolt of lightning conducts through sand, it heats up the sand to very high temperatures. The sand melts and quickly solidifies again to form a substance called fulgurite. The interior of the fulgurite channel is hollow, and the outside is glassy. The longest fulgurite specimen ever found, produced by a lightning flash in Florida in 1996, is nearly 5 m (16 ft) in length.

LIGHTNING, BUT NOT AS WE KNOW IT

Strong electric fields in clouds produce other electrical discharges in addition to lightning. Dubbed 'blue jets', 'sprites' and 'elves', these are dim flashes of coloured light high in the atmosphere. They normally occur above a mesoscale convective system (thunderclouds joined together over a large area), and are as transient as the lightning flashes down below. Barely visible to the naked eye from ground level, tantalising reports of high-altitude flashes nevertheless date back nearly 300 years. Sprites and blue jets were first captured on video by Space Shuttle astronauts in 1989, and elves during another Space Shuttle mission in 1990. Since then, several teams of scientists have observed and investigated these intriguing phenomena.

Blue jets shoot out of the top of thunderclouds like bright fireworks, at speeds of up to 100 km/s (60 mps), reaching an altitude of about 40 km (25 miles) – almost the height of five Mount Everests. Sprites are larger, more commonplace and extend even higher than blue jets. They come in a variety of shapes and sizes, and often occur in clusters. They are reddish orange at the top – at altitudes of around 70 km (40 miles) – but the lower portions, which look like hanging tendrils, are blue and extend down to around 40 km (25 miles). The highest of all, which are found at the very edge of space, are the elves – red haloes some 400 km (250 miles) in diameter that often form crowns above sprites, but sometimes occur in isolation.

Rainbows and auroras

Sunlight is essential – without it, life on Earth would not be possible. But the Sun's light also provides us with a range of strikingly beautiful visual phenomena, such as rainbows, sun dogs and haloes. Solar wind interacts with Earth's magnetic field, creating its own stunning light displays: the auroras.

UNLIGHT IS WHITE light: a mixture of all the colours of the spectrum. The white light spectrum includes more than just the seven individual colours we associate with rainbows (red, orange, yellow, green, blue, indigo and violet). In fact, it is a continuous range, consisting of countless colours between red and violet. As sunlight passes through the atmosphere, it encounters air molecules – mostly nitrogen and oxygen. These molecules absorb light and reradiate it a moment later – a process that is known as scattering. Because of their size, the air molecules scatter light at the blue end of the spectrum much more than light at the red end. Air molecules scatter light in all directions, so when you look at the sky on a clear day, predominantly blue, scattered light will enter your eyes.

Stand under a clear blue sky in the daytime, and far to the east of you (a few time zones ahead) people will be enjoying an early evening sky illuminated by the same sunlight that has just passed over your head. But because the sunlight has to travel further through the atmosphere, much of the blue is scattered out – so their sky will be a glorious pinkish red colour. If they observe the Sun at the moment it sets – one of the only times you can safely look at the Sun – they may see a flash of green light on the horizon for a second or two. This is the last morsel of light coming directly from the Sun, but it has been refracted (bent) by the atmosphere. The blue end of the spectrum is refracted more than the red, so the red light is the first to disappear below the horizon, blue last. But since nearly all the blue light has been scattered out on its way through the air, the last significant colour to disappear is green.

CLOUDS, MISTS, CREPUSCULAR RAYS

The droplets that make up clouds and mists are much bigger than individual air molecules – about 100,000 times bigger, or the equivalent of comparing a grape pip to a football field – yet the width of each water

droplet is less than half the diameter of a human hair. They also scatter light, but they scatter all parts of the spectrum equally – that is why clouds appear white.

Rays of light formed by gaps in clouds are scattered by mist, dust and any other particles, forming long, bright beams that spread across the sky. Known as crepuscular rays, they appear to lead back to a Sun that is only just above the clouds. But this is an illusion: the Sun is much further away. Although the rays appear to converge when you look along their length, they are actually parallel – similar to when you look at parallel railway tracks. Crepuscular rays only appear when the Sun is low in the sky, as the beams of light approach us at a shallow angle.

THE FULL SPECTRUM

To make a rainbow, you need rain. Raindrops are much bigger than cloud and mist droplets – about 10 to 50 times as large. When a ray of sunlight enters a raindrop, it refracts; each colour bends by a different amount and takes a unique route through the raindrop. The light bounces off the back of the raindrop, and refracts again as it exits. The result is that the various colours are fanned out, forming a bright spectrum. This is the source of the colours of a rainbow.

RAINBOW
Glacier National Park in British Columbia, Canada, has a high annual precipitation rate, thanks to moist air from the Pacific Ocean hitting the mountainous terrain – perfect conditions for stunning rainbows.

However, light does not enter the raindrop as a thin beam: it enters at all points on the side of the raindrop facing the Sun. Light entering at the centre will reflect straight back on itself – it is deviated by 180 degrees, the maximum deviation possible. No light ends up travelling down or turning left or right, a 90-degree deviation. So you won't see any refracted light from raindrops directly above your head or on your left or your right. You need to have the Sun behind you, and the rain in front, to catch any of the light that has been refracted and reflected by raindrops. The minimum deviation for any light passing into a raindrop is about 138 degrees.

Imagine the raindrops frozen in time for a moment: a vast array of droplets of water suspended right in front of you. You will see light from raindrops within a 42-degree cone (from 180 to 138 degrees), where 0 degrees is straight ahead. (In fact, the ground truncates the cone into the familiar semicircular bow; occasionally, you can see a complete circle from an aeroplane.) The light is brightest – and the colours most differentiated – around the 42-degree edge; this

BROCKEN SPECTRE
During this odd phenomenon, the observer's shadow often seems to be magnified, and a faint halo-like ring can sometimes be detected around the shadow's head.

is the actual rainbow. Red is always on the outside, blue inside. The dramatic presence of a rainbow will remain for as long as the conditions are right. The longest duration ever recorded was six hours, in Sheffield, United Kingdom, in 1994.

MORE BOWS

Inside the rainbow (at angles of less than 42 degrees), the colours combine to form a whitish disc. You can sometimes also see purple and green fringes, which are called supernumerary bows. They are caused by a phenomenon called interference – the same phenomenon that is responsible for coloured fringes in soap bubbles. Outside the rainbow, at angles of greater than 42 degrees, is Alexander's dark band, which was named after the third-century AD philosopher Alexander of Aphrodisias, who was the first to describe it. It is a 'band' because,

SUN HALO
Long before modern meteorology, sun haloes were seen as a sign of impending rain, because the cloud type that creates the halo is often observed near weather fronts.

EXTREME FACT

Rainbows and haloes both produce highly polarised light. If you are wearing polarised sunglasses, the top of the arc will be invisible – blocked out by the polaroid filter.

ALEXANDER'S DARK BAND

The space between the two rainbows appears darker because raindrops there do not reflect light towards the observer.

HALOES AND ARCS

Sunlight creates another set of optical phenomena in our skies when it interacts with ice crystals in cirrus clouds, at an altitude of several kilometres. Individual ice crystals are all hexagonal prisms: they have six faces aligned at 60 degrees to each other, and two faces at 90 degrees to the others. Some are elongated columns, while others are flat, thin plates.

In a manner similar to the formation of a rainbow – but with the Sun in front of you rather than behind – sunlight passing through column crystals can create a ring of light called a halo. The ring has a radius of 22 degrees – about the size of your hand, with fingers outstretched, when it is held at arm's length. When observing a halo, it is important to block out the Sun – to protect your eyes and to see the effect more clearly.

Plate crystals tend to float with their large, flat sides horizontal, and this gives rise to another 22-degree feature often seen when cirrus clouds are present. Bright spots on either side of the Sun called sun dogs. Light reflecting off the top or bottom of plate crystals is responsible for sun pillars – columns of light stretching vertically above and below the Sun. Yet another feature created by plate crystals is the circumzenithal arc, often described as an upside-down rainbow, or a colourful smile. In this case, sunlight enters through one of the large, flat faces and leaves through one of the smaller slanting faces, creating a perfect dispersion of colours. On a dark night, the Moon's light is sometimes enough to produce moon haloes, moon pillars and moon dogs.

in the right conditions, a second rainbow is visible, at an angle of around 51 degrees, and the dark band straddles the space between the two bows. This secondary rainbow is produced by sunlight that has reflected twice at the back of the raindrops. The colours are reversed, with red on the inside, and the secondary rainbow is less than half as bright as the primary one, so it is not always visible. There are even higher-order rainbows that are fainter, which result from multiple reflections within raindrops.

Although fog droplets are much smaller than raindrops, and tend to scatter light, they can also refract and deviate light in the same way as raindrops, forming a 'fogbow'. Because of the drops' small size, the colours are not as well differentiated, and fogbows are often perceived as white diffuse rings with only very faint colours. In certain circumstances, fog does produce colourful rings, but by interference rather than refraction. In this case, the fogbow becomes a series of concentric, beautifully coloured rings, suitably named a 'glory'. The coloured rings of a glory are only a few degrees in diameter, so you can normally see complete circles. You will sometimes observe your own shadow at the centre, since the Sun is behind you. This creates an eerie effect known as a Brocken spectre.

SOUTHERN LIGHTS

An emperor penguin colony seems unfazed by the shimmering of the aurora australis light over Atka Bay in Antarctica.

NORTHERN LIGHTS

Greenish auroral light illuminates the night sky over Antigun Pass, a natural passageway through northern Alaska's Brooks Range.

AURORA FROM ABOVE

NASA astronaut Joe Acaba photographed the aurora australis from the International Space Station's Tranquility node on 15 July 2012.

STRANGE LIGHTS IN THE SKY

Stay a night or two under a clear, dark sky somewhere in or around the Arctic or Antarctic, and chances are you will witness one of nature's most intriguing and beautiful spectacles: an aurora. During one of these displays, shimmering green curtains of light shift and swirl high up in the cold sky; higher still, you may see red or pink columns pointing out to space.

Auroras occur in two auroral zones – oval rings about 5000 km (3000 miles) in diameter at their widest point, each of which is centred on a magnetic pole. There is nearly always a weak, diffuse aurora in the auroral zones, which is sometimes too faint to see with the naked eye. More dramatic displays occur every two or three days on average. The auroras that appear in the north polar region are called the northern lights, or the aurora borealis; in the south, they are known as the southern lights, or the aurora australis. There is more opportunity to see the northern lights than the southern lights, simply because there is more land close to the auroral zone in the north. Night-time is your best chance of viewing these phenomena, because auroras are brighter and more energetic on Earth's non-illuminated side.

Auroras vary greatly in their brightness and activity, and the auroral zone expands and contracts. Particularly energetic auroras can be seen over a much wider area. You can't see an aurora if it is overcast, because their

WHERE TO SEE AURORAS

Tromsø, Norway, is one of the best places to see the northern lights, but you can find resorts dedicated to 'aurora hunting' in all Scandinavian countries, Iceland, Canada and Alaska. In the Southern Hemisphere, New Zealand's Stewart Island is one of the best places to go to see the southern lights.

light originates in the ionosphere, which begins about 90 km (55 miles) above ground – much higher than clouds, and about 10 times as high as a jet aircraft's cruising altitude. Some auroras extend up to an altitude of 400 km (250 miles) – about level with the orbit of the International Space Station, which sometimes passes straight through them.

SOLVING THE MYSTERY

The ethereal glow of auroras was a mystery until quite recently. In ancient times and the Middle Ages, many

people thought they were of supernatural origin – spirits of ancestors, or messages from gods. In the eighteenth century, scientists realised that auroras are connected to magnetism, because of their association with Earth's magnetic poles; some even observed how auroras cause the needle of a magnetic compass to change direction.

In the nineteenth century, scientists suggested that auroras are an electrical phenomenon, too – because the light was reminiscent of the eerie glow achieved in their laboratories by sending electrical discharges through low-pressure gases, a glow that is most familiar to us today in neon signs and orange streetlights. And the scientists of the nineteenth century were right: the way these gas-discharge lamps generate their light is indeed the same as the way auroral light is produced.

Inside a discharge lamp – and in an aurora – electrons shoot through a low-pressure gas, knocking into the atoms and ions that make up the gas, and transferring energy to them. The energy kicks each electron within the atoms and ions up to a higher energy level. A short time later, the electron falls back down to a lower level, releasing the excess energy as a burst of light called a photon. The colour of the light depends on the difference in energy between the two electron levels, and that hinges on what kind of atom or ion it is – in other words, which element. Oxygen and nitrogen make up nearly 99 per cent of the atmosphere, so these two elements are responsible for the colours of auroras. Green, the most common hue, is produced by oxygen, which can also give a reddish light. Nitrogen yields blue and red lights.

THE SOLAR CONNECTION

What no one quite realised until the twentieth century was how auroras are driven by the Sun – although there were clues. The biggest clue came in late August 1859, when very bright auroras were observed as far north as Queensland, Australia, and as far south as the Caribbean – just hours after English astronomer Richard Christopher Carrington had become the first person to observe a solar flare (a violent eruption on the Sun's surface). One witness in San Salvador, the capital city of El Salvador, reported that the sky was so red the houses and trees looked as if they had been covered with blood, while campers in the Rocky Mountains of the United States wrote that they were able to read by the aurora's light. Meanwhile, a large number of magnetic compasses went haywire; telegraph networks worldwide became electrified, working even without being connected to their batteries. Scientists suspected some kind of solar-terrestrial link, but no one could come up with a convincing explanation of what went on. The exact mechanism behind auroras was not fully worked out until the early 2000s.

The temperature of the Sun's outer atmosphere, the corona, is a staggering 2 million°C (3.6 million°F) – so it is no surprise that material is constantly boiling off. That material – mostly protons and electrons – streams out into space in all directions, and forms the solar wind. Some of it reaches Earth, and Earth's magnetic field funnels it down towards the magnetic poles – like water spiralling down a plughole – causing the diffuse auroras.

Our planet's magnetic field extends for thousands of kilometres into space. It is called the magnetosphere, despite the fact that it is not spherical; in fact, it is teardrop-shaped, its long tail extending from Earth's night side, moulded by the solar wind's insistent pushing. During times of increased solar activity, the solar wind is stronger than usual, and this causes a 'solar substorm': the magnetic field lines in the magnetosphere are pushed back still further, until something called 'reconnection' happens. Magnetic field lines at the teardrop come together, stretch to their limit and finally 'snap' like rubber bands. Protons and electrons from the solar wind are flung towards Earth, where they arrive at high speed, giving glorious, bright, active auroras.

The very brightest auroras – those that are visible over a very wide area – are caused by coronal mass ejections (CMEs): huge globs of gas expelled from the corona after particularly violent solar flares. When a CME hits Earth, it can produce geomagnetic storms that cause significant disruption to telecommunications and power systems. The 1859 storm was the most energetic ever recorded. In one of the most energetic storms of recent times, in March 1989, major power cuts were experienced in several locations, including Quebec, Canada, where more than 6 million people were without power for nine hours. On the plus side, the lack of electric lights meant that people could clearly see and enjoy the spectacular auroras!

Cyclones and tornadoes

Air is a fluid, like water. But unlike water, it is invisible, almost imperceptible … until it moves.
A gentle breeze can rustle leaves and keep you cool on a hot summer's day, but the powerful winds
of a cyclonic storm or a tornado can wreak havoc, destroying property and taking lives.

WINDS ARE CAUSED by the differences found in atmospheric pressure: air moves from high to low pressure. Atmospheric pressure is the result of the weight of the gases that make up the atmosphere. It pushes on the top of your head – but also, since air is a fluid, against the side of your body and even the soles of your feet. The weight of the atmosphere is surprisingly large. The column of air directly above a tennis court weighs about the same as five fully loaded Airbus A380 airliners, for example – and that weight constantly pushes down on the tennis court's surface (as well as the players!).

UNDER PRESSURE

Changes in temperature and humidity cause variations in atmospheric pressure. Warm air weighs less than cold air and so exerts less pressure. Likewise, humid air weighs less than dry air. The atmosphere contains huge conveyor belt-like circulations of air, because the Sun heats areas close to the Equator much more than areas around the poles. One result of the global circulation patterns is that dense cold air is constantly deposited at the poles, creating a calm 'polar high'. In 2009, a team of astronomers from the United States and Australia studied satellite data, climate models and ground-based weather data to find the most stable atmospheric conditions in which to make their observations. They came up with Ridge A, on top of a plateau in Antarctica – the least windy place on Earth. Nearby, this high pressure air drains off plateaus, resulting in Earth's most consistent high winds, with speeds typically around 300 km/h (190 mph). These 'katabatic winds' also drain off plateaus in Greenland.

Landscape can play another role in determining the strength and direction of winds: mountain ranges funnel winds along valleys and through narrow passes, dramatically increasing their speed. In southern France, winds from the north-west caused by high-pressure air over the Bay of Biscay are squeezed along the valleys of the rivers Rhone and Durance. The resulting wind, called the mistral, has consistent speeds of around 60 km/h (40 mph), but they can be much greater. A similar

? EXTREME FACT
English–Indian scientist and merchant sailor Henry Piddington coined the term 'cyclone' in 1845, after noting that a tropical storm near Mauritius blew a ship around in circles.

▣ TORNADO
An ominous brown vortex appeared west of the city of York, Nebraska, on 20 June 2011. Several farms were damaged and a train was derailed as the tornado made its way across the state.

▣ WEATHER FRONT
Meteorological Armageddon seemed to have come to Sydney on 25 October 2005, when a dark and stormy weather front loomed over the previously sunny sands at Bondi Beach.

KATABATIC WINDS
The mountainous terrain on the subantarctic island of South Georgia helps to funnel winds down to sea level.

phenomenon makes New Zealand's capital Wellington the world's windiest city, where mountains focus the winds blowing off Cook Strait directly onto the city.

CRITICAL MASSES

As a result of differences in both solar radiation and geographical location, vast masses of air form, each with broadly similar densities throughout, which become the main players in the drama of the world's weather. These air masses constantly shift and clash in the daily and yearly cycles of solar illumination, creating the atmospheric instabilities that unleash their power on people and their property. Cold, dry 'continental polar' air masses exert the highest pressure, while warm, humid 'maritime tropical' air masses exert the least.

While the weather underneath a high-pressure area – like that found at Antarctica's Ridge A – remains calm, the weather under a low-pressure area tends to be unsettled. The most unstable weather happens at the boundaries between air masses: weather fronts. At a cold front, for example, cold dense air can force warm wet air aloft, producing torrential downpours, and the juxtaposition of the two air masses creates strong winds.

The largest and most dramatic weather systems arise around very low-pressure areas – deep depressions – created when the Sun heats one patch of ocean more

than another. Cooler, denser air spills into the depression from all directions. The lowest sea-level pressure ever recorded formed over the ocean north-east of Papua New Guinea in October 1979. The pressure dropped to 870 millibars (mb) – 14 per cent lower than the standard atmospheric pressure of 1013 mb. A severe tropical cyclone, Typhoon Tip, developed around the depression, and went on to become the largest tropical cyclone on record, with gale-force winds at distances of more than 1000 km (600 miles) from the storm centre.

ROUND AND ROUND

Cyclones are large masses of circulating air, surrounded by vast walls of cloud called rainbands, which form as evaporated water condenses in the cold incoming air. The rainbands give these storms the familiar spiral patterns often seen in weather maps and satellite images. Cyclones rotate because higher-pressure air pushing in towards the depression from all directions circulates rather than moves in straight lines. The circulation happens because air is deflected – to the right in the Northern Hemisphere and to the left in the Southern Hemisphere, irrespective of the direction in which it is moving in the first place. The deflection is due to the planet's rotation.

To understand why being on a rotating planet deflects the path of moving air, imagine standing at the edge of a turntable rotating clockwise. Try rolling a ball straight towards the centre of the turntable, and it will travel in a curved path. It will be deflected to the left, because it has a high initial sideways velocity before travelling into the part of the turntable that is moving more slowly. The same thing will happen if you try rolling a ball straight out from the centre of the turntable. Again, the deflection will be to the left – because now the ball begins with less sideways velocity, but then travels into the faster-moving part of the turntable. If the turntable is rotating anticlockwise, the deflection will be to the right in both cases. This phenomenon is called the Coriolis effect.

◢
CYCLONE DAMAGE
On 29 October 1999, a super cyclonic storm struck the Indian state of Orissa (now known as Odisha), killing almost 10,000 people, destroying 275,000 houses and leaving more than 1 million homeless.

▶▶
SUPER TYPHOON HAIYAN
The Moderate Resolution Imaging Spectroradiometer (MODIS) on NASA's Terra satellite captured this stunning image of a slightly weakened Super Typhoon Haiyan approaching the coast of Vietnam on 10 November 2013.

As a result of the Coriolis effect, cyclonic winds always circulate anticlockwise in the Northern Hemisphere and clockwise in the Southern Hemisphere. (An anticyclone is a large mass of air that is centred on an area of high atmospheric pressure, and it rotates in the opposite direction – clockwise in the Northern Hemisphere and anticlockwise in the Southern Hemisphere.)

NAMING CONVENTIONS

Cyclones that originate over tropical or subtropical oceans are known as tropical cyclones. They are categorised according to the speed of their circulating winds. The categories and the names vary frustratingly, depending on the part of the world in which they form. If they have wind speeds of up to 61 km/h (38 mph), they are normally referred to as 'tropical depressions' or 'tropical disturbances' by meteorologists everywhere.

However, with increasing wind speeds, they become category 1 or 2 tropical cyclones and then category 3, 4 and 5 severe tropical cyclones in Australia and the South Pacific; tropical storms and then typhoons and super typhoons in the north-western Pacific; cyclonic storms and then severe, very severe and super cyclonic storms in the northern Indian Ocean; moderate or severe tropical storms and then tropical cyclones and intense or very intense tropical cyclones in the south-western Indian Ocean; and tropical storms and then category 1 to category 5 hurricanes in the north-eastern Pacific Ocean and the North Atlantic Ocean.

DOING DAMAGE

Tropical cyclones gather energy from warm tropical oceans, but they are soon carried away from the tropics – northwards in the Northern Hemisphere and southwards in the Southern Hemisphere – and they are also initially pushed in a westerly direction in both hemispheres by trade winds. Once they are out of the tropics, their path is largely unpredictable. A 1994 tropical cyclone – the longest lived and most travelled ever known – was first called Hurricane John, but the name changed to Typhoon John and then back again, as it crossed the International Date Line twice. Despite the uncertainty about the path of tropical cyclones, huge amounts of money and expertise are put into the effort to track tropical storms and predict their course, because of the damage they can cause when they make landfall.

The fastest gust of wind ever recorded in a tropical cyclone – 408 km/h (254 mph), considerably quicker than a Formula One car racing along a straight – occurred when Severe Tropical Cyclone Olivia passed over Barrow Island, just off the coast of Western Australia, in 1996. Super Typhoon Haiyan, which caused devastation across the Philippines in November 2013, had 'one-minute sustained wind speeds' of around 315 km/h (196 mph) when it hit the town of Guiuan, in the Eastern Samar

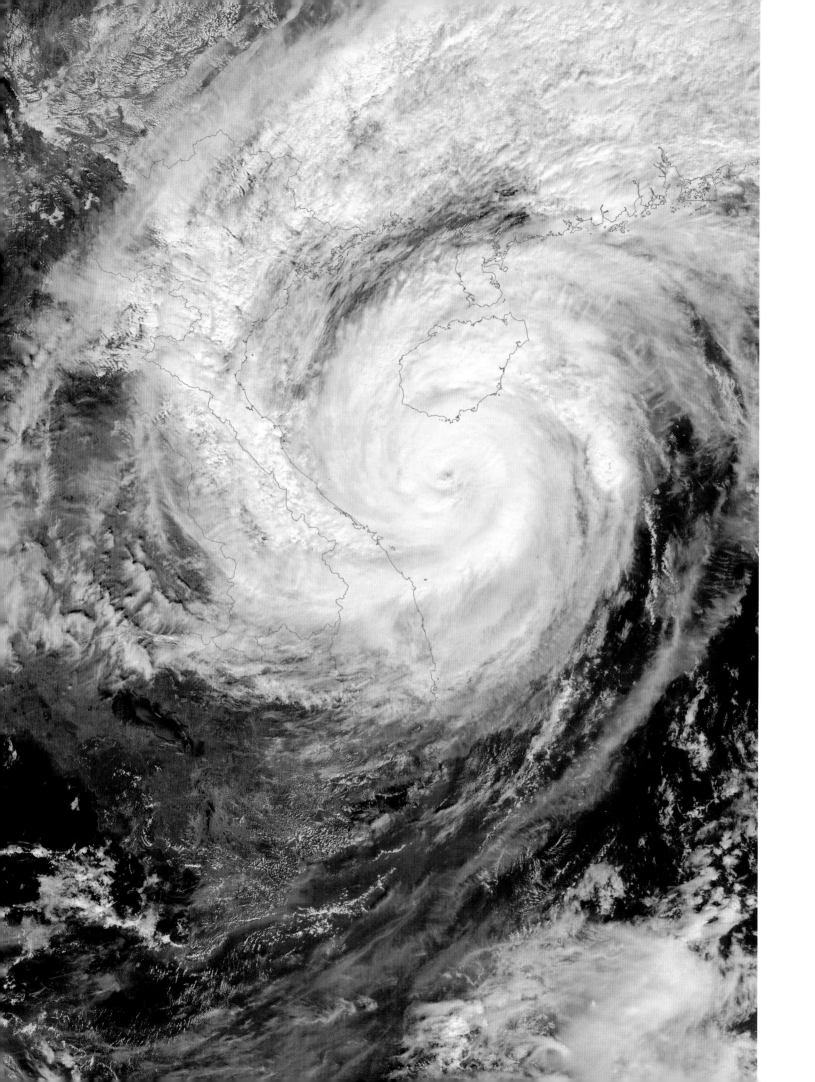

SUPERCELL
Fortunately, this sinister-looking storm that formed over Glasgow, Montana, in July 2010 was one of the 70 per cent of supercells that do not spawn tornadoes.

province. This is the highest recorded sustained wind speed of any tropical cyclone making landfall.

With their high-speed winds, tropical cyclones can uproot trees and cause significant damage to buildings and crops. But the wind is not the only problem, and is often not the worst. Torrential rain and hail can cause widespread flooding and devastation. And perhaps the biggest threat to coastal areas is an ocean swell called a storm surge, which is caused by a combination of the sea level rising – as a bulge in the low-pressure centre – and the strong winds making waves. The highest-recorded storm surge measured 13 m (43 ft); it was caused by Tropical Cyclone Mahina, which hit Bathurst Bay in Queensland, Australia, in 1899, killing 400 people.

When Hurricane Katrina struck the US city of New Orleans in 2005, the storm surge breached the levees that were designed to protect the city from flooding. Sea water pushed several kilometres inland, leaving many thousands of people stranded, homeless or without power. It was one of the deadliest natural disasters in American history – more than 1800 people lost their lives – and the most costly, with damages estimated at US$81 billion.

As the world's warmest ocean, the Indian Ocean is particularly prone to powerful tropical cyclones. To make matters worse, storm surges can easily flood the vast low-lying areas along the coastline of the Bay of Bengal, which is shared between India, Bangladesh, Myanmar, Sri Lanka and the western part of Thailand. As a result, most of the deadliest tropical cyclones have begun life in the Indian Ocean and struck these countries.

TERRIFYING TWISTERS

Tornadoes are just as damaging and deadly as tropical cyclones – albeit on a more intense, localised scale. A tornado is a rapidly spinning column of air. Wind speeds can be even higher than in tropical cyclones. The highest wind speed recorded inside a tornado was an incredible 486 km/h (302 mph), at Bridge Creek in Oklahoma, in May 1999. By virtue of its movement, the extremely fast-flowing air of a tornado exerts up to 100 millibars less pressure than the atmosphere outside. The low pressures inside a tornado present a particular danger, creating a kind of suction force that can lift roofs off buildings and make windows burst outwards, for example.

Tornadoes form in thunderclouds – in fact, the name 'tornado' comes from the Spanish word *tronada,* meaning 'thunderstorm'. But swirling horizontal vortices below a thundercloud – like rolling tubes of air – are the ultimate source of a tornado's rotation. These vortices are fairly commonplace in the air just above ground level, even when a thundercloud is not present. They owe their existence to the fact that wind speed increases as altitude rises. Faster wind above a pocket of air drags the top of that air pocket with it, while the bottom, nearer to the ground, is left behind – like pushing your hand

over a rolling pin on a table. The resulting turning force causes the pocket of air to rotate. The effect is more marked where two different streams of air approach from different directions at different altitudes. The horizontal vortices can be lifted into a thundercloud and flipped to a vertical position by the strong updraught of air that is a feature of thunderclouds. The result is that the updraught itself, and much of the interior of the thundercloud, begins to rotate. The rotating section of the cloud is called a mesocyclone – and the thundercloud is now known as a supercell.

Adjacent to the main updraught, falling rain and hail drags cold air downwards, creating a down draught. This can sometimes wrap around the updraught and drag it downwards. The mesocyclone then bulges from the base of the cloud, and a tornado is born as the rotating air meets the ground. Normally, the low pressure inside the tornado causes water vapour to condense, forming the familiar funnel-shaped cloud. Where the tornado makes contact with the ground it can stir up dust and 'suck up' small or even large objects. The rotating updraught is often made to spin faster by air flowing into the narrow updraught at ground level – and a tornado can rage for anything from 10 minutes to more than an hour.

EXTREME TOP 10
DEADLIEST TROPICAL STORMS*

1 GREAT BHOLA CYCLONE (BANGLADESH, 1970)
400,000 DEATHS

2 HOOGHLY RIVER CYCLONE
(INDIA AND BANGLADESH, 1737)
300,000 DEATHS

3 HAIPHONG TYPHOON (VIETNAM, 1881)
300,000 DEATHS

4 CORINGA CYCLONE (INDIA, 1839)
300,000 DEATHS

5 BACKERGANJ CYCLONE (BANGLADESH, 1584)
200,000 DEATHS

6 GREAT BACKERGANJ CYCLONE
(BANGLADESH, 1876)
200,000 DEATHS

7 CHITTAGONG CYCLONE (BANGLADESH, 1897)
175,000 DEATHS

8 SUPER TYPHOON NINA (CHINA, 1975)
170,000 DEATHS

9 CYCLONE 02B (BANGLADESH, 1991)
140,000 DEATHS

10 CYCLONE NARGIS (MYANMAR, 2008)
140,000 DEATHS

Some figures are equal due to rounding up and down.

STAY SAFE

It is not always obvious where or when tornadoes will strike, as some tornadoes have no visible funnel cloud; look for whirling dust underneath a thundercloud.

If a tornado is heading towards you:

✦ Find a strong shelter, ideally in a basement – you are not safe in a stationary vehicle or a mobile home.

✦ Stay away from windows.

✦ Lie face-down in the nearest ravine or ditch, away from trees and cars (if you cannot find shelter).

✦ Drive away from the tornado at a right angle to its path (if you are in a vehicle).

TORNADO TRACK

Gouges in the greenery near Westminster, Texas, clearly reveal the path of destruction of a 2006 tornado.

If a tornado ventures onto water, it can become a powerful waterspout. Most waterspouts, however, are not associated with the mesocyclones within supercell thunderstorms, and therefore they are weaker – although they, too, inherit vorticity from the air below a cloud. Over dusty ground, similar weak rotating systems called dust devils form, again in the same way.

MEASURING THE WIND

Meteorologists use one of two scales to categorise tornadoes' ferocity. The Enhanced Fujita (EF) scale originated in the United States, and is the most widely used. Tornadoes are classified into six categories, from EF0 to EF5. The TORRO (T) scale originated in Britain, and is an extension of the standard Beaufort wind-speed scale. Although both scales are based on the speeds of tornadoes' winds, in practice, tornadoes are categorised according to the damage they cause. The reason is that it is nearly impossible to measure wind speeds inside a tornado directly: not only because of the risk to personnel and equipment, but also because of the unpredictability of the tornado's track across the landscape.

During the 1980s, meteorologists at the US National Oceanic and Atmospheric Administration did try to take measurements from inside tornadoes. They used a specially built device called the Totable Tornado Observatory. (Totable means portable, and conveniently gives the device the acronym 'TOTO' – a reference to the dog in *The Wizard of Oz,* whose plot centres around a violent tornado in Kansas.) TOTO comprised a metal drum containing various meteorological instruments, which could be carried on a pick-up truck. The team of scientists behind the device tried many times to place

it in the path of approaching tornadoes, but they failed every time – the closest they came was in 1984, when TOTO was blown over by only a moderate tornado.

The invention of Doppler weather radar in the 1980s made it possible to accurately measure wind speeds inside a tornado from a distance. The equipment sends microwaves to the edge of a tornado, and the beams bounce off water droplets carried around by the wind. Measuring the frequency of the reflected microwaves reveals the speed at which the droplets are moving. The same technology allows meteorologists to identify mesocyclones spinning inside thunderclouds, which can help to provide advance warning of an impending tornado. Mounting a Doppler radar unit on a truck makes it possible for researchers to get close enough to a storm to obtain readings while still remaining at a safe distance, and means that they can drive away quickly should the tornado move towards them.

ACROSS THE WORLD

Tornadoes happen all over the world, apart from the polar regions. They are most common in middle latitudes, between 30 and 60 degrees above and below the Equator. It is here that cold, dry polar air mixes with warm, wet tropical air, at the 'polar front'. That mixing, and the resulting instability, is most active during the spring and autumn months, as the polar front shifts position.

Each continent has tornado hot spots, where the geographical and meteorological conditions are just

NORTH CAROLINA 2011

TORNADO DAMAGE

Survivors are often left stunned by the discriminating nature of tornado damage. Winds can upturn cars and boats, and shatter houses, but leave pianos intact; a fork becomes a deadly projectile, while a fragile clock remains whole, stopped at the exact time of the twister.

INDIANA 1925

OKLAHOMA 2013

right for breeding these terrifying spinning winds. As is true for tropical cyclones, the area around the warm sea in the Bay of Bengal is at an elevated risk of tornadoes – in particular, Bangladesh and eastern India. On 26 April 1989, what turned out to be the deadliest single tornado on record passed through the Manikganj District of Bangladesh. Around 12,000 people were injured, and 1300 lost their lives. Tornadoes also occur in South Africa, Australia, New Zealand, Argentina, Brazil and Uruguay, and across much of Europe and eastern China.

The United States experiences more tornadoes than any other country – around 1200 per year. One region of North America in particular, stretching across the Great Plains of the United States and into southern Canada, is rightly renowned for its high tornado activity. This region suffers nearly as many tornado outbreaks as the rest of the world put together – a fact that has earned it the nickname 'Tornado Alley'.

RECORD BREAKERS

So frequent and powerful are the tornadoes that hit Tornado Alley that it holds many of the world's tornado-related records. In April 2011, Tornado Alley set a record for the number of tornadoes in a region in a single month, at 760. That same month saw the largest number of tornadoes in a 24-hour period, when 209 tornadoes blasted their way across the region – part of a three-day outbreak that killed 324 people; a further 24 people were killed by weather events relating to the thunderstorms, such as lightning and hail. The widest-ever recorded tornado, defined by the breadth of its spinning cloud, was 4.2 km (2⅗ miles) wide – equivalent to the combined lengths of 84 Olympic-size swimming pools. It passed through El Reno, Oklahoma, on 31 May 2013. The previous record holder, a 4-km (2½-mile) wide twister, struck Hallam, Nebraska, on 22 May 2004.

The longest lived and farthest travelled single tornado ever recorded was the so-called Tri-State Tornado, which raged for three-and-a-half hours on 18 March 1925. It devastated communities in Missouri, Illinois and Indiana, killing nearly 700 people along its 352-km (219-mile) path. This was also a particularly fast-moving tornado, tracking across the ground at an average of 100 km/h (60 mph) around twice the normal speed for a tornado. Also in Tornado Alley, Oklahoma City has been hit by more tornadoes than any other city – more than 100 have been recorded there. And Texas has an average of 125 tornadoes per year – more than any other US state.

CARRYING IT OFF

Tornadoes can carry objects very long distances, by virtue of the powerful updraught, their very high winds and low air pressures – and the fact that they travel across country. Often, the debris that travels the furthest is lightweight and has large surfaces that make them

TORNADO ALLEY

There is no exact definition of the extent of Tornado Alley, but at its heart are the US states of Texas, Oklahoma, Kansas and Nebraska. The reason this area is so prone to tornadoes is that cold, dry air pushing southwards from Canada often meets warm, moist air moving northwards from the Gulf of Mexico, forming frequent unstable weather fronts – and lots of violent thunderstorms. The two air streams often clash in the right way to introduce a spin into the air – the vorticity that can spawn tornadoes.

prone to aerodynamic lift. In 1925, the Tri-State Tornado carried a pair of trousers 63 km (39 miles) – without disturbing the US$93 in cash that was in a pocket of the trousers. In May 1991, a tornado carried a personal cheque from Stockton, Kansas, to Winnetoon, Nebraska – a distance of 359 km (223 miles), the furthest confirmed distance travelled by tornado debris.

It is not just small, light items that tornadoes pick up. Flying debris – anything from small rocks to roofs and even cars – poses a real threat to people near a tornado. Even people themselves are sometimes carried off by tornadoes. In May 1930, four members of the Kern family were carried through the air when a tornado ripped through their hometown of Kickapoo, Kansas. Mother Augusta Kern and two of her children were carried about 180 m (590 ft) away, but the father, Lawrence, was found, with his head and shoulders lodged into the ground, about 1.8 km (1.1 miles) away. This is the furthest any person has been carried by a tornado. More recently, in March 2006, a tornado near Fordland, Missouri, lifted 19-year-old Matt Suter and deposited him, virtually unscathed, 399 m (1309 ft) away. This is the furthest someone has been carried by a tornado and survived – beating the previous record of 300 m (984 ft), which was held by a young girl from South Dakota; a 1955 tornado scooped up both the girl and her horse, and both were unharmed.

Storms and floods

Ancient Egyptian farmers depended upon the annual flooding of the Nile to provide fertile ground for their crops. In Egyptian mythology, the floodwater represented the tears of the goddess Isis; in reality, the flooding was the result of seasonal rain rushing down from the highlands every summer. Rain and other forms of precipitation are not always so predictable – or so beneficial.

THE RAIN THAT flooded the Nile each year – laying down a layer of rich silt – was caused by the West African monsoon, which blows moist air from the Gulf of Guinea eastwards in the summer months, across the Sudan and the Sahel and eventually over Ethiopia. Rainfall on the highlands of Ethiopia varies from an average of just 80 mm (3 in) in November to an average of 2800 mm (110 in) in the month of August, at the height of the monsoon rains. It is monsoon rainwater from the Ethiopian highlands that finds its way northwards down the Blue Nile, into the Nile proper and into Egypt. The flow rate of the Blue Nile as it empties into the Nile varies from a minimum of about 200 cubic m (7000 cubic ft) per second in May to as much as 5700 cubic m (200,000 cubic ft) per second – equivalent to more than half a million bucketfuls – in late August. The monsoon rains still come to this day, but since 1970, the High Dam at Aswan has prevented the flooding upon which the ancient farmers depended, and more controlled irrigation and the use of artificial fertilisers has taken over.

TORRENTIAL RAIN

A monsoon is a seasonal shift in wind direction that results in dramatic changes in precipitation. Monsoons are like sea breezes on a grand scale; they result from the fact that land heats up more quickly than sea water, and sea water holds more heat. Sea breezes – blowing inland in the morning, and out to sea in the afternoon – are always present on an otherwise calm, sunny day by the sea. In the morning, the land heats up quickly, causing air above it to rise, which draws in cooler air from above the sea. By late afternoon, the land is cooling, but the sea has retained much of its heat, so the breeze is reversed. In a monsoon, similar changes take place, but over months not hours, and across whole regions, not just a small patch of coastline. Vast masses of air moving inland from oceans carry moisture, which is deposited as rain.

The archetypal monsoon – the first large-scale weather phenomenon to be recognised, hundreds of years ago by Arabian navigators – is the South Asian

?

EXTREME FACT
The word 'monsoon' comes from the Arabic word *mawsim* which means 'seasons'.

EGYPTIAN FLOOD
Before the Aswan High Dam was completed in 1970, flooding of the Nile occurred regularly. In 1927, the floodwater almost reached the pyramids situated on the Giza Plateau.

SOUTH ASIAN MONSOON
Thin plastic raincoats are no match for the deluge that happens during the South Asian monsoon. Streets in many cities, such as Hanoi in Vietnam, can overflow with murky floodwater.

monsoon. The water it deposits upon India accounts for around 80 per cent of that country's total rainfall – and it also drenches Bangladesh, Pakistan and Sri Lanka every year. The rainwater, which originates in the warm waters of the Indian Ocean, is hotly anticipated, and arrives from the south-west during the summer month of June. Weather conditions swiftly shift from hot and dry to warm and wet, with the rainfall highest where the humid air is forced upwards by enormous mountains. Moist air encountering the Himalayas in north-eastern India produces the heaviest and most persistent rain. The wettest place on Earth, by average annual rainfall, is the Indian district of Meghalaya, in the Himalayan foothills. Average annual rainfall here is 12,000 mm (470 in) – although this can vary significantly from year to year. The town of Cherrapunji, in Meghalaya, holds the record for the highest rainfall in a single year. Between August 1860 and July 1861, an amazing 26,467 mm (1042 in) of rain fell there.

REMARKABLE RAINDROPS

There is a good reason why rain often falls over high ground – as the South Asian monsoon winds approach the Himalayas, or the West African monsoon winds approach the Ethiopian highlands, for example. A mass of moist air encountering higher ground has no option but to rise up. As it does so, it cools; the invisible vapour it carries becomes visible as tiny droplets, and rain clouds form. Rain clouds also form where the Sun's heat creates a warm, low-pressure area into which water can evaporate – this air, too, is pushed upwards, but this time by cooler, denser air from all around, and not by geographical features. Water droplets coalesce inside a rain cloud, forming drops big enough to fall.

Most raindrops are spherical, even as they fall; the classic teardrop shape, with a streamlined, pointed top, is a fallacy. Drops with diameters greater than about 2 mm (1/10 in) become slightly flattened as they fall, shaped by air resistance, so that they resemble hamburgers. If they are above 4 mm (1/6 in) diameter,

they tend to form into tubes and then break apart, although the largest intact raindrops ever recorded had diameters approaching 1 cm (²⁄₅ in) – the size of a typical blueberry.

HEAVY WATER

Despite the relatively small size of individual raindrops, a downpour can release huge volumes of water. Just 10 mm (²⁄₅ in) of rain falling over an area of 1 sq km (²⁄₅ sq miles) amounts to 10 million litres (2.6 million gallons) – enough to fill four Olympic swimming pools. This amount of water has a weight of approximately 10,000 tonnes (11,000 tons) – the same as 1500 adult male (bull) African elephants. That amount of water can fall in less than a minute in a heavy downpour: the highest recorded one-minute rainfall, on 4 July 1956 in Unionville, Maryland, deposited 31.2 mm (1⅕ in) of rain. The greatest recorded 60-minute downpour drenched the town of Holt, Missouri, with rain to a depth of 305 mm (12 in), on 22 June 1947. The island of Réunion, surrounded by the warm waters of the Indian Ocean, holds several rainfall records, including the greatest 24-hour rainfall, a staggering 1825 mm (72 in), in January 1966.

If all the water in the atmosphere at any one time fell out of the air – all the vapour, ice crystals and droplets – it would be enough to cover Earth's surface to a depth of about 1.25 cm (½ in). But water is constantly being recycled, so the total amount of precipitation (rain, snow, hail and so on) falling each year across the whole world is much greater: enough to cover the planet's surface with a layer of water more than 1 m (3 ft) deep.

DISASTROUS DELUGES

Floods can devastate an area, destroying crops, cutting electricity and, of course, ruining people's property. A flash flood is caused by a single downpour of torrential rain that is not absorbed into the ground – as can

RÉUNION ISLAND
The abundant rainfall over this small island has created some spectacularly tall waterfalls, including a number of cascades that drop into the Trou de Fer canyon.

FLASH FLOOD
Residents of Toowoomba in Queensland, Australia, were shocked on 10 January 2011 when a deadly flash flood – described as an 'inland tsunami' – swept through the city.

happen with very dry or already saturated soil. During a flash flood, fast-flowing water just 15 cm (6 in) deep can push a person's feet so forcefully that they are knocked to the ground; a depth of just 60 cm (24 in) is sufficient to cause a car to begin floating away. Larger-scale flooding typically occurs with more prolonged rainfall, after the water held by soils eventually makes rivers swell and break their banks. In the aftermath of a widespread (or 'broadscale') flood, water supplies may be contaminated, and many deaths associated with such flooding happen as a result of waterborne diseases, such as cholera, typhoid and leptospirosis. To make matters worse, sewer systems are often unable to cope with a large flow of water.

Millions of years of flooding, especially on natural flood plains, have led to the evolution of plants and birds that can survive in the relatively hostile environment of wetlands. One feature common to many wetland plants is the existence of air tubes called aerenchyma in the stems, which allow for the exchange of oxygen and other gases between submerged plant tissues and

HEAVY RAIN
*A large downpour of
rain can release huge
amounts of water. A
road quickly becomes
slippery, as water
reduces the friction
between car tyres
and the road surface.*

BIRD LIFE
A great egret uses its long, graceful legs to stroll casually through floodwater in Australia's Kakadu National Park, searching for food.

the air above. Many wetland birds, such as the blue heron, have long legs that keep their bodies above the level of floodwater, while others have nostrils high up their beaks, so they can sweep their beaks through shallow water in search of food without drowning.

Humans are not so well adapted to flooding – and urban development, so often found along river courses and coastlines, increases the risk of flooding. Many of the world's largest cities have developed around ports built near the wide, slow-flowing tidal estuaries of large rivers. Here, heavy rainfall combined with high tides and storm surges can pose a threat to millions of people. Wetlands and forests act as sponges, absorbing water and then releasing it gradually, keeping the flow of a river fairly constant. Covering these environments with tarmac and concrete increases the likelihood of flash floods.

VARIATIONS ON A THEME

More than half the world's people live in areas with a climate that is dominated by monsoons, and are dependent upon the seasonal rainfall. Indians, for example, celebrate the monsoon rains in a number of festivals across the country. However, the amount of rain a monsoon brings can vary considerably – and with such huge amounts of water involved, even a small variation can have dire consequences. Acutely aware of the year-to-year variation in the amount of water coming down the Nile – and completely at its mercy – inhabitants of ancient Egypt would throw offerings into the river, imploring the gods to inundate the land with enough water to grow crops, but not so much that their crops, and even their mud-brick houses, would be washed away. The offerings would have made no difference of course, because the strength of the

▲
MONSOON FESTIVAL
Indian farmers participate in a bull race at a paddy field during the monsoon festival in Altekhali village, some 110 km (70 miles) south of Kolkata, on 20 June 2013. The race occurs before the field is ploughed, in the belief that it will bring a better monsoon and a richer harvest.

monsoon in a particular year depends upon climatic events far away, and not on the whim of the gods.

One of the main factors affecting the strength of monsoons is a meteorological phenomenon called the El Niño Southern Oscillation (ENSO), characterised by a reversal of the winds and sea currents in the equatorial Pacific Ocean. An ENSO event has two distinct phases: El Niño – in which the eastern side of the Pacific Ocean is much warmer than usual, and the western side of the Pacific Ocean is much cooler than usual – and La Niña, in which the situation is reversed. El Niño has long been known to Peruvian fishermen, as it dramatically reduces their catch. It was they who named it: *el niño* means 'little boy' in Spanish, but when it is capitalised it more specifically relates to the Christ child, a reference to the fact that the warming of the eastern Pacific Ocean usually becomes apparent

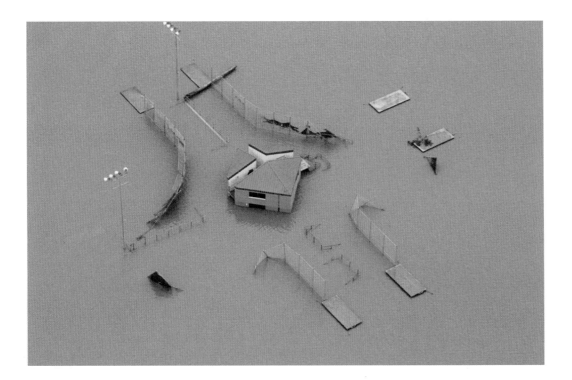

TEXAS FLOODS
Baseball fields and other parts of Gonzales were swamped by floodwater from the Guadalupe River in October 1998. The river peaked at just over 15 m (50 ft).

around Christmas time. La Niña is derived as an accompanying term, and is based on the Spanish *la niña,* which means 'little girl'.

ENSO events can have a profound effect on the world's monsoons, but they also affect rainfall patterns in non-monsoon areas, as warmer, moister air masses occur in out-of-the-ordinary locations. During an El Niño, increased rainfall tends to affect Peru, northern Bolivia and Chile, northern coastal Africa and the eastern Mediterranean, Iran and Afghanistan, with knock-on effects in several other parts of the world. All of these areas are then at risk of flooding. The coastal deserts of South America also typically receive significant rainfall in El Niño years – normally they receive virtually no rain at all. The 1997–98 El Niño was particularly strong, and brought devastating floods to the normally arid west coast of Peru. That same year, the El Niño boosted the amount of rain delivered by the monsoon in Mexico and south-western United States. The resulting floods in Texas caused an estimated US$2.6 billion in property damage and destroyed US$2 billion worth of crops. The overall burden on the US economy of the 1997–98 El Niño event was estimated at US$25 billion.

During a La Niña event, it is normally Central America, Venezuela, Colombia, Australia and Southeast Asia that experience increased rainfall – again, with far-reaching consequences. Tropical cyclones that develop over the warmer waters tend to have more power – and bring more rain – during La Niña events than in other years.

DOUBLE TROUBLE

The 2009–10 El Niño and 2010–11 La Niña events were among the strongest on record, and resulted in a number of catastrophic floods. Huge areas of eastern Africa suffered devastating flooding in both 2009 and 2010 as a result of a strengthening of the West African monsoon. In September 2009, Burkina Faso experienced its heaviest rainfall for 90 years, and the equivalent of one-quarter of the region's entire average annual rainfall tumbled down in just one day. In South America, up to 400 mm (16 in) of rainfall in a single week led to severe flooding in Brazil, Argentina and Uruguay, killing dozens of people and displacing many thousands of others during November and December 2009.

The 2010–11 La Niña phase caused similar problems, but in different locations. One-fifth of the land area of Pakistan was under water in July 2010, after unusually intense monsoon rains there; over 20 million people were affected, and around 2000 died. In Australia, 2010 ranked as the second-wettest year on record, with many parts of the country experiencing widespread flooding between September 2010 and February 2011 – a result of a disruption to the Australian monsoon, known as 'the wet'. In Queensland, more than 200,000 people were affected by the most infamous flood in Australian history, with economic damage estimated at AU$2.38 billion. The flooding began after heavy rains in September 2010, and was made worse by a tropical storm, Tropical Cyclone Tasha, hitting the region in December. In the state capital, Brisbane, the river peaked at 4.5 m (15 ft) in January, flooding nearly 30,000 homes and leaving 100,000 homes with no electricity supply. Another storm, Severe Tropical Cyclone Yasi, hit in February, causing more damage to towns already under water.

PAKISTAN FLOODS
In September 2010, the town of Khairpur Nathan Shah in Pakistan resembled Venice in Italy when once-dry streets became waterlogged canals during the country's flood crisis.

EXTREME TOP 10
WORLD'S DEADLIEST FLOODS*

1 YELLOW RIVER (HUANG HE) (CHINA, 1931)
1,000,000 TO 3,700,000 DEATHS

2 YELLOW RIVER (HUANG HE) (CHINA, 1887)
900,000 TO 2,000,000 DEATHS

3 YELLOW RIVER (HUANG HE) (CHINA, 1938)
500,000 TO 900,000 DEATHS

4 YELLOW RIVER (HUANG HE) (CHINA, 1642)
300,000 DEATHS

5 RU RIVER AND BANQIAO DAM (CHINA, 1975)
230,000 DEATHS

6 YANGTZE RIVER (CHINA, 1931)
145,000 DEATHS

**7 ST FELIX'S FLOOD
(THE NETHERLANDS AND ENGLAND, 1530)**
100,000 DEATHS

**8 HANOI AND RED RIVER DELTA
(NORTH VIETNAM, 1971)**
100,000 DEATHS

9 ST LUCIA'S FLOOD (THE NETHERLANDS, 1287)
50,000 TO 80,000 DEATHS

10 STORM SURGE (THE NETHERLANDS, 1212)
60,000 DEATHS

Some figures are equal due to rounding up and down.

MILLIONS UNDER WATER

Most of the deadliest floods of all time have occurred within China. This is a result of the huge expanse of lowlands fed by several large rivers that receive much of their water from the warm, wet South Asian monsoon winds – the same ones that deposit so much water on northern India – as they extend beyond the Himalayas. China has a long history of building defences along its rivers, to control the waters and reduce the impact of flooding but those schemes have repeatedly been beaten by the immense forces of the water as it flowed across the country. In some cases, the defences have been burst on purpose: in 1642, the governor of the city of Kaifeng gave the order that dikes protecting the city should be broken, in an attempt to end a siege of the city by peasant rebels. More than 300,000 people died – around three-quarters of the area's residents.

Sometimes the flood defences are simply not sufficient – as happened in the deadliest natural disaster of all time. After three years of particularly dry weather, heavy snow fell in western China in

EUROPEAN WINDSTORM

Walkers on the beach at the coastal town of Scheveningen, near The Hague, struggled against the wind on 25 November 2012 as a storm raged about the Netherlands. Most European windstorms strike in autumn or winter.

MASSIVE HAILSTORM

Firefighters shovelled ice from around cars trapped in one of Bogotá's main streets after a hailstorm hit Colombia's capital on 3 November 2007. Melting ice added to residents' woes, as roads quickly became slushy rivers.

December 1930, during the country's winter. China's three greatest rivers – the Yellow River (Huang He), the Yangtze and the Huai – all swelled with the melt-water in the spring. In the summer of 1931, a particularly strong monsoon unleashed huge amounts of water into the already swollen rivers. To make matters worse, several severe cyclonic storms hit China that year, bringing more torrential rain. The Yangtze burst its banks in July 1931, flooding vast areas of the eastern Chinese lowlands. A series of dikes along the Yellow River broke down, releasing a terrifying wall of water; entire villages were buried by floodwater and mud. Hundreds of thousands of people died in their sleep. The capital at the time, Nanjing, was completely cut off by deep water. Throughout the autumn, hundreds of thousands more died from waterborne diseases. The exact death toll is unknown, with conservative estimates by the Chinese government of the time in the hundreds of thousands, and more realistic ones by other agencies at between 3 and 4 million. Around 80 million people were left homeless.

FEARSOME STORMS

Also making several appearances in the top 10 list of deadly floods is The Netherlands, which is at particular risk of inundation because much of the country is reclaimed land that lies below the level of the North Sea. North-west Europe is prone to a class of cyclones called European windstorms. Although the main threat from these storms is damage caused by gale-force winds, huge amounts of water picked up from the North Atlantic, where the storms develop, are also unleashed.

Cyclonic storms have a warm, low-pressure centre, and air moistened by evaporating sea water rises up, forming dense rain clouds. This strong convection forms towering thunderclouds, whose tops experience temperatures that are well below freezing. Ice crystals grow there and fall, only to be carried upwards again by strong updraughts. An individual ice crystal can make the journey from top to bottom and back up again many times, accreting a new layer of water each time, which freezes. The result is a ball of ice with concentric layers like an onion. Eventually, the ball of ice becomes too heavy to be supported, and it falls from the cloud as a hailstone.

ICE FROM THE SKY

Although a typical hailstone is only the size and mass of a small pea, intense storm clouds can produce much larger ones. The heaviest hailstone on record weighed 1.02 kg (2¼ lb), the same as a large fresh pineapple. It fell on 14 April 1986, during a hailstorm that killed 92 people in the Gopalganj district of Bangladesh. The largest hailstone on record fell at Vivian, South Dakota,

on 23 July 2010. It had a diameter of 20 cm (8 inches), and was only slightly lighter than the Gopalganj hailstone.

Hail causes billions of dollars' worth of damage to property every year – hail-related insurance claims totalled US$3.9 billion across North America alone in 2012. Some areas are more prone to hail than others. Cheyenne, Wyoming, is sometimes referred to as the 'hail capital of America'. A storm in August 1985 left hail drifts that measured about 1.8 m (6 ft) in height. Meanwhile, the Hail Research Station in the Kericho area of Kenya, close to Lake Victoria, records hailstorms on around 130 days per year.

One of the costliest hailstorms of all time hit in and around Denver, Colorado, on 11 July 1990. Hailstones ranging in size from 4 to 7 cm (1½ to 2¾ in) – the size of golf balls and baseballs – injured dozens of people, punched holes in roofs, battered tens of thousands of cars, smashed windows, stripped paint off buildings and ripped up golf courses. The total cost of this single storm was estimated at US$605 million. But the most expensive hailstorm in recorded history took place on an otherwise sunny afternoon in southern Germany on 12 July 1984. The storm began over Lake Constance at around 3.30 pm and continued unabated until it passed through Munich at around 6 pm. It left behind a 300-km (185-mile) long, 20-km (12-mile) wide trail of destruction. Four hundred people were injured, while 150 aeroplanes, 70,000 houses and 200,000 cars were damaged, and many areas suffered flooding as the hail melted. The total insurance bill was estimated at 1.5 billion Deutsche Marks – the equivalent of more than US$1 billion today.

Snow and blizzards

Every snowflake that floats down towards the ground is light, delicate and unique. But countless trillions of them falling in the same region over a short period of time paint the landscape a heavy, solid, uniform white. The result can be extremely treacherous – especially when the wind is blowing.

A BLIZZARD IS simply a combination of snowfall and sustained strong winds. In the United States and some other countries, meteorologists use a more precise definition: a snowstorm with winds of at least 56 km/h (35 mph), and visibility less than 400 m (1300 ft), lasting for three hours or more. If the conditions remain similar after the snow stops falling – because the winds whip up snow that has already fallen – meteorologists refer to the event as a 'ground blizzard'.

SAVAGE SNOWSTORMS

Unfortunately, severe blizzards can often have fatal consequences. The deadliest of all time occurred in western Iran, in February 1972. Over 8 m (26 ft) of snow fell – equivalent to the height of two double-decker buses – more or less continuously over a period of six days, with snowdrifts burying cars, trains and even entire villages. Around 4000 people died either during the storm itself or because of its after-effects – as communities were cut off when roads became blocked and telephone cables broke. Many people

CAROLEAN DEATH MARCH

In January 1719, nearly 6000 exhausted Swedish soldiers from the Carolean army set out on a retreat back to Sweden after a disastrous defeat in Trondheim, Norway. A powerful snowstorm hit on 12 January, and continued into the next day. Extremely low temperatures claimed many lives, while high winds reduced visibility to almost nothing. More than 3000 of the soldiers froze to death in the mountain camp or while they were trying to find their way across the hills to safety. By 17 January, when the surviving soldiers reached safety, a further 700 of them had died from the effects of the snowstorm.

❓

EXTREME FACT

On two occasions in living memory, it has snowed in the Sahara – first in 1979, then in 2012.

⬒

WINTER MAGIC

One of the prettiest sights in countries where winter brings consistent snowfalls is a leafless tree decorated with nature's frosting – a covering of snow that sparkles in the Sun.

⬓

RURAL BLIZZARD

Relentless blizzards can soon become dangerous white-outs, where the clouds and snow merge into a single white expanse, the horizon is invisible and the lack of shadows is disorientating.

remained without essential utilities such as water and electricity for weeks. Only one winter storm, known as the Carolean Death March, has come close to claiming as many lives – but that happened 300 years ago.

In living memory, the second-deadliest blizzard occurred in Afghanistan, in February 2008. Nearly 1000 people died in a snowstorm during the country's coldest winter on record. The temperature reached a low of -30°C (-22°F) across most of the country. Hundreds of thousands of goats, sheep and cattle also died, and more than 700 houses were completely destroyed by the weight of snow and the strong winds.

BATTLING A NOR'EASTER

Blizzards are fairly common in central and north-eastern Asia – but even more so in Russia, northern Europe, Canada and the United States. In most of these countries, the regions in which blizzards are commonplace lie in the cold Arctic. Most of the United States, however, is not in the Arctic; here, it is the battle between warm, moist air from over the Gulf of Mexico and cold polar air from over Canada that brings winter snowstorms. The north-east coast is hit the most, by huge cyclonic storms called nor'easters. These storms are so big that they sometimes straddle the whole US east coast and beyond, from Cuba in the south to Canada in the north. They bring in humid air from the Atlantic Ocean, produce strong winds and, if cold polar air is also present, they will deposit snow over large areas. One of the most notorious winter nor'easters – nicknamed the 'Storm of the Century' – struck in March 1993. Hundreds of roofs collapsed under the weight of the heavy snow, and more than 3 million people were without power. A total of 318 people lost their lives, most of them in the United States and Canada, as a result of the blizzard, but others also died in Cuba as a result of the strong winds and storm surge.

The most infamous blizzard in North American history was also the result of a nor'easter. The Great Blizzard of 1888 – dubbed the Great White Hurricane – brought 120 km/h (75 mph) gusts and, in some areas, 130 cm (50 in) of snow, which paralysed essential services and claimed some 400 lives. Not all of North America's snowstorms are the result of nor'easters. Earlier in that same year, to the south-west, a huge mass of very cold Arctic air swept across the Great Plains, rapidly creating a devastating snowstorm on what had been a fine day. Huge amounts of snow fell, and powerful winds made visibility very low. The event has been called the Schoolhouse Blizzard, because many schoolteachers sent children home at the first signs of the storm, unaware that conditions would change so quickly. Many of the 235 people who died during the blizzard were children.

ICE CRYSTALS

The crucial ingredient of a snowstorm, snowflakes are born when tiny cloud droplets freeze around microscopic particles called ice nuclei. These particles provide a surface onto which water molecules can cling and begin joining together to form an ice crystal. In air devoid of ice nuclei, the droplets can exist well below freezing – even at temperatures lower than -30°C (-22°F). Ice nuclei are often minute soot particles, volcanic ash or tiny flecks of clay or sand dust, but they can also be living bacteria. One species of bacterium in particular is commonly found right at the heart of snowflakes, as well as hailstones and raindrops: *Pseudomonas syringae*. This species has long been known to cause disease in a wide range of plants: the bacteria produce a protein that binds water molecules in just the right way to encourage the formation of ice crystals; when ice forms on crops' leaves, the leaf cells break open, allowing the bacteria in to infect the plant. Inside a cloud, those same proteins allow *P. syringae* to be an extremely efficient nucleator.

As soon as a few water molecules have connected together on an ice nucleus, an ice crystal begins growing; it enlarges as more and more water molecules join up. Ice crystals have a sixfold symmetry because of the shape of individual water molecules and the way the molecules bond together. This symmetry results in the beautiful patterns that are revealed when gazing at snowflakes under a microscope. The exact shape of ice crystals depends on many factors, including the humidity and temperature of the air, but several forms are commonly seen. Needles, star shapes, flat plates and columns are the most prevalent – but the likelihood of any two snowflakes being molecule-for-molecule identical is virtually zero, since a typical ice crystal contains many trillions of molecules.

BIG AND BEAUTIFUL

A snowflake can be a single ice crystal – but most are aggregations of tens or even hundreds of individual ice crystals. A typical snowflake is around 1 cm (⅖ in) across. At Fort Keogh, Montana, in January 1887, farmer Matt Coleman claimed to have come across

WILSON BENTLEY'S SNOWFLAKE
Late in the nineteenth century, Wilson Bentley became the first person to photograph snowflakes.

MAGNIFIED SNOWFLAKE
Using an electron microscope, scientists have been able to see the dendritic arms of a snowflake.

MODERN SNOWFLAKE IMAGE
Photographed under a microscope in 2009, this snowflake exhibits the classic six-armed shape.

'STORM OF THE CENTURY'

Snowploughs could only do so much to clear the roads after the infamous nor'easter that struck North America in March 1993. Residents were left to dig out their cars by hand.

snowflakes that measured 38 cm (15 in) in diameter and 20 cm (8 in) in thickness, describing them as 'larger than milk pans'. Although the dimensions of these remarkable snowflakes were almost certainly exaggerated, very large flakes do sometimes occur.

People have been studying snowflakes under microscopes since the seventeenth century, and photographing snowflakes resting on cold surfaces since the 1880s. The first to capture snowflakes on film was American farmer Wilson Bentley. During his lifetime, he photographed more than 5000 snowflakes, and in 1925 he stated that snowflakes are 'a miracle of beauty' and that this beauty should be 'seen and appreciated by others'. Since the 1950s, electron microscopes have revealed still more incredible detail, almost down to the level of individual molecules. But it is only recently that people have photographed snowflakes in any detail while they are still in the air. Since 2011, a team from the University of Utah, led by Dr Tim Garrett, has been capturing remarkable images of snowflakes in free fall – as well as measuring their speed – as they pass through a specially designed instrument called the Multi-Angle Snowflake Camera. The research will help to improve the forecasting of winter storms, by extending scientists' understanding of the structure and behaviour of snowflakes.

LET IT SNOW

Surprisingly, snowflakes can remain intact as they fall, even if the air is slightly above freezing. In this case, each snowflake melts slightly during its descent, and some of the liquid water then evaporates; the evaporating molecules take heat from the rest of the snowflake, which keeps it frozen. The result is wet snow, which is good for making snowmen. But if the air is warmer than about 2°C (36°F), snowflakes melt on their way down, forming a mixture of rain and snow (sometimes called 'sleet'), or simply cold rain.

If the temperature of the air underneath a cloud is below freezing, a snowflake remains whole as it falls – typically at about 3.6 km/h (2 mph) – and it lands gently on the ground or another available surface. Contrary to the saying 'it's too cold to snow', there is no temperature too low for snowfall – as long as there is moisture in the air. The two requirements, low temperature and moisture, come together most successfully where cold wind blows over a large area of water. So-called 'lake-effect' or 'ocean-effect' snow lies at the heart of the heaviest and most consistent snowstorms. The most snow ever to fall in an inhabited area in a single day was 193 cm (76 in), at the small mountain resort of Silver Lake, Colorado, on 14 April 1921. The largest recorded amount of snow to have fallen in a single location over the course of a year was 31.1 m (102 ft), on Mount Rainier in Washington State, between 19 February 1971 and 18 February 1972.

It snows in every month of every year on Mount Rainier, because of the combination of the altitude and the humid air blowing in off the Pacific Ocean to the west. With an average of 17 m (56 ft) of snowfall per year, Paradise Ranger Station on Mount Rainier is the snowiest place on Earth. Valdez in Alaska is the world's snowiest town close to sea level. An average of 8 m (26 ft) of snow falls there each winter. Meanwhile, highland areas of Japan have the deepest seasonal accumulations of snow. On Mount Tate in the Toyama Prefecture of Honshu, an average of 7 m (23 ft) of snow falls each year – although in some years, depths can be as high as 20 m (65 ft). Every April, a 500-m (1640-ft) long, high-walled passage is cut through the deep snow, making a unique and breathtaking 'snow canyon' that is a popular tourist attraction.

POLAR EXTREMES

Although snow can form at very low temperatures, it rarely does – because very cold air normally has very little moisture in it. The world's coldest continent, Antarctica, is also the driest. There are many 'dry valleys' where no snow ever falls – and, because the air is so dry, the whole of Antarctica is considered a desert. The continent holds the official record for the very lowest ambient temperature ever recorded on Earth: -89.2°C (-128.6°F) in July 1983, during the long, dark polar winter.

The temperature in Antarctica as a whole has stayed below freezing for around 15 million years, so when snow does fall, it covers snow already laid down. The result is an ever-growing covering of snow and ice – the Antarctic Ice Sheet – which is an average of 2 km (1¼ miles) thick. The ice sheet holds 90 per cent of all the frozen water on the planet. If you could divide the Antarctic Ice Sheet among the more than 7 billion people who are alive today, each of us would receive over 300 million tonnes (330 million tons) of snow and ice – which is equivalent to the weight of 600 fully loaded Airbus A380 airliners. If the entire Antarctic Ice Sheet were to melt, the sea level would rise by around 60 m (200 ft).

The age of the packed snow in the Antarctic Ice Sheet increases with depth. In 2004, a team of European scientists completed drilling an ice core to a depth of 3270.2 m (10,729 ft) – just 5 m (16 ft) above the continent's bedrock. By studying the water along the length of the ice core (the ratios of different isotopes of hydrogen and oxygen present in the ancient snowfall), the team constructed a record of average global temperatures as far back as 740,000 years ago. There are only two ice sheets in the world today – although during ice ages, there are many more. The other one, also the result of millions of years of snowfall, covers most of Greenland. If that were to melt, the sea level would rise about 7.2 m (24 ft).

VALDEZ, ALASKA
Heavy snowfall contributed to the sinking of a boat in the harbour at Valdez on 21 December 2006. Over a 24-hour period, the city received 53 cm (21 in) of snow, breaking the record of 19 December 1985 when 31.75 cm (12½ in) of snow fell on Valdez.

SNOW CANYON
Known by locals as Yuki-no-Otani, this roadway on Mount Tate, in the Toyama Prefecture of Japan's island of Honshu, is completely cleared by snowploughs every spring, leaving behind snow walls that are up to 20 m (65 ft) high – as tall as a six-storey building.

FROZEN NIAGARA
In January 2014, a strong polar vortex – a swirling mass of frigid air originating in the Arctic – brought bitterly cold weather to both Canada and the United States, leading to an unusual sight on the border between these two countries – Niagara Falls, with its flow partially frozen.

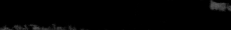

RIVERS OF ICE

The pressure of accumulated snow on ice sheets – and their smaller cousins, ice caps – causes the ice at the bottom to flow slowly outwards. The resulting rivers of ice – known as glaciers – play an important part in shaping the landscape, especially during ice ages, and their melt-water provides precious drinking water for people in many parts of the world. Glaciers are the largest moving objects on Earth. The very largest of all is the Lambert Glacier, in East Antarctica. It measures about 100 km (60 miles) wide, and for most of its 400-km (250-mile) length, it is about 2.5 km (1½ miles) deep.

If the foot, or terminus, of a glacier meets the sea, huge chunks break off, or 'calve', to become icebergs. Some glaciers are substantial enough that their terminus extends out into the sea in one piece, sometimes for tens or even hundreds of kilometres, as an 'ice shelf', with icebergs calving at the outer edge. The Ross Ice Shelf in Antarctica, the world's largest, has a surface area about the same as Cameroon. It is also one of the thickest, around 800 m (2600 ft) thick in places – although, like all ice shelves, most of the thickness is below water, as these huge structures are basically floating platforms of ice.

Glaciers' inexorable movement down a slope, driven by their own weight, is very slow. Typical speeds range from a few centimetres per decade to perhaps 500 m (1600 ft) per year, depending upon their thickness and the angle and type of terrain. The edges and bottom of a glacier move more slowly than the centre and top, because of friction with the ground; the same is true for rivers. Most of the world's glaciers are thinning and retreating, contributing to a rise in the sea level.

TROUBLE ON THE MOUNTAIN

While glaciers move accumulated snow very slowly down mountains, avalanches achieve the same result much faster. Avalanches are most common in the Alps

HINDU KUSH AVALANCHE
Severe winters often see an increase in deadly avalanches in this mountain range found in Pakistan and Afghanistan.

in France, Austria and Switzerland. Worldwide, they claim an average of 150 lives every year. There is often little warning of where and when they will happen – and this unpredictability adds to their immense danger. Accumulated snow on a mountain can collapse in a number of different ways, and often a single avalanche will include two or more of them. Loose, fresh snow, for example, tumbles down a mountain slope, often creating a plume of snow powder as it does so. Powder snow comprises countless small, individual grains, and as they tumble, they may be suspended in the air for much of the time, acting like a fast-flowing fluid. Avalanches involving powder snow tend to be the largest, fastest-moving and most deadly. Older, more compact snow tends to fracture, forming large slabs that slide down a slope more or less intact at first, before breaking up. A slab avalanche can accelerate from standing to 130 km/h (80 mph) in a matter of seconds.

While most avalanches kill no one, or just a very few people, large ones can kill many, many people – the biggest cause of death being asphyxiation under the snow. During World War I, avalanches killed tens of thousands of Italian and Austrian soldiers at military bases in the Alps. Often, the avalanches were set off deliberately, by bombing the tops of mountains. Another extreme example of avalanches killing on a huge scale involved the renowned military commander Hannibal, in 218 BC. As he crossed the Alps to fight the Roman army, around 18,000 of his soldiers and hundreds of horses and elephants were killed by a number of avalanches.

The biggest and deadliest avalanche in recorded history happened in Peru on 31 May 1970, when a large part of the north face of the country's tallest peak, Mount Huascarán, collapsed – a result of a major

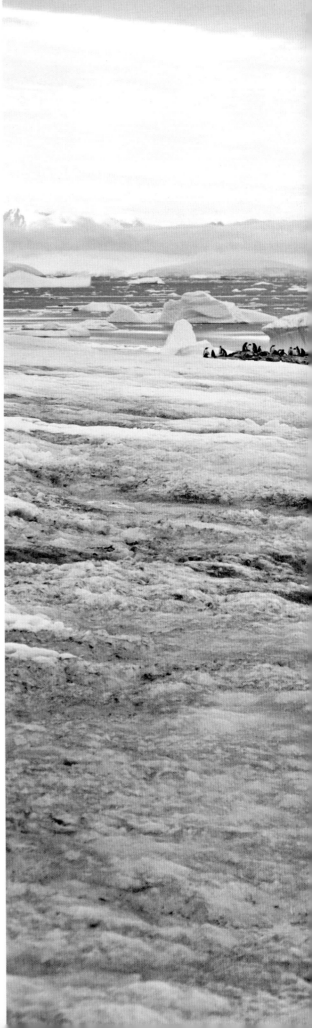

undersea earthquake centred 35 km (22 miles) off the coast. Unusually for an avalanche, the debris hurtling down the mountain was made up mostly of glacial ice, mixed with substantial amounts of fresh snow, rock and mud. The avalanche completely buried two small towns, killing an estimated 20,000 people. Just eight years earlier, in 1962, snow laid down on the same mountain by a heavy snowstorm tumbled down the mountainside along with huge and heavy pieces of glacial ice, killing more than 4000 people.

SURVIVING THE SNOW

It is clear that snow can be very hazardous to humans – but it can also threaten plants, animals and other living things. Buried under snow at temperatures below freezing, plants have little access to the sunlight they need to photosynthesise and grow – so food becomes scarce for those animals that depend upon plants for nourishment. Some animals – particularly birds – simply migrate. The Arctic tern has the greatest migratory range of any animal, travelling 35,000 km (22,000 miles) twice a year so that it can experience two summers – one in the Arctic and one in the Antarctic.

Those animals that stick around during harsh winter conditions have various ways of surviving, or even thriving. For some, camouflage is essential: the mountain hare and the Arctic fox turn white just for the winter. Some animals grow an extra layer of fat or extra fur to insulate them more effectively against the cold. Emperor penguins are well-known huddlers, standing together in groups to reduce heat loss; they also balance their eggs on their feet, to prevent them touching the freezing snow. Many amphibians and small mammals slow their metabolisms for a long winter hibernation, keeping their bodies warm enough to survive but otherwise using minimum

ARCTIC FOX

In addition to its snow-white fur, the Arctic fox has several other adaptations that help it to survive winter in the harsh environment in which it lives. It has thick fur – even on the soles of its paws – as well as small ears to reduce heat loss.

'WATERMELON SNOW'

Red and green algal blooms add a burst of bright colour to the Antarctic landscape. In 2012, a large patch of vibrant green algae floating in the frigid water off Antarctica – probably blown there along with snow from the continent – was so big it could be seen from space.

energy. Some animals, such as the snowshoe hare,
have wide feet that allow them to walk on top of
delicate, freshly laid snow without falling through.
Freshly fallen snow is typically 90 to 95 per cent
air, which makes it a good thermal insulator. Ruffed
grouse, native to North America, spend most of their
winter days burrowed deep in snow for this reason,
emerging briefly each day to feed.

One of the major hazards for living things that exist
in temperatures below freezing is the growth of ice
crystals. A living cell depends upon liquid water for
many of its essential functions, including transporting
nutrients. If the cell water freezes, all functions cease;
in addition, the ice formed in the cell takes up a greater
volume than the liquid water, bursting open the cell.
A wide range of living things produce 'antifreeze'
proteins inside their cells to prevent this from
happening. Unlike the antifreeze used in car coolant
systems, these molecules do not lower the freezing
point of water. Instead, they bind to tiny ice crystals,
preventing them from growing. These proteins are
commonplace in plants, fish, insects and many
microorganisms that live in very cold environments.
Some cold-adapted microorganisms can be seen as
coloured patches in the otherwise pristine white of a
snowpack. In particular, red algae appear as bright
red or pink 'watermelon snow'. Red algae are cryophilic,
or 'cold-loving', one of a huge number of microorganisms
called extremophiles that have adapted to the extreme
environments of our planet.

CRACKED EARTH
All over the world, lakebeds in drought-affected regions crack up as the moisture evaporates and the Sun-baked soil contracts.

Droughts and dust storms

A long spell of reduced rainfall can have dramatic effects, from drying up rivers upon which entire regions depend to reducing crop yields and putting people at risk of famine and disease. Extended periods of drought can even play a major part in the downfall of civilisations.

L IKE MANY thriving civilisations, the Khmer Empire in Southeast Asia relied heavily on seasonal monsoon rains brought inland from the Indian Ocean. To this day, these rains account for three-quarters of the region's total rainfall. In the empire's capital city, Angkor – well known for its magnificent temple Angkor Wat – engineers built huge reservoirs to store rainwater. The water was used to irrigate rice paddies and to maintain a vast system of canals that provided avenues for travel and commerce within the sprawling city. In addition, the sophisticated water management system was designed to sustain the population through the dry season.

Studies of tree rings from the region reveal long periods of drought around the time the civilisation began to collapse, in the late fourteenth century. Recent analysis of cores taken from the bed of the largest reservoir has shown that very little sediment was laid down at these times, indicating that water levels were indeed very low. Doubtless several factors played a part in the decline of the Khmer Empire, but it is becoming clear that drought was one of the major causes.

A TERRIBLE TRANSITION

Scientists have put the unusual cluster of long droughts down to a particular transition in global climate – from the 'Medieval Climate Anomaly' to the 'Little Ice Age'. During the Medieval Climate Anomaly, which lasted from around 950 to around 1250, countries around

COLORADO'S MESA VERDE
A severe drought forced the Ancestral Pueblo people to leave their cliff dwellings in the late thirteenth century.

the North Atlantic were warmer than usual, while elsewhere was colder. The situation was reversed in the Little Ice Age, with Europe and the Americas enduring very cold winters.

The Medieval Climate Anomaly – and particularly, the long transition into the Little Ice Age – affected rainfall patterns in many parts of the world. In the Yucatán Peninsula of what is now Mexico, the Mayan civilisation – already in decline after reduced rainfall in the ninth century – documented severe, multiyear droughts in the fourteenth and fifteenth centuries. Scientists have estimated that half of the Yucatán population died from famine and disease during these episodes. Further north, in what is now the south western United States, tree rings reveal a period of drought from 1276 to 1299; it was at this time that settled communities of Ancestral Pueblo and Hohokam people dispersed and returned to a nomadic life.

FEELING THE PRESSURE

The civilisation-busting droughts of the thirteenth and fourteenth centuries were due to long-term disruptions of rain patterns associated with large, slow fluctuations in climate. But such is the importance of water in

---

❓ EXTREME FACT
Recent analysis of mysterious layers of red soil on the island of Bermuda has revealed that the soil most likely originated from Africa; it was brought to Bermuda by dust storms.

KENYAN DROUGHT

In 2011, nomads in Kenya's Chalbi Desert struggled to find enough water for their herds of goats and sheep, with many of their traditional springs rapidly drying up because of the local drought conditions.

people's lives that droughts lasting a few years or even a few months can also be troublesome. For example, one of the triggers of the French Revolution, which began in 1789, was the single dry summer of 1788, which dramatically reduced the wheat crop, pushing bread prices unaffordably high.

Droughts continue to do economic damage to this day. Until the appearance of Hurricane Katrina in 2005, the most costly natural disaster in North American history was not a tropical cyclone, an outbreak of tornadoes or an earthquake: it was a severe drought that ran from 1987 to 1989. In several parts of the United States, the spring of 1988 was the driest on record. At its peak, the drought affected more than

one-third of the country. It is notoriously difficult to work out the true economic impact of droughts; most of the losses are associated with crops and livestock, but fishing and tourism also suffer, as does forestry, with slowed growth of timber and trees lost to wildfires exacerbated by the dry conditions. The cost of the 1987–89 drought has been estimated at US$90 billion (2013 value) in the United States, and more than CAN$2 billion in Canada.

The main cause of the 1987–89 drought was the presence of huge high-pressure air masses that sat stubbornly over much of North America, bringing week after week of virtually cloudless skies. Unlike low-pressure air, which rises and draws moisture

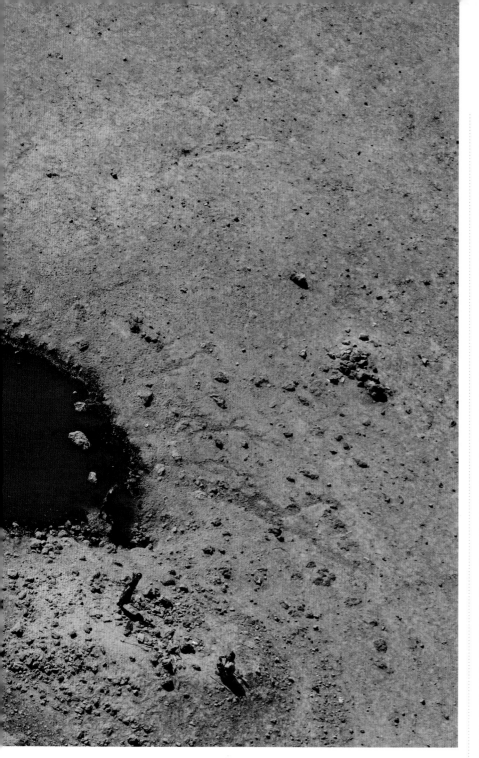

into the atmosphere to form clouds, high-pressure air descends, preventing evaporation. Normally, high-pressure areas dissipate: the cloudless skies allow the Sun's heat to warm the land and evaporate water – this evaporation cools the ground and the vapour forms rain clouds. Condensation releases heat in the atmosphere, and the pressure is reduced, leading to a change in the weather. But in 1987, soils across much of the United States were already dry; when sunlight hits dry soil, all it can do is warm the surface. The subtropical jet stream – a speedy river of air high in the atmosphere – was also important: it shepherded the high-pressure air mass, keeping it in place.

A PACIFIC CAUSE

The high-pressure air that was to blame for the 1987–89 North American drought was itself largely the result of a strong La Niña event. La Niña is part of a major climate cycle called the El Niño-Southern Oscillation (ENSO), which affects atmospheric and oceanic currents in the equatorial Pacific Ocean. Under normal conditions – outside an ENSO cycle – trade winds blowing across the Pacific Ocean create an upwelling of deep, cool waters near the west coast of South America. This cools the air along that coastline; the air sinks, and the resulting 'ridge' of high pressure keeps much of Chile and Peru in desert conditions. During a La Niña event, the upwelling of cold water is increased, and the western coast of South America receives even less rainfall.

The effects of a La Niña go far beyond North and South America; climate scientists call the far-reaching consequences 'global teleconnections'. As the eastern Pacific Ocean cools, the western Pacific Ocean warms, bringing moist, stormy, low-pressure air to Australia and Southeast Asia; this has the knock-on effect of drawing moist air away from East Africa, disrupting the normal rainy season there. During the 2010–11 La Niña, much of eastern Africa received only one-quarter of its normal rainfall. The resulting drought affected millions of people in Somalia, Kenya, Ethiopia and Tanzania. It was the worst drought in the region for decades – tens of thousands of children died during the famine in Somalia alone.

MAKING THE SWITCH

The other phase of an ENSO cycle, El Niño, also has global teleconnections, affecting rainfall patterns across similarly widely separated regions. During an El Niño event, the trade winds and ocean currents switch: the upwelling of cold water near the west coast of South America ceases, and descending, high-pressure air occurs on the other side of the Pacific Ocean, bringing dry conditions to the east coast of Australia, and much of Indonesia and southern Asia. In Indonesia, the drought caused by the 1997–98 El Niño created a huge shortfall

DROUGHT AND FAMINE IN AFRICA

Beginning in the 1950s, central Africa suffered decades of below-average rainfall, resulting in a series of droughts and famines. A detailed study involving weather records, satellite images and climate modelling suggests that particles emitted by coal-burning power stations and factories in Europe and the United States led to a cooling of the Northern Hemisphere; as a result, the normal rain patterns shifted south, drastically reducing rainfall in the Sahel, a region that spans the African continent just below the Sahara. After legislation was passed to control the release of these particles, the rainbands returned to their normal position, and the drought eased.

AUSTRALIAN DROUGHT

Some 40,000 sheep were auctioned off in Hay, New South Wales, in October 2007. While sheep sales are common during spring, most of these animals were sold in response to the drought that had plagued the Murray–Darling Basin since the late 1990s.

KALAHARI DESERT

The quiver tree is the most prominent type of flora in the South African portion of the Kalahari Desert. It has many adaptations to help it survive the arid conditions, including succulent leaves, white powder on its branches that reflects heat, as well as a trunk that can hold a lot of water.

in cereal production, estimated at 3.5 million tonnes (3.9 million tons). Food prices rose considerably, putting pressure on those already struggling against famine.

In Australia, El Niño events almost always bring drought to the northern or the eastern half of the country. During the 1982–83 El Niño, the states of Victoria and New South Wales experienced record low rainfall. However, the most notorious Australian drought in recent times was the Millennium Drought, known colloquially as the 'Big Dry', which affected huge swaths of the country between 1995 and 2009. It was the worst drought on record for south-eastern Australia. Global climate models have suggested that while some of the drought is explained by El Niño events in that period, the rest may have been due to global warming.

According to most climate scientists, including those on the Intergovernmental Panel on Climate Change (IPCC), it is extremely likely that human activity – in particular, the production of greenhouse gases by the burning of fossil fuels – has been the main cause of global warming in at least the past 60 years. Our use of fossil fuels, and the subsequent warming of the planet, is likely to increase – and droughts such as Australia's Big Dry could become more frequent and more extreme. The burning of fossil fuels was also probably the cause of decades of drought in northern Africa in the second half of the twentieth century, including some of the deadliest droughts since 1900.

PERMANENT DROUGHT

All the world's deserts – areas that are always in drought – are created and maintained by 'ridges' of high pressure, which provide stable conditions with little cloud cover. The high-pressure air that keeps the deserts along the coast of Peru and Chile dry is caused by the upwelling of cold water in the Pacific Ocean. But most deserts occur in two bands of high-pressure air that encircle the globe: the 'subtropical highs'. The elevated pressure is the result of air descending from high altitude, as part of a convection current that begins near the Equator. Heating is greatest near the Equator, where the Sun is directly overhead. Air rises there, drawing in cooler air from the tropics. The tropical air converges, is heated and also rises. The rising air splits at high altitude and forms two streams, one moving northwards and one southwards. Each stream cools and descends at around 30 degrees north and south, finishing the cycle and forming the subtropical highs.

The subtropical highs are responsible for the Sahara, Namib and Kalahari Deserts, the deserts of Australia and the Middle East, and the arid conditions in much of Mexico and the south-western United States. They also play a part in the aridity of the Atacama Desert in Chile. Some of the driest and hottest places are found under the mostly cloudless skies in these regions. The highest recorded and verified ambient temperature,

EXTREME TOP 10
DEADLIEST DROUGHTS*

1 CHINA, 1928 3 MILLION DEATHS

2 BANGLADESH, 1943 1.9 MILLION DEATHS

3 INDIA, 1942 1.5 MILLION DEATHS

4 INDIA, 1965 1.5 MILLION DEATHS

5 INDIA, 1900 1.25 MILLION DEATHS

6 SOVIET UNION, 1921 1.2 MILLION DEATHS

7 CHINA, 1920 500,000 DEATHS

8 ETHIOPIA, MAY 1983 300,000 DEATHS

9 SUDAN, APRIL 1983 150,000 DEATHS

10 ETHIOPIA, DECEMBER 1973 100,000 DEATHS

*Since 1900. Some figures are equal due to rounding up.

56.7°C (134°F), was measured at Furnace Creek Ranch in Death Valley, California, on 10 July 1913. (A slightly higher temperature – 57.8°C [136°F] – recorded in the Libyan town of Al-Aziziya in 1922 is now disputed.) The Atacama Desert is the driest region on Earth, with average rainfall of little more than 10 mm (⅖ in) per year. Arica, on the desert's Pacific edge, is the driest inhabited town in the world: it receives an average of just 0.76 mm (²/₁₀₀ in) of rain per year. No rain fell there at all between 1903 and 1918 – the longest recorded dry period anywhere in the world.

KICKING UP THE DUST

Although deserts have very little rain, they do have their very own storms: dust storms. The winds that cause the storms are often the result of unsettled weather in neighbouring regions drawing air across the desert. In North Africa and the Arabian Peninsula, the result is a hot, dry wind called the khamsin, which blows from the south-west at speeds of up to 140 km/h (90 mph). The khamsin can blow for two days at a time, rapidly increasing temperatures by 20°C (36°F) and whipping up immeasurable amounts of sand.

A single dust storm in the Sahara can hoist hundreds of tonnes of sand into the air, and warm air can lift some of the smaller particles to altitudes of around 4500 m (15,000 ft). Saharan dust storms dislodge an estimated 1.3 billion tonnes (1.4 billion tons) of sand each year. One-third of the sand ends up in the Atlantic Ocean; occasionally, some of the lighter sand particles can make it all the way across the ocean to Central America, the Caribbean and the south-western United States. Sand lifted into the air by dust storms in the Gobi Desert in China and Mongolia can also travel large distances. In 2001, through data from satellites and ground-level air-quality monitoring stations, scientists tracked the movement of millions of tonnes of dust

》》

DUST STORM

Vehicles travelling on a main road through the city of Bikaner in Rajasthan, India, were confronted by the frightening leading edge of a dust storm on 13 June 2013. Arid parts of western Rajasthan are hit by up to 20 dust storms every year.

》》

BLOOMING DESERT

Joshua Tree National Park in California protects a precious section of the Mojave Desert. White dune evening primroses and pinkish purple desert sand verbenas flower profusely after rain falls in the desert during the winter months.

carried from the Gobi Desert – during a period of just a few weeks, winds carried dust eastwards over the Pacific Ocean and then right across the United States. Records from the fourteenth century show that large dust storms occurred in the Gobi Desert every 30 years or so. Since the 1990s, they normally occur every year – because of deforestation and changes of land use in China.

A dramatic change in land use was also to blame for the terrifying and ecologically disastrous dust storms – known as the 'Dust Bowl' – that occurred across the prairies of the United States and Canada in the 1930s. Decades of ploughing had removed grasses and other small plants and shrubs, and loosened the topsoil. The grasses had held the soil in place, and they retained some moisture – essential functions in these semiarid regions. Without them, the loose topsoil dried out and became mobile. Winds blew the dusty topsoil into huge dark clouds nicknamed 'black blizzards', eroding the soil, rendering the land uninhabitable and leading to a mass migration away from the affected areas.

SURVIVING IN THE DRY

Dry conditions present a major challenge to plants and animals as well as to humans, since every living thing depends upon a reliable supply of water. Evolution has provided an incredible array of adaptations. For example, the kangaroo rat – native to arid regions within North America – drinks very rarely, and manufactures its own water inside its body from the oils in seeds. Camels use a similar strategy, laying down fat inside their humps from which they can later produce water. Desert-dwelling reptiles – and some mammals that live in arid regions, such as the rhinoceros – have extra-thick skin with no sweat glands, which helps to prevent water loss.

When rain does fall in deserts, the landscape quickly becomes covered with a glorious multicoloured coat, as flowering desert plants undergo their entire life cycle in just a few weeks – blossoming brightly to attract the scarce pollinating insects, then making and releasing seeds. The seeds lie dormant until the next downpour. Some plants survive extreme dehydration by shutting down completely; they drift around the desert for years or even decades as tumbleweeds, all but dead, until they land in water. Within hours of making contact with water, their seeds sprout into life, and so they are referred to as 'resurrection plants'.

CLEVER PHOTOSYNTHESIS

Succulent plants such as cactuses have a different strategy – they store water in their fleshy leaves. They also use a form of photosynthesis called crassulacean acid metabolism (CAM), which is much less wasteful of water than ordinary photosynthesis. Most plants open their stomata (leaf pores) during the day, allowing carbon dioxide in but also encouraging the evaporation of water from the leaves, which draws up more water from the roots. In CAM photosynthesis, the stomata are held tightly shut during the hot, dry day, and opened only at night, to allow carbon dioxide in. The carbon dioxide is held in the leaves, and is processed inside the sealed leaf the next day, when the Sun is shining.

Some drought-tolerant plants use another form of photosynthesis, called C4 carbon fixation, in which the stomata are open during the day, as for normal plants. The stomata stay open for much less time, however, as C4 carbon fixation utilises carbon dioxide more efficiently than normal photosynthesis. Maize and sugar cane are the best-known plants that use this photosynthesis type.

Wildfires and fire whirls

Fire requires three things: fuel, oxygen and a source of heat. Once ignited, a fire will continue burning until it exhausts its fuel or is smothered. Out in the wild, fires rage largely out of control, consuming trees, shrubs and whatever else will burn, until there is nothing left – or until the rain comes.

WILDFIRES GO BY many names – including bushfires, forest fires and prairie fires – depending upon what is being burned. Every year, wildfires blaze across an average of more than 3.5 million sq km (1.4 million sq miles) of forest, bush, brush and grassland worldwide – equivalent to nearly four times the combined area of Germany and France, or half the area of Australia. Wildfires in Africa account for more than two-thirds of that total – and most of them are started deliberately. Farmers across Africa use fire for a variety of purposes – including forcing grazing animals off land set aside for growing crops, removing stubble left behind after the previous year's harvest and destroying unwanted plants on agricultural land. Nowhere is this approach used more than in the Sahel, the semiarid belt that stretches across the continent just below the Sahara. Remote-sensing instruments on board satellites detect a band of fire shifting north and south each year, matching the seasonal greening of the region.

Farmers in rainforest areas also set deliberate fires, but mostly to create new pastures and new fields for planting, rather than to replenish existing ones. This slash-and-burn agriculture is much cheaper and quicker than clearing an area with machinery – especially in remote areas. With high densities of fuel in the lush forests, there is always a danger that fires can burn out of control. In Indonesia in 1997, fires started by slash-and-burn agriculture quickly accelerated, consuming nearly 100,000 sq km (39,000 sq miles) of rainforest and spreading a choking haze across much of Southeast Asia. It was by far the worst wildfire event of the twentieth century, and probably of all recorded history.

HOT AND DRY

As is the case for most of the world's worst wildfires, the 1997 Indonesia fires took hold after a period of reduced rainfall. The risk of fires growing and spreading out of control is greatest when vegetation is tinder-dry and temperatures are high. In these conditions, a small fire started by a carelessly discarded cigarette or even broken glass magnifying the Sun's rays can quickly grow into a widespread and dangerous conflagration.

?

EXTREME FACT
Coal has been smouldering beneath the ground on Mount Wingen – commonly known as Burning Mountain – in the Australian state of New South Wales for at least 6000 years.

DRAMATIC WILDFIRE
Caused by lightning, the deadly Dude Fire killed six firefighters as it burned through ponderosa pine forests in Arizona for 10 days in June 1990. Fire is an important process in maintaining healthy ponderosa pine forests, and without it the whole ecosystem is affected.

The paucity of rainfall in Indonesia in 1997 was largely the result of El Niño – part of a cycle of changing sea and air temperatures across the Pacific Ocean that affects rainfall patterns in various regions. Rainfall across much of Australia is also drastically reduced during an El Niño event – and the result is normally an increase in the number and extent of bushfires across the country. An El Niño that began in 1982, for example, led to rainfall reducing to one-quarter of its normal value by early February 1983. On the sixteenth of that month – Ash Wednesday – nearly 200 bushfires raged across the states of Victoria and South Australia, razing to the ground an area of forest and bush equivalent to twice the area of the city of Melbourne and claiming 75 lives. The Ash Wednesday bushfires were the worst, costliest and deadliest wildfires in Australia's history – until the Black Saturday bushfires of 7 February 2009, during another El Niño event. Over 400 individual fires began that day across Victoria, and 173 people lost their lives.

As the driest inhabited continent, Australia is often struck by large wildfires, even in non-El Niño years. The country's most extensive wildfire began on Friday 13 January 1939, at the height of a particularly hot, dry summer. The Black Friday bushfires affected around three-quarters of Victoria, and destroyed approximately 20,000 sq km (8000 sq miles) of bush – equivalent to the entire area of Slovenia. The fires killed 71 people and destroyed several towns, and were only extinguished by a heavy rainstorm two days later.

WHERE AND WHEN

Large wildfires occur in places that receive enough rainfall for plant life to flourish, but are not so wet that fires cannot take hold. There are no wildfires in hot deserts, despite the dry conditions and high temperatures, simply because there is so little biomass to burn. And in the absence of slash-and-burn agriculture, rainforest environments suffer few wildfires. Fires do happen naturally in untouched rainforest – usually as a result of lightning strikes – but they are normally confined to saplings and leaf litter, with the amount of water held by mature trees and the general damp conditions preventing fire from growing and spreading.

Most accidental or natural wildfires occur at middle latitudes; as well as Australia, they are common in Russia, the Middle East, North and South America and parts of Europe. In the twentieth century, management of the United States' vast expanses of forest and large open prairies and shrub lands involved a policy of determined fire prevention. Consequently, forests grew denser – a phenomenon wildfire experts call 'fuel loading' – and resulted in larger, more sustained fires than would have happened naturally. Today, forest and prairie management involves setting 'prescribed' fires to help reduce this problem.

The deadliest wildfire in the United States happened before the fire suppression policy began – on Sunday 8 October 1871, near the small town of Peshtigo, Wisconsin, in the heart of a heavily forested area. There were actually several fires, which grew quickly, after seven weeks with almost no rain. Some began when sparks from steam locomotives ignited brush alongside the railway, others when slash-and-burn land clearing got out of hand. The Peshtigo wildfires killed nearly 2000 people and consumed approximately 5000 sq km (1900 sq miles) of forest. The fires spread rapidly, as strong winds from a cyclonic storm fanned the flames. Several other devastating fires happened on that very same day, because similar conditions existed across the rest of Wisconsin, as well as the states of Michigan and Illinois.

FIERY WEATHER

Witnesses of the destruction in Peshtigo reported that the conditions were similar to extreme weather, with some structures destroyed by very strong winds even though the fire did not touch them directly; one house was lifted cleanly off its foundations. The terrible fire in Peshtigo was a 'firestorm' – an inferno so hot and energetic that it creates its own weather. In a firestorm, cooler air from around the fire rushes in to take the place of the hot air rising quickly from the fire. The inflowing air creates strong winds at ground level, and the wind intensifies the fire as it brings with it a fresh supply of oxygen, as well as feeding it with loose debris such as fallen branches and leaf litter. Often – especially when two or more large fires join together – a cloud forms above a firestorm, from the huge amounts of water vapour created by the fire itself, cooling as it rises in the air. The cloud is made all the more dark and ominous because of the presence of heavy smoke. Meteorologists refer to these clouds as 'pyrocumulus', or 'pyrocumulonimbus'. Just like a thundercloud (cumulonimbus), a pyrocumulus cloud reaches several kilometres in height, and typically produces lightning and thunder, and often some rain. The lightning can even ignite new fires.

In extreme circumstances, and if prevailing winds are just right, a powerful vortex called a mesocyclone

can form inside a pyrocumulus cloud, as happens inside a supercell thundercloud – and with the same result: a tornado. This almost certainly happened in the Peshtigo fire, and several other huge wildfires since – although the first true fire tornado to be studied and confirmed by scientists was one that wreaked havoc on Australia's capital, Canberra, in January 2003. As it approached the edge of the city, scientists were able to measure the tornado's diameter – around 500 m (1600 ft) – and to estimate the wind speeds inside: over 250 km/h (150 mph). Swirling vortices of fire called fire whirls can form in much smaller fires – but even these can be very energetic and destructive.

WILD IN THE CITY

At exactly the same time the wildfires were burning around Peshtigo, the US city of Chicago, Illinois, was ablaze. That fire also created a firestorm, with whirlwinds that lifted wooden planks and hurled them hundreds of metres. The potential for a city fire to spread and keep burning is greater where the population density is high, and where wooden buildings dominate. The Great Fire of Rome, in 64 AD, completely destroyed one-third of the city, and left much of the rest in ruins. History is littered with many other infamous city fires, including the Great Fire of London in 1666, and the less well-known fire in London in 1212, which killed

PYROCUMULUS CLOUD

These sinister-looking clouds can loom over a fire-ravaged landscape for days, or be carried many kilometres away from the fire by strong winds. The biggest clouds may transport pollutants up to 16 km (10 miles) into the atmosphere, impacting on the ozone layer.

FEARSOME FIRE WHIRLS

All fires feature horizontal vortices – swirling masses of air caused by the rolling convection of the hot air they produce. But sometimes they also create vertical vortices – twisting columns of air and smoke reaching high above the ground. This normally happens where the air currents of two or more adjacent wildfires interact. These 'fire whirls' or 'fire devils' draw ash up from the ground, which ignites, along with unburnt gases from the fires themselves, to produce a tall, rapidly rotating pillar of fire. Fire whirls are the spectacular cousins of dust devils and waterspouts; they can last for an hour or more, and pose considerable hazards to firefighters.

REGROWTH

Signs of vibrant green regeneration abounded on the trees around the Victorian town of Marysville, Australia, just six months after the area was devastated by the disastrous Black Saturday bushfires on 7 February 2009.

SAVANNA FIRE

A female African elephant and her two calves move away from a grassland fire in the Maasai Mara National Reserve, Kenya. A reduction in the number of savanna fires here has allowed acacia trees to take hold.

3000 people. In 1812, two-thirds of the city of Moscow was destroyed by a three-day blaze. That fire was started deliberately, in an attempt to deny soldiers of the French emperor Napoleon I entry to the city.

The most extreme, devastating and deadly city fire occurred as a result of a magnitude 7.9 earthquake that hit Tokyo on 1 September 1923. Altogether, the earthquake, the fires and a tropical cyclone that hit the following day claimed at least 100,000 lives, with another 40,000 people missing, presumed dead. The greatest single loss of life was caused by an extremely powerful fire whirl – which was almost certainly a large fire tornado – that killed 38,000 people who had gathered in a large open space, trying to stay away from crumbling buildings.

Some bombing campaigns in World War II were modelled on wildfires and city fires – and were designed to create huge firestorms. In particular, the bombing of Hamburg (1943), Dresden (1945) and Tokyo (1945) led to firestorms covering several square kilometres, each killing tens of thousands of people. The colossal amount of energy released by the detonation of the atomic bomb dropped on Hiroshima on 6 August 1945 also created a firestorm, but it killed no one, because it happened over an area that had already been completely decimated by the bomb's initial blast.

STAYING ALIVE

Fire was commonplace long before humans arrived. Lightning is by far the most frequent natural cause, but sparks caused by falling rocks and the heat of lava have both also been known to start fires. Some animals take advantage of wildfires, skirting the outer edge looking for potential prey fleeing the flames. Birds, for example, can often be seen swarming dangerously close to wildfires, hunting for insects flying or hopping away from the heat.

Like any other disruption to an ecosystem, wildfires have been a driver of evolution. In particular, a great number of plants have physical adaptations that allow them to take advantage of – or even rely on – wildfires. Most involve either surviving the fire and quickly resprouting while other species perish, or producing seeds that germinate immediately after a fire. For example, arbutus trees found in Mediterranean biomes have their crown – from which branches grow – just above the root. They are extremely successful at regrowing after a fire destroys the above-ground parts of the tree. Native to California, the giant sequoia has a trunk that is covered with very thick bark, which allows it to survive a forest fire relatively unscathed. Its seeds litter the forest floor, and germinate quickly after a fire. The ash acts as a fertiliser, and the sunlight streaming down to the ground thanks to the loss of branches from the canopy enables the seedlings to become established. The eucalyptus, native to Australia,

has evolved a similar strategy, and the volatile, flammable oil it produces seems to actively encourage fire.

The Aleppo pine, which is found in countries around the Mediterranean Sea, has several strategies that allow it to thrive in fire-prone areas. Like many species of pine, it retains most of its seeds, on cones, in the branches – a kind of seed bank. The seeds only fall to the ground when the branches burn – an adaptation that botanists call 'serotiny'. Aleppo pine seedlings flourish in the acidic conditions of ash-ridden soil, and they mature and produce new cones quickly, in case a fresh fire kills the young trees. Oddly, however, natural wildfires are very rare in the part of the Mediterranean basin where these trees originated. Researchers suggest therefore that these adaptations probably evolved since humans began using fire in agriculture in the region, nearly 800,000 years ago – a time span of around 6200 of the tree's generations.

OTHER CLEVER PLANTS

Grasses also quickly regrow after fires. They gained an evolutionary foothold tens of millions of years ago, in the savannas of Africa – an area frequently struck by lightning. In grasses, the part of the plant from which new leaves grow – the basal meristem – is safely located just beneath the ground, which means that the only parts above ground are the leaves (the blades of grass) and the reproductive parts (the flowers). This strategy also allows them to regrow after grazing animals have eaten the visible parts of the plant.

The chaparral biome, which covers large parts of California, but also extends into northern Mexico, has long been subject to fairly frequent fires. As a result, it features a large number of plants adapted to surviving them. One of the most successful plants, buckbrush has seeds coated in a thick, durable cuticle that only cracks open in the heat of a fire, allowing them to

germinate. Harvester ants often hoard the seeds under the soil, where they lie dormant until the next fire sweeps through the chaparral region.

GOING UNDERGROUND

As Captain Meriwether Lewis and William Clark explored the Missouri River, as part of their epic journey across what is now the United States (1804–06), they observed grass fires igniting coal seams alongside the river. The coal fires smouldered long after the grass fires had been extinguished. The coal seams Lewis and Clark observed were exposed – but coal and peat under the ground can also burn, albeit slowly, so that smoke and even flames escape through fissures in the rocks above. Fire can sometimes start spontaneously where oxygen reaches hydrocarbons like those found in coal, peat and oil: very slow oxidation of the hydrocarbons produces a little heat, which increases the rate of the reaction, and eventually leads to ignition. But underground fires can also be started by accident – the fires of Indonesia's slash-and-burn agriculture often ignite peat and coal fires underground, for example.

There are many thousands of fires in abandoned coalmines, mostly in China and India, which have ignited spontaneously or by accident. Underground fires like these burn slowly for months or even years, spreading along coal seams, releasing poisonous gases

DOOR TO HELL
In 1971, a Soviet drilling rig collapsed into a gas-filled cavern near Derweze, a town in Turkmenistan. Scientists set the toxic gas alight, thinking that it would eliminate the fumes – and the 70-m (230-ft) wide hole has been burning ever since.

CHAPARRAL FIRE
In August 2009, the Lu Breu Fire burned through approximately 360 sq km (140 sq miles) of chaparral in California's Santa Barbara County. While many fires in this region start naturally, this one was caused by a stove at an illicit marijuana plantation.

IT'S ABOUT TIME

There has only been enough oxygen in the air to sustain fire for about 10 per cent of Earth's history – since around 470 million years ago. Wildfires have only been possible since plants began colonising the land, around 420 million years ago. The earliest fossilised charcoal that has been discovered anywhere on Earth dates to that time.

to the surface and increasing the risk of ground subsidence. There are also many underground fires in Powder River Basin, the site of the United States' largest oil field, which straddles Montana and Wyoming. A scientific study of the ash under the ground revealed that there have been fires there for at least a million years – long before people lived there. Sometimes, it is methane and other flammable gases escaping from underground coal or oil deposits that burn. Methane leaking out from the Baba Gurgur oil field in Iraq has been burning continuously since at least the time it was described by ancient Greek writers, nearly 3000 years ago.

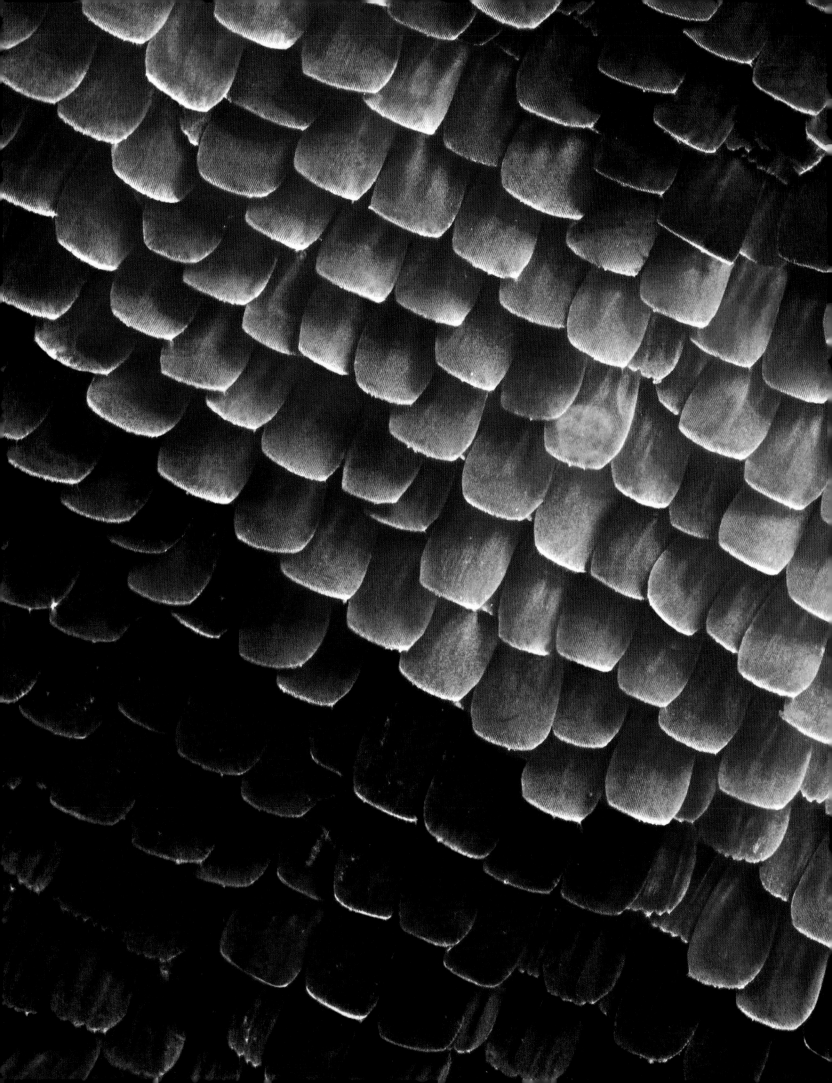

PART
6

REFERENCE

Extreme 100 – Earth's record holders
Glossary
Index
Acknowledgements
Photo credits

BUTTERFLY WING
*Photographed under a microscope, the fragile wing of a red admiral
butterfly clearly comprises rows of minuscule coloured scales.*

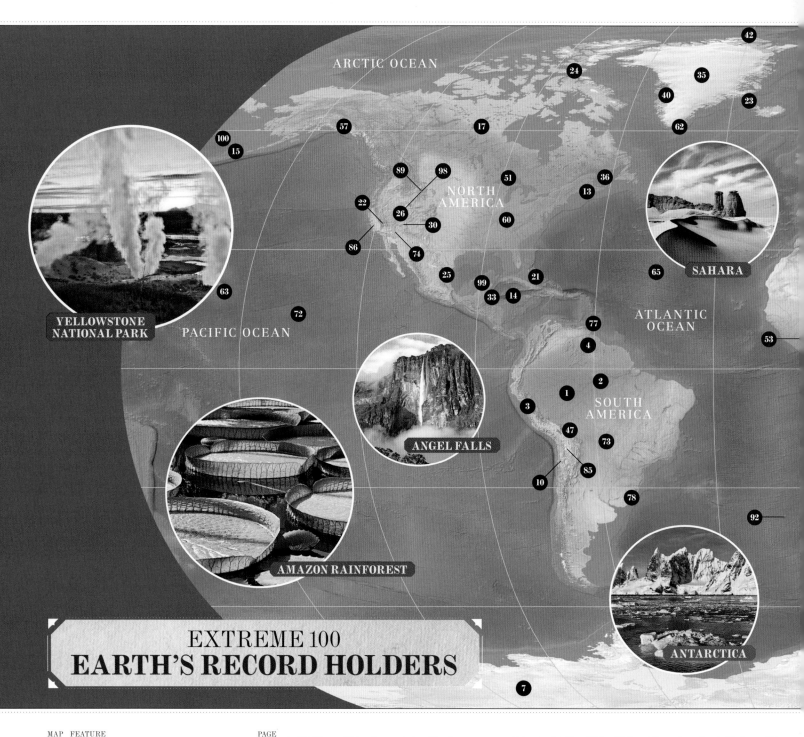

ARCTIC OCEAN

NORTH AMERICA

SAHARA

YELLOWSTONE NATIONAL PARK

PACIFIC OCEAN

ATLANTIC OCEAN

ANGEL FALLS

AMAZON RAINFOREST

SOUTH AMERICA

ANTARCTICA

EXTREME 100
EARTH'S RECORD HOLDERS

MAP	FEATURE	PAGE
1	**Amazon rainforest**, largest tropical forest	135
2	**Amazon River**, widest river	193
3	**Andes**, longest land-based mountain range	94
4	**Angel Falls**, tallest land-based waterfall	200
5	**Antarctic Desert**, largest desert	126
6	**Antarctic Ice Sheet**, largest ice sheet	231
7	**Antarctica**, coldest and driest continent	126
8	**Arctic Ocean**, smallest ocean	161
9	**Asia**, largest continent	123
10	**Atacama Desert**, driest region	118
11	**Australia**, smallest, driest inhabited continent	298
12	**Barberton Mountain Land**, oldest intact mountain range	90
13	**Bay of Fundy**, largest tidal range	177
14	**Beebe Vent Field**, deepest and hottest hydrothermal vents	169
15	**Bering Canyon**, longest submarine canyon	170
16	**Bouvet Island**, most isolated land	154
17	**Canada**, longest coastline	181
18	**Caspian Sea**, largest lake (by area)	212
19	**Challenger Deep**, deepest natural point	167
20	**Congo River**, deepest river	193
21	**Dean's Blue Hole**, deepest submarine sinkhole	186
22	**Death Valley**, highest recorded temperature	295
23	**Denmark Strait Cataract**, largest waterfall	208
24	**Devon Island**, largest uninhabited island	149
25	**El Zacatón**, deepest water-filled sinkhole	80
26	**Fountain Paint Pot**, largest mud pool	71
27	**Frying Pan Lake**, largest hot pool	69
28	**Ganges delta**, largest delta	199
29	**Grand Canal**, longest artificial waterway	196
30	**Grand Canyon**, largest enclosed canyon	101
31	**Great Australian Bight/Nullarbor Plain**, longest cliff face	97
32	**Great Barrier Reef**, largest coral reef ecosystem	189
33	**Great Blue Hole**, widest submarine sinkhole	186
34	**Great Rift Valley**, longest rift	43
35	**Greenland**, largest island	149
36	**Gulf of St Lawrence**, largest estuary	199
37	**Hang Son Doong**, largest cave passage	109
38	**Indus Gorge**, deepest canyon	103
39	**Inga Falls**, largest waterfall (by average volume)	203
40	**Jakobshavn Glacier**, fastest-moving glacier	233
41	**Japan**, most tsunami-prone country	172
42	**Kaffeklubben Island**, most northerly permanent land	149
43	**Kati Thanda–Lake Eyre**, largest ephemeral lake	218
44	**Khone Falls**, widest waterfall	200
45	**Kifuka**, most lightning-prone place	240
46	**Krubera-Voronja Cave**, deepest cave system	112
47	**La Paz**, highest capital city	94
48	**Lake Baikal**, oldest and deepest lake	212

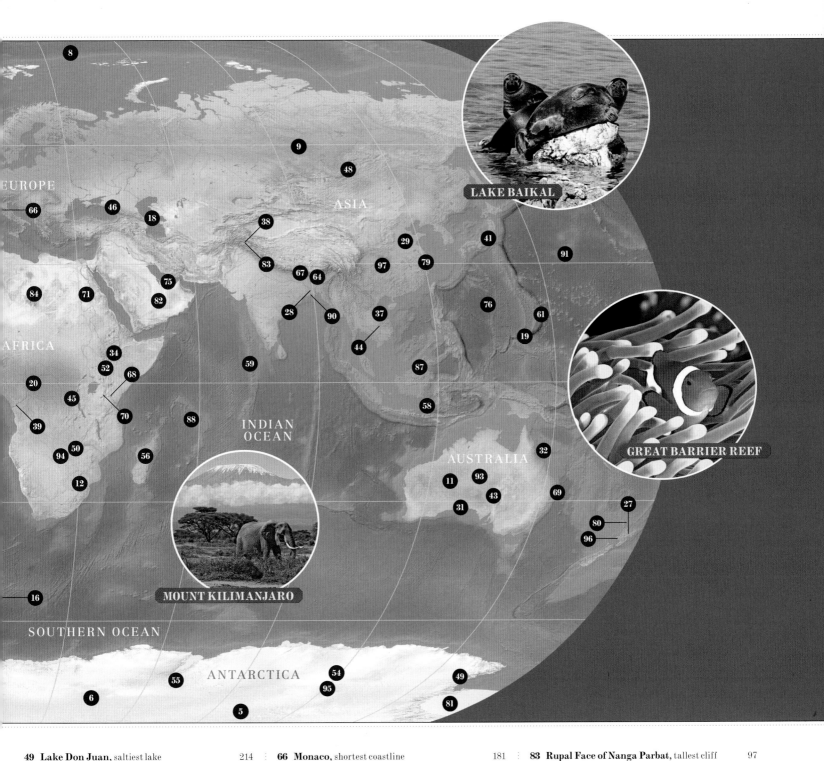

LAKE BAIKAL

GREAT BARRIER REEF

MOUNT KILIMANJARO

EUROPE

ASIA

AFRICA

INDIAN OCEAN

AUSTRALIA

SOUTHERN OCEAN

ANTARCTICA

49	**Lake Don Juan**, saltiest lake	214
50	**Lake Kariba**, largest reservoir (by volume)	218
51	**Lake Superior**, largest freshwater lake (by area)	214
52	**Lake Turkana**, largest alkaline lake	215
53	**Lake Volta**, largest reservoir (by area)	218
54	**Lake Vostok**, largest underground lake	218
55	**Lambert Glacier**, largest alpine glacier	235
56	**Madagascar**, oldest island	153
57	**Malaspina Glacier**, largest piedmont glacier	235
58	**Malay Archipelago**, largest collection of islands (by area)	150
59	**Maldives**, flattest and lowest-lying country	152
60	**Mammoth Cave**, longest cave system	112
61	**Mariana Trench**, deepest ocean trench	167
62	**Maujit Qaqarssuasia**, tallest sea cliff	182
63	**Mauna Kea**, tallest mountain (base to summit)	92
64	**Meghalaya district**, wettest region	268
65	**Mid-Oceanic Ridge**, longest mountain range	94

66	**Monaco**, shortest coastline	181
67	**Mount Everest**, tallest land-based mountain	88
68	**Mount Kilimanjaro**, tallest freestanding land-based mountain	92
69	**Mount Tempest**, tallest coastal dune	182
70	**Ngorongoro Crater**, largest intact caldera	62
71	**Nile**, longest river	191
72	**Pacific Ocean**, largest ocean	161
73	**Pantanal**, largest wetland	221
74	**Parker Dam**, deepest reservoir	218
75	**Persian Gulf**, warmest ocean water	163
76	**Philippine Sea**, largest sea (by area)	171
77	**Pitch Lake**, largest tar pit	226
78	**Praia do Cassino**, longest beach	182
79	**Qiantang River**, largest tidal bore	178
80	**Rikoriko Cave**, largest sea cave	184
81	**Ross Ice Shelf**, largest ice shelf	233
82	**Rub' al Khali**, largest sand desert	120

83	**Rupal Face of Nanga Parbat**, tallest cliff	97
84	**Sahara**, largest hot desert	118
85	**Salar de Uyuni**, largest saltpan, flattest place	120
86	**San Andreas Fault**, largest overland fault zone	40
87	**Sarawak Chamber**, largest cavern	109
88	**Saya de Malha Banks**, largest seagrass beds	189
89	**Steamboat Geyser**, tallest geyser	68
90	**Sundarbans**, largest mangrove forest	186
91	**Tamu Massif**, largest volcano	58
92	**Tristan da Cunha**, remotest inhabited island	153
93	**Uluru (Ayers Rock)**, largest monolith	97
94	**Victoria Falls**, largest land-based waterfall	203
95	**Vostok Station**, lowest recorded temperature	142
96	**Wellington**, windiest city	259
97	**Xiaozhai Tiankeng**, deepest sinkhole	80
98	**Yellowstone National Park**, largest geyser field	68
99	**Yucatán Peninsula**, longest subterranean river	195
100	**Zhemchug Canyon**, largest open canyon	169

GLOSSARY

abyssal plains Flat or gently sloping sediment-rich expanses that form much of the seabed

aftershock A tremor that follows an earthquake in the same area

alpine glacier A slow-moving frozen river of snow and compacted ice that forms on mountains

archipelago A large group of islands

arête A narrow, steep-sided, sharp ridge formed by adjacent glaciers pushing past each other

atoll A ring-shaped island or archipelago formed by coral reefs

BASE jump A parachute jump from a fixed point such as a cliff, rather than from an aeroplane; BASE stands for Building, Antenna, Span and Earth

biodiversity The variety of plant and animal life that is found in a particular habitat

'black smoker' A hydrothermal vent with a dark, chimney-like structure formed from zinc, iron and copper sulfides and manganese and iron oxides

brackish Slightly salty

calcite A light-coloured crystalline mineral comprising calcium carbonate

caldera A large basin-like crater that forms when a volcano erupts and collapses in on itself, or explodes violently and blows away its summit

calving The process whereby end pieces of a tidewater glacier break free and float off into the ocean

carotenoid A yellow, orange or red pigment that gives colour to organisms

cataract A large waterfall

cenote A water-filled sinkhole, particularly in Mexico's Yucatán Peninsula

claustrophobia A fear of confined spaces

cone geyser A geyser with a jet that erupts out of a cone of rock deposit known as geyserite

constellation An internationally recognised group of stars that often forms a visible pattern or figure in the night sky

continental drift See plate tectonics

crater A bowl-shaped depression that marks the opening of a volcano; sometimes a crater lake forms that contains lava or water

cryoconite hole A water-filled cylindrical melt-hole that is found on the surface of some glaciers

cryophile A cold-loving organism

cyanobacteria Ocean-dwelling blue-green algae (also called blue-green bacteria)

delta An often-triangular alluvial plain that forms when a river deposits sediment near its mouth

desiccation Extreme dehydration or dryness

'dip-slip' fault A rupture in Earth's crust where most of the movement is vertical or on an incline

'eight-thousander' One of the few mountains with a height that exceeds 8000 m (26,000 ft)

endemic species A plant or animal that is found in a particular place and nowhere else in the world

endorheic basin A closed drainage area that retains most of its water because it has no outflow and only loses water through evaporation and seepage

ephemeral Lasting for a very short time

epicentre The point on Earth's surface that is directly above an earthquake's place of origin

estuary The mouth of a river, where salty tidal water from the ocean or sea meets fresh water from the river

eukaryote A modern cell that contains many important structures within its own membranes such as a nucleus with genetic material, chloroplasts for photosynthesis and mitochondria that burn fuel for energy

extremophile A microorganism that lives in an extreme environment (such as one that is very hot or very cold)

fault A rupture in Earth's crust that is caused by the movement of plates

firestorm An inferno that is so hot and energetic it creates its own weather

flowstone A calcite deposit that has been left in a cave by flowing or dripping water

foreshock A tremor that precedes an earthquake in the same area

fountain geyser A geyser with a jet that erupts out of a pool

fulgurite The glassy substance that is created when sand is melted during a lightning strike and then quickly becomes solid again

fumarole A vent in Earth's surface that allows underground steam and gases to escape

geologist A person who studies the history and structure of Earth

geomorphology The study of the development and structure of the physical features of Earth's surface

geothermal Of or relating to heat produced internally by Earth

geyser An intermittent eruption from the ground of water that has been geothermally heated to boiling point

gigantism The state of being larger than normal in size or stature

glacial trough A U-shaped valley carved by a glacier

glacier A slow-moving mass of snow and compacted ice on mountains and near the poles

Gondwana The supercontinent formed when a number of major plates collided 600 million years ago

horizontal waterfall A frothing flow of tidal water that is squeezed between two narrowly spaced cliffs

hydrologic cycle The circuit followed by Earth's water, as droplets fall from the sky, are channelled into bodies of water and evaporate back into the sky

hydrothermal vent An area on the seabed from which geothermally heated water emerges

ice cap A large glacier that covers an area of less than 50,000 sq km (19,000 sq miles)

ice sheet A large glacier that covers an area of more than 50,000 sq km (19,000 sq miles)

ice shelf A thick slab of ice from an ice sheet or other large glacier that stretches from the land over nearby water

igneous rock Hot, molten rock (magma) that has cooled and 'frozen' into solid shapes

katabatic winds Gusts that occur when gravity forces high-pressure air to travel from a high elevation to a low elevation down a slope

'king' tide See macro tide

lahar A destructive and/or deadly mudflow that occurs when hot gases, rock and ash from an erupting volcano melt the snow and ice at the summit

limnic eruption A sudden release of deadly carbon dioxide gas from a lake

liquefaction The process whereby waterlogged soil that has been agitated (such as during an earthquake) loses its strength and cohesiveness and is consequently unable to support weight

macro tide A tide that regularly reaches heights of 4 m (13 ft) or above; also known as a 'king' tide

mantle The layer of hot, pressurised rock beneath Earth's surface crust

megathrust earthquake The large release of energy that occurs when two plates in the process of subduction – which have had their movement impeded by friction – suddenly jolt into motion once again

mesocyclone A rising vortex of air that rotates around a vertical axis within a thundercloud

metamorphic rock Sedimentary or igneous rock that has been subjected to heat, pressure or chemistry-altering fluids, which changes the structure of the rock

meteorologist A person who studies the weather

meteotsunami A tsunami caused by a weather-related increase in air pressure over a large body of water

Mid-Atlantic Ridge The 10,000-km (6200-mile) long mountain range that runs down the middle of the Atlantic Ocean

monolith A mountain that is made up of a single type of rock

monsoon A seasonal shift in wind direction that results in dramatic changes in precipitation (predominantly rain)

moraine Deposits of sediment and rock that build up in front, beneath and to the sides of a glacier, which remain long after the glacier has retreated

oasis A fertile area in a desert, where water can be found

onsen A Japanese hot spring, bathing house or spa

palaeontologist A person who studies the fossils of ancient plants, animals and humans

palaeotsunami A tsunami that occurred in the geological past, prior to written records

Pangaea The supercontinent formed when Gondwana collided with the other major plates 250 million years ago

permafrost The layer of soil in polar regions that remains frozen throughout the year

photosynthesis The process whereby green plants use sunlight to manufacture nutrients from carbon dioxide and water

piedmont glacier An alpine glacier that spreads out like a river delta at its terminal end

piping pseudokarst A type of sinkhole that is caused by leaking sewage or stormwater pipes

plate Earth's surface crust is divided into eight major and seven minor sections (plates), which are constantly in motion

plate tectonics The geological process whereby large pieces of Earth's crust (known as plates) slide past each other, collide or pull apart; also known as continental drift

polynia An area of open water that is surrounded by sea ice

primordial Primitive or original

rift A fissure or break in the landscape that is caused by the movement of plates away from each other

Ring of Fire The 40,000-km (25,000-mile) long zone of heightened seismic and volcanic activity that circles the Pacific Ocean

sedimentary rock A type of rock that is made up of sediment deposited over millennia in shallow seas and lakes

seismic Of or relating to an earthquake

seismic sea wave See tsunami

seismograph A machine (often featuring a revolving drum and stylus) that prints out seismic data recorded by a seismometer

seismometer An instrument that detects and measures the strength of earthquakes

shield volcano A broad, dome-like volcano created by the constant outpourings of fluid lava rather than explosive lava

speleologist A person who studies caves

speleothem A cave formation created by deposits of crystalline minerals

spelunker A person who explores caves

stratovolcano A conical volcano created by a build-up of alternating layers of lava and ash; forces beneath the volcano often cause it to erupt explosively

'strike-slip' fault A rupture in Earth's crust where most of the movement is horizontal; also known as a 'transform' fault

stromatolite A rocky mound made from layers of microbes and grainy sediment

subduction The geological process whereby two plates meet, and the heavier one is forced under the lighter one

supercell A thundercloud that features a rotating updraught, or mesocyclone

supernova A giant exploding star

supervolcano A volcano that is capable of ejecting at least 1000 cubic km (240 cubic miles) of ash and rocks in a single eruption

thermophile A heat-loving organism

tidal bore A surge of water that is driven inland and upstream against a river's normal flow, creating waves

tidewater glacier A type of alpine glacier that flows to the ocean or sea

'transform' fault See 'strike-slip' fault

travertine Light-coloured calcareous rock that has been deposited by mineral springs

tributary A stream or river that flows into a larger river or lake

troglobite An animal that spends its entire life in the dark parts of caves

tsunami A large and destructive series of waves that travels across an ocean, sea or lake, which is caused by an earthquake, landslide, volcanic eruption or other force displacing a large body of water; also known as a seismic sea wave

tundra The treeless Arctic area of North America, Europe and Asia

virga Rain or snow that evaporates before it touches the ground

volcanic plug A vertical feeder pipe of solid lava that remains after the rest of an ancient volcano has worn away

vorticity A spinning motion

wadi A dry riverbed usually found in deserts

weather front A boundary between two different air masses

'white smoker' A hydrothermal vent with a pale, chimney-like structure formed from barium, silicon and calcium minerals

zoological Of or relating to the biology and behaviour of animals

INDEX

Italicised page numbers
refer to images.

abyssal plains, 170–1, 310
Acaba, Joe, *254*
acacia (wattle) trees, 135, *302*
Aceh, Sumatra *see* Indian Ocean
    Tsunami (2004)
acid water bodies, 71–2, *73*, 78, 80
Aconcagua mountain, Argentina, 94
aerenchyma (air tubes), 270, 273
Afar Triple Junction, 44
Afghanistan, blizzards in, 279
Africa
    canyons in, 105
    drought and famine in, 293,
        295
        ENSO events and, 274
        fire in, 298
        Great Rift Valley, 43
African Plate, 39, 43–4, 72
aftershocks, 48, 51–3, 310
agriculture, use of fire in, 298, 303
Agulhas Current, 163
Agulhas landslide, 85
Ahaggar Mountains, Algeria, 120,
    121
airliners, 54, 240
Aitape, Papua New Guinea, 175
Akosombo Dam, Volta River, 218
Alamere Falls, California, 200
Alaska, *50*, 51, *131*, *145*
Alaskan Tsunami (1958), 174–5
Al-Aziziya, Libya, 295
Aletsch Glacier, Switzerland, 234,
    234
Alexander of Aphrodisias, 252
Alexander's dark band, 252–3, *253*
algae, on snow, 236, *288–9*, 289
Alicella gigantea, 168
alkaline lakes, 215, 217
Alofaaga Blowholes, Samoa, 184,
    184
Alpine fault, New Zealand, 40, 43,
    43
alpine glaciers, 231–6, *235*, 310
Alps, avalanches in, 287
Altekhali village, India, *273*
Altiplano (central plateau of the
    Andes), 95
altitude sickness *(soroche)*, 94–5
Amazon rainforest, Brazil, *134–5*,
    135, *192*, 193, *308*
Amazon River, 178, 193, 196
amphipods, 168, *169*
Amundsen–Scott South Pole Station,
    140, 142
Ancestral Pueblo people, 101, *101*,
    291
Anchorage, Alaska, earthquake
    in, *50*
Andes mountain chain, 83, 94–5,
    94–5, 97, 102–3
Andrews, Roy Chapman, 13, 124
Angel Falls (Salto Ángel,
    Kerepakupai Merú),
    Venezuela, 200, *201*, *308*
Angel, Jimmie, 200
Angkor, Khmer Empire, 291

animals, 123
    Antarctic and Arctic regions,
        126–7, *144–5*, 145, 147
    at extreme altitudes, 95, *96*, 97
    fires and, *302*, 303
    in calderas, 62
    in caves, 115–17, *116*
    in deserts, 118, *121*, 297
    in forests, 131–2, 134–5, 137,
        138–9
    in lakes and reservoirs, 212,
        214–15
    in oceans and seas, *164–6*,
        168–71, *168–9*, *171*
    in rivers and deltas, *192*, 199
    in snow, 288–9, *288*
    in swamps and wetlands, 221–2,
        222–3, 226, 270, 273
    in tidal bores, 178
    in waterfalls and cascades,
        204–5, 207
    largest and smallest, 34–5
    livestock in droughts, *292–3*,
        294
    on coastlines and seashores,
        184, *187–8*, 189
    on glaciers and sea ice, 236,
        237
    on islands, 150, 153–4
    trapped animals, 115–16, 226,
        227
    volcanoes and, 54
    see also biodiversity; birds;
        invertebrates; reptiles
Annapurna 1 (mountain), 88, 103
Antarctic Bottom Water, 163
Antarctic Circumpolar Current, 163
Antarctic Convergence, 147
Antarctic Ice Sheet, 282
Antarctica, *143*, 233, *308*
    desert in, 126–7, *126–7*
    snow in, 282
    underground lakes, 218
Antelope Canyon, Arizona, 106, *107*
anticyclones, 260
Aoraki/Mount Cook, *43*
apes, 34
Apollo 12 mission, lighning and,
    243
Appalachian Mountains, 90, *91*, 92
Arabian Plate, 39, 43–4, 72
Archaeopteryx fossil, *30*
Archipelago Sea, 150
archipelagos, 150, 310
    see also islands
archways, 184, 186
arcs, 253
Arctic Circle, *144–5*, *144*, 147,
    149–50, 221
Arctic fox, 288, *288*
Arctic Ocean, 140, 161
Arctic tern, 288
Arctic willows, 131
arêtes, 236, 310
Argentinosaurus, 34–5
arid conditions *see* deserts;
    drought
Armero, Colombia, 85
army ants, 137

ash, volcanic, 54, *56–9*, 65
    fertile soil from, 92
    lahars and, 83, 85
    lightning and, *242*
    tuff rock for statues, 153
Ash Wednesday bushfires (1983),
    298
Asia
    canyons in, 103, 105
    deserts in, 123–4
Asian tsunami *see* Indian Ocean
    Tsunami (2004)
asphalt, 226
asteroids, 20, 33, *33*
astronomy *see* space
Aswan Dam, Egypt, 268
Atacama Desert, South America,
    118, *118–19*, 120, 122, 295
Atlantic Ocean, 161
atmosphere, oxygen levels in, 32–3
atmospheric pressure
    aridity and, 292–3, 295
    tsunamis and, 177
    winds and, 259–60
atolls (coral islands), 150, 152, *152*,
    310
    see also coral reefs
auroras, *254–6*, 255, 257
Aurornis xui, 33
Australia
    classified as a continent, 149
    coral reefs in, 189
    deserts in, 120, 122
    drought in, *294*
    dry rivers in, 196, *198*, 199
    El Niño events, 295
    fires in, 298
    floods in, 274
    trees in, 130, 135
Australopithecus afarensis, 44
Australopithecus sediba, 34
avalanches, 287–8
    staying safe, 288–9
Ayers Rock *see* Uluru (Ayers Rock)

B-15 iceberg, 233
Baatara Gorge Waterfall (Balaa
    Gorge Waterfall), Lebanon,
    207, *207*
Baba Gurgur oil field, Iraq, 305
bacteria *see* microorganisms
Badain Jaran Desert, China, 122,
    122–3
Baikal Rift Valley, 44
Baker Three Glacier *see* Lambert
    Glacier, Antarctica
Ball's Pyramid, Lord Howe Island,
    154, 186
balneotherapy, 74
Balteo Glacier, 236
bamboo forest, 86, *86*
Banda Aceh, Sumatra *see* Indian
    Ocean Tsunami (2004)
Bangladesh, cyclones and
    tornadoes in, 263, 267
baobab trees, 135
Barberton Mountain Land, South
    Africa, 90, *90*
barchan dunes, 122

bar-headed geese, 97
BASE jumping, 97, 115, 310
Bath, United Kingdom, 69
Bathurst Bay, Queensland, 263
bats in caves, *116*, 117
Bay of Bengal, cyclones and
    tornadoes in, 263, 267
Bay of Fundy, Canada, tides in,
    177–8, *177*, 209
Bayn Dzak (Flaming Cliffs),
    Mongolia, 124
Beacon of Maracaibo, 246, *246*
Beacon Valley, McMurdo Dry
    Valleys, Antarctica, 231, 233
Beaufort wind-speed scale, 264
Beebe Vent Field, Cayman Trench,
    169
Beijing–Hangzhou Canal, China, 196
Belize, Caribbean, *80*, 81
Bengal delta (Ganges delta), 199,
    199
Bentley, Wilson, *280*, 282
Beppu, Kyushu, Japan, 74
Bering Sea, 169–70
Bermuda, red soil on, 291
Bialowieza Forest, Europe, 135
big bang, 17–18
Big Blowhole, Kiama, 184
billabongs, 218
Bingham, Hiram, 94
biodiversity, 310
    abyssal plains, 170–1
    coastlines and seashores, 186,
        189
    estuaries, 199
    lakes and reservoirs, 212, 214,
        218
    swamps and wetlands, 222
    see also animals; plants
birds
    Antarctic and Arctic regions,
        140, 145, *145*, 147, *147*
    at extreme altitudes, *96*, 97
    Atacama Desert, 118
    coastlines and seashores, 182
    descendants of dinosaurs, 33
    in boreal forests, 132
    in canyons and gorges, *102*, *106*
    in caves and canyons, *102*, 106,
        116–17
    in lakes and reservoirs, 215,
        216, 217–18, *217*
    in snow, 288–9
    in swamps and wetlands, 221–2,
        222–3, 226, 270, *272*, 273
    largest ancient, 35
    on islands, 61, 152, 154, *156–7*
    smallest, 34
    use of natural heat by, 74
    wildfires and, 303
birdwing butterflies, 137
Black Friday bushfires (1939), 298
Black Saturday bushfires (2009),
    298, *302*
'black smokers', *168*, 169, 310
blizzards, *278*, 279–80
blobfish, 167
Blood Falls, Taylor Glacier,
    Antarctica, 203

blowholes, 182, 184
blue heron, 273
blue hyacinth macaw, 221, *222–3*
blue jets (coloured lights), *248*, 249
Blue Lake (Rotomairewhenua), New
 Zealand, 217
Blue Mountains, canyons in, *104*,
 105–6
Blue Nile Gorge, Ethiopia, 105
Blue Nile (river), 191
blue skies, from scattering of light,
 250
blue whales, *34–5*, 35
blue-green algae (cyanobacteria),
 32, *32–3*, 310
Bogotá, Colombia, *276*
bogs, 222, 224, *224*
 fires in, 305
 human remains in, 225–6, *225*
Bondi Beach, Sydney, *258*
boreal forest (northern forest),
 130–2, *131*, 144
Boscia albitrunca, 120
Bosut, Croatia and Serbia, 199
boundaries *see* plate boundaries
boundary currents, 163
Bourtanger Moor, Netherlands,
 226
Bouvet de Lozier, Jean-Baptiste
 Charles, 154
Bouvet Island (Bouvetøya), 154
Boxing Day Tsunami *see* Indian
 Ocean Tsunami (2004)
Boyoma Falls (Stanley Falls),
 Democratic Republic of the
 Congo, 195
Bracken Cave, Texas, *116*, 117
Branson, Richard, 10
Bridal Veil Falls, Colorado, ice-
 climbing at, *210*, 211
Bridge Creek, Oklahoma, 263
Brisbane, Queensland, floods, 274
Brocken spectres, *252*, 253
bromeliads, *136*, 137
Brooks Falls, Katmai National Park
 & Preserve, Alaska, *204–5*
brown bears, *204–5*
Bryde's whale, *164–5*
buckbrush, 303, 305
Buckskin Gulch, Utah, 106
Bunsen, Robert, 67
Burkina Faso, 274
Burning Mountain (Mount Wingen),
 298
bushfires *see* wildfires

C4 carbon fixation, 297
calcite, defined, 310
calcium deposits
 in caves, 109–10, *110*, 112–14,
 114–15
 in coral reefs, 189
 in volcanic areas, 71–2, *71*
 tufa rock, *26*
calderas, 62, 68, 310
 creation of, 62, 64
 towns in, 64, *64–5*, 72
 see also craters
California, earthquakes in, 25
calving, of icebergs, 233, 287, 310
Cameron, James, 167
Canada
 drought in, 292, 297
 Tornado Alley, 267
Canaima National Park, Venezuela,
 200
canals, 196, *197*

Canary Islands, landslides predicted
 in, 85
canyons and gorges, 100–7, *100–7*
 see also submarine caves and
 canyons; valleys
Cape Coral, Florida, 196
capybaras, *223*
Caraballeda, Venezuela, *82*
carbon sinks, 189, 225
Caribbean islands, sinkholes in,
 80, 81
Caribbean Sea, 169, *170*
caribou (reindeer) migration,
 144–5, 145
Carlsbad Caverns, New Mexico, 109
carnivorous plants, 222, *225*
Carolean Death March, 279
carotenoids, 72, 74, *75*, 217, 310
Carrington, Richard Christopher,
 257
Carson, Rachel, 13
cascades *see* waterfalls and
 cascades
Caspian Sea, 212, 214
cataracts *see* waterfalls and
 cascades
Cataracts of the Nile, 191
Catatumbo Lightning (Relámpago
 del Catatumbo), 246, *246*
Catatumbo asteroid, 33, *33*
Caucasus Mountains, caves in, 112
cave diving, 117, *117*
Cave of the Swallows, *114–15*, 115
cave swiftlets, 117
caves and caverns, 108–17, *108–17*
 drilling rig collapse into, *305*
 lava tubes in, 62
 longest, 110
 subterranean rivers in, 196
 see also sea caves; spelunkers
Cayman Trench, Caribbean Sea,
 169
cenotes (water-filled sinkholes),
 80–1, 81, 310
Census of Marine Life, 170–1
Cerro Blanco (White Hill), Sechura
 Desert, Peru, 122
Chalbi Desert, Kenya, *292–3*
Challenger Deep, 167–8
Chamarel Waterfall, Mauritius, 208,
 208–9
chaparral biome, California, 303,
 304, 305
Chelyabinsk meteor, 21–2
Cherrapunji, Meghalaya, India, 268
Cheyenne, Wyoming, 277
Chicago fire, Illinois (1871), 301
Chicha, Chad, dust storms, 126
Chicxulub asteroid, 33, *33*
China
 canyons in, 105
 coal mines burning in, 305
 floods in, 275, 277
Chinchorro people, 118
Chlamydomonas nivalis (snow
 algae), 236, *288–9*, 289
chlorophyll, 72, 74, *75*, 134
Choco–Darien ecoregion, Ecuador,
 136
Christchurch Earthquake (2010),
 53, *83*
Christchurch Earthquake (2011),
 48, *48–9*, 83
Christchurch, New Zealand, 43, *82*
circumzenithal arcs, 253
cirrus clouds, 253
cities *see* towns and cities
Clark, William, 305

Claustral Canyon, Blue Mountains,
 104, *104*
claustrophobia, 109, 310
cliffs, 97, *291*
 see also sea cliffs
Cliffs of Moher, Ireland, 182
climate change
 coal-burning power station
 particles, 293
 coral reefs and, 189
 drought and, 291, 295
 global temperatures, 282, 295
 melting glaciers, 234
 melting ice sheets, 231
 rising sea levels, 152, 189
 sea-ice cover and, 236
 thawing of peat bogs and, 225
climbing, 88, *88*, 92, 95, 97
 frozen waterfalls, *210*, 211
clouds, 243, *243*
 fires and, 300–1, *301*
 light scattering and, 250
cloud-to-cloud lightning, 243
cloud-to-ground lightning, 246
CN Tower, Toronto, lightning and,
 240
coal
 earthquakes and mining of, 53
 underground fires and, 298, 305
coast redwoods, 128, *129*, 130
'coastal paradox', 181
coastlines and seashores, 180–9,
 180–9
 longest coastlines, 189
 measuring coastlines, 181
cobalt-rich crusts, 171
coca leaves, for altitude sickness,
 94
cockles, collecting, 186
coco de mer palm seed, 134, *134*
Colca Canyon, Peru, 102–3, *102*,
 106
cold fronts, 259
coldest places, 88, 142, 282
Coleman, Matt, 280, 282
colloid hydrogels, 227
Colorado River, Arizona, 100–2
comets, 20
condors, 96, 97, *102*, 106
cone geysers, 68–9, 310
Congo River, *192*, 193–5
conifer trees, 128, *129*, 130, 132,
 134, *137*
 fire and, *299*, 303
constellations, 310
 see also stars
continental drift (plate tectonics),
 23, 25, *28–9*, 33, 167, 310
 faults and rifts and, 38–44
 islands and, 149, 152
 Japan at junction of four plates,
 51
 mountain formation and, 88,
 90, 92
continents, 23, 149
Convention on Wetlands of
 International Importance, 222
convergent boundaries, 39, 43
Coongie Lakes, South Australia, 220
Copper Canyon, Mexico, 102
coral islands (atolls), 150, 152, *152*,
 310
coral reefs, *171*, *188*, 189
Coral Triangle, 189
Corcovado National Park, Costa
 Rica, *138–9*
core (Earth), 23, *23*, 144

Coriolis effect, 260
coronal mass ejections (CMEs), 257
Cotahuasi Canyon, Peru, 102
Cousteau, Jacques-Yves, *80*
cows killed by lightning, 249
Cox's Bazar, Bangladesh, 182
crassulacean acid metabolism
 (CAM), 297
Crater Highlands area, Tanzania, 62
crater lakes, 61–2, *62*, 64, 217–18
craters, *33*, 310
 see also calderas
crayfish, in caves, 116
crepuscular rays, *238*, 250
cross-sea bridges, 180
crust (Earth), 23–4, *23*
cryoconite holes, 236, 310
Cryogenian period, 31
cryophiles, 289, 310
Cueva de los Cristales, Mexico,
 24–5, 25, 114
Cumbre Vieja volcano, La Palma,
 Canary Islands, 85
cumulonimbus clouds
 (thunderclouds), 243, *243*,
 249, 263–4
currents *see* oceans and seas
cyanobacteria (blue-green algae),
 32, *32–3*, 310
cyclones, *258–67*, 259–60, 263–4,
 267, 274
 European windstorms, *276*, 277
 origin of word, 259
cyclonic storms, 260, 277, 279

Dallol geothermal field, Ethiopia,
 44, 72, *73*
dams *see* reservoirs and dams
Danakil Depression (rift valley),
 72, *73*
Darwin, Charles, 31
Dean's Blue Hole, Bahamas, *186*
Death Valley, California, 118, 295
'Death Zone' (extreme altitudes), 88
Decade for Natural Disaster
 Reduction (1990s), 61
'Decade Volcanoes', 61
deciduous trees, 134
Deepsea Challenger (submersible),
 167
deep-sea creatures, *166*
deep-sea mining prospects, 171
deep-sea trenches *see* oceans and
 seas
Del Norte Coast Redwoods State
 Park, California, *129*
deltas, 199, 310
 origin of word, 191
 see also rivers
Dendrosenecio kilimanjari, 92, *93*
Denmark Strait Cataract, 208
Denver, Colorado, 277
desert pavement, 120
deserts, 118–27, *118–27*, 294, 295,
 296
 desert lakes, 214–15
 world's largest, 127
 see also dust storms; sand dunes
dessication, defined, 310
 see also deserts; drought
Dévoluy Mountains, France, *108*
Devon Island, Canadian Arctic, 149
Dhaulagiri I (mountain), 103
Dinaric Alps, 203
dinosaurs, 33, *33*, 34–5, *34*, 124,
 124
'dip-slip' faults, 39, 310

Disko Bay, Greenland, *233*
divergent boundaries, 39
diving *see* cave diving; scuba diving
Dolina Geizerov (Valley of the
   Geysers), *66*, 67–8
Dome A, East Antarctic Ice Sheet,
   142
Don Juan Pond, McMurdo Dry
   Valleys, Antarctica, 214, *215*
Donjek Glacier, Kluane National
   Park and Reserve, Canada,
   232, 233
Doppler weather radar, 264
double islands, 150
Douglas fir trees, 130
Drake Passage, *160–1*
Dream Lake, Colorado, 236
driver ants, 137
drought, *290–4*, *291–3*, 295, *296–7*,
   297
   see also dust storms; rainfall
dry caves, 112
Dry Falls Cataract, Washington
   State, 209
dry rivers, 120, 196, *198*, 199
dry slot canyons, 107, *107*
Dude Fire, Arizona (1990), *299*
dugongs, *188*
Dunaliella salina, 217
Dune 7, Namib Desert, 122
dunes *see* sand dunes
dust devils, 264
dust storms, 124, *125*, 126, 291,
   295, 297, *297*
Düzce earthquake (1999), 40, *41*
dwarf planets, 20
dykes, *98–9*

eagles, 106
Earth, *16–18*, 18–19
   extremes in, 10–13, 308–9
   internal structure, 22–9, *23*
   rotation of, 47
earthquakes, 47–53
   faults and, 39–40, *41*, 43
   landslides and, 83
   Reservoir-Induced Seismicity, 218
   sinkholes and, 81, 83
   tectonic plates and, 25
   volcano belt, 64–5
   see also aftershocks; foreshocks;
      megathrust earthquakes
East African Rift, 43–4, *45*, 218
East Antarctic Ice Sheet, 142
East Pacific Rise, 168–9
Easter Island (Rapa Nui), 152–3
echolocation, 117
Eiffel Tower, Paris, lightning and,
   240, *240*
'eight-thousanders', 88, 310
El Capitan, Yosemite National Park,
   97
El Niño-Southern Oscillation
   (ENSO), *153*
   drought and, 293, 295
   monsoons and, 273–4
El Reno, Oklahoma tornado (2013),
   266, 267
El Tatio, Atacama Desert, Chile, 68
El Valle de Antón, Panama, 64
electrical discharges, 257
   see also lightning
elephants, *302*
   cleaning debris in Sumatra, *50*
   salt caves and, 117, *117*
Elliot, William (Captain), 149
elves (coloured lights), 249

Emerald Island (phantom island),
   149
Emerald Lake, Colorado, 236
emperor penguins, 147, *147*, *255*,
   288
enclosed canyons, 102
endemic species, 154, 310
endorheic basins, 214, 310
English Harbour, Antigua, 170
Enhanced Fujita (EF) scale, 264
ENSO events *see* El Niño-Southern
   Oscillation (ENSO)
ephemeral, defined, 310
ephemeral lakes, 218
epicentre, 47–8, 51, 310
Erasmus of Formiae, St, 257
erosion
   after land clearing, 297
   by ice, 235–6
   coastlines and seashores, 182
   waterfalls and, 200
eruptions *see* geysers; volcanoes
estuaries, 199, 310
Ethiopian highlands, rainfall in, 268
Étretat, France, *180*
eucalyptus trees, 130, *131*, 135,
   303
eukaryotes, 32, 310
Eurasian Plate, 23, 25, 44, 51
European Alps, 92, *93*
European bison, 135
European windstorms, *276*, 277
evolution, *30*, 31–2, 34
   fire and, 303
   human, 34, 44
   of wood, 128
   see also fossils
'exploding lakes', 217
extinctions, 31–3, *33*
extreme record holders, list of,
   308–9
extremophiles, 236, 289, 310
Eyjafjallajökull volcano, Iceland,
   54, *242*

The Fang, Vail, Colorado, ice-
   climbing, 211, *211*
Farafra Oasis, Egypt, *122*
farming, use of fire in, 298, 303
faults, 38–43, *42–3*, 310
   see also earthquakes
fennec foxes, 118, *121*
fens *see* swamps and wetlands
finches, as evidence of natural
   selection, 31
fire whirls (fire devils) and fire
   tornadoes, 301, *301*, 303
fires, underground, 298, 305
   see also wildfires
firestorms, 300–1, 310
   from bombing campaigns, 303
fish, 150, 152, *166*, *169*
   ascent of waterfalls by, *204–5*,
      207
   ENSO events and, 273
   evolution of, 34
   fossils, 30
   in lakes and reservoirs, 214, 217
   in swamps and wetlands, 222
Fish River Canyon, Namibia, 105
Fishlake National Forest, Utah,
   132, *133*
Fjallsjökull glacier, Iceland, *230–1*
flamingoes, 217, *217*
flash flooding, 270, *270*, 273
flooded lands *see* swamps and
   wetlands

floods, 193–4, 268, *269–76*, 270,
   273–5, 277
   cyclones and, 263
   deadliest, 275, 277
   defences against, 275, 277
   ENSO events and, 274
   flash flooding, 270, *270*, 273
   from monsoons, *269*
   glacial flooding, 209
   wetlands as mitigators of, 221–2
   see also storms
Florida, United States, sinkholes in,
   78, *78–9*, 80
Florida Everglades, 221
flowstone, 110, *110*, 114, 310
fogbows, 253
Fordland, Missouri, tornado near,
   267
foreshocks, 40, 47, 52–3, 310
forest fires *see* wildfires
forests, 128–37, *128–37*
   see also trees
fossils, *30–1*, 31–4
   bacteria in rocks, 90
   dinosaurs, 34–5, *34*, 124, *124*
   human evolution, 34, 44
   petrified forests, 128, *128*
   snakes, 35
   trapped animals, 115–16, 226,
      227
   see also dinosaurs
fountain geysers, 68, 310
Fountain Paint Pot, Yellowstone
   National Park, *70*, 71
fractals, in measuring coastlines,
   181
frazil ice, 211
Frying Pan Lake, New Zealand,
   69, 71
fulgurite, 249, 310
fumaroles, 68, 72, *73*, 310

Gagarin, Yuri, 10
Galápagos Islands, 31, 168–9
galaxies, 20–1
Ganges delta (Bengal delta), 199,
   199
Garrett, Tim (Dr), 282
Gates of Hell, Congo River, 194–5
gemstones, 25, 27
General Sherman (giant sequoia),
   132
Geoffroy's side-necked turtle, *192*
geologists, 310
   see also rocks and minerals
geomagnetic poles, 144
geomagnetic storms, 257
geomorphology, defined, 310
geothermal phenomena, 67–77
   geothermal, defined, 310
geyserite, 68
geysers, 66–9, *67–9*, 72, 310
giant groundsels, 92, *93*
giant otter, *223*
giant sequoias, 132, 134, 303
Giant's Causeway, Northern Ireland,
   27, *27*
gibber (desert pavement), 120
gigantism, 168, 310
Gilboa, New York State, 128
ginkgo trees, 128
Glacier National Park, British
   Colombia, *251*
glaciers, 92, *93*, 149, *230–7*, 231–6,
   286, 287, 310
   blue colour, 217, 231
   glacial flooding, 209

'glacial rebound', 150
   glacial troughs, 236, 310
   in Antarctic Desert, 126
   landslides and, 83
   movement of, 233, 287
Glasgow, Montana, *262*
glass squid, *166*
global teleconnections, 293, 295
global warming *see* climate change
glories (fogbows), 253
GNS Science, 43, 48, 53
Gobi Desert, *12*, 13, 123–4
   dust storms, 295, 297
gold, 40, 94
Golovanovo, Russia, *300*
Goma, Democratic Republic of the
   Congo, 62
Gondwana, 23–4, 310
Gonzales, Texas, *274*
Gopalganj district, Bangladesh, 277
gorges *see* canyons and gorges
Gouffre Berger, France, 112, *113*
Gouffre de la Baume des Crêtes,
   Verneau cave system, France,
   110
Gouffre Mirolda, France, 112
Grand Canal, China, 196
Grand Canal, Venice, *197*
Grand Canyon, Arizona, *100–1*,
   101–2, 106
   thunderstorms, *247*
Grand Coulee riverbed, Washington
   State, 209
Grand Geyser, Yellowstone National
   Park, 68
Grand Prismatic Spring, Yellowstone
   National Park, 72, 74, *75*
grassland fires (savanna fires), *302*,
   303
Graballe Man, 226
Great Alaskan Earthquake (1964), *50*
Great Australian Bight, cliff faces
   at, 97
Great Barrier Reef Marine Park,
   189, *169*
Great Blizzard of 1888 (Great White
   Hurricane), 279
Great Chagos Bank, Indian Ocean,
   152
Great Chilean Earthquake (1960),
   47–8, 51–2
   Easter Island statues and, *153*
Great Dividing Range, Australia,
   90, 92
great egrets, *272*
Great Fire of London (1666), 301
Great Fire of Rome (64 AD), 301
Great Geysir, Haukadalur Valley,
   Iceland, 67
Great Glen Fault, Scotland, *42*, 43
great grey owl, 132, *132*
Great Hanshin Earthquake, Kobe,
   Japan (1995), *46*
Great Lakes, Africa, 214
Great Lakes, North America, 214,
   236
Great Otway National Park,
   Australia, *131*
Great Rift Valley, 43
Great Vasyugan Mire, 222, 224
Green Bridge of Wales,
   Pembrokeshire, Wales, 184,
   186
Green Swamp, North Carolina, *225*
Greenland, 149, *149*, 182, *183*
Greenland Ice Sheet, 102, 231, 282
Greenland Sea, 208

grey whales, 145, 184
griffon vulture, 97, 106
ground blizzards, 279
Gua Nasib Bagus (Good Luck Cave),
    Sarawak, Borneo, 109
Guadalupe River, Texas, *274*
Guaíra Falls, Paraná River, Brazil–
    Paraguay border, 211
Guangxi province, Dashiwei
    Tiankeng, 80
Guatemala City, 81, *82*
Guinan, Eastern Samar province,
    Philippines, 260, 263
Gulf of St Lawrence, Canada, 199
Gulf Stream, 163
Gulfs of Finland and Bothnia, Baltic
    Sea, 163
Gunung Mulu National Park,
    Sarawak, Borneo, 109
Gurbantünggüt Desert, China, 123
Gyala Peri (mountain), 103
gypsum crystals, 114

habitats *see* animals; plants
hail, *276*, 277
Hail Research Station, Kericho,
    Kenya, 277
Haiti Earthquake (2010), *52–3*, 53
Haiyuan County, China, landslides
    in, 83
halite (salt) crystals in caves,
    114–15
Hallam, Nebraska tornado (2004),
    267
Halley's Comet, 20
haloes, 253
Hang Son Doong (Mountain River
    Cave), Vietnam, 109, *109*, 196
Hannibal, 287
Hanoi, Vietnam, *269*
'harbour waves' *see* tsunamis
hatchetfish, *166*
Hawaii, tsunami deaths in, 47
Hay, New South Wales, *294*
Heart Mountain, Wyoming, 85
heat *see* hottest places
Henley-on-Todd Regatta, *198*
Hercules beetles, 137, *137*
Hickey, John, 215
hills *see* mountains
Himalayan mountain range, *24–5*,
    25, 88, 92
    canyons in, 103, *103*
    rainfall in, 268
Himalayan yak, 95, *96*
Hindu Kush mountain range, 88
Hirondellea gigas, 168
Hiroshima, Japan, atomic bomb
    firestorm, 303
Hoggar Mountains *see* Ahaggar
    Mountains, Algeria
Holt, Missouri, 270
hominids *see* human remains
Homo floresiensis, 34
Homo sapiens, 34
Honshu Island, Japan, 51
'horizontal waterfalls', 178, *178*,
    208–9, 310
Horn of Africa, 43–4
'hot spots', volcanoes above, 54, 58
hot springs and pools, 69, 71, *71*, *75*
    Japanese macaques in, 74, *76–7*
hottest places, 72, 114, 118, 169,
    295
Hubbard Glacier, Alaska, *232*, 233–4
Hubble Space Telescope, *11*
Hukou Waterfall, China, *202*, 203

human activities
    dust storms and, 297
    earthquakes and, 53
    floods and, 273
    hurricanes and, 221
    landslides and, 83
    sinkholes and, 81
    see also climate change
human remains, 34, 44
    in peat bogs, 225–6, *225*
Hurricane Isaac (2012), 199
Hurricane John (Typhoon John)
    (1994), 34, 260
Hurricane Katrina (2005), 221, 263
hurricanes, 260
    see also cyclones
hydroelectric projects, 195, 200,
    203, 211, 218
hydrogen sulfide *see* sulfurous
    gases
hydrologic cycle, 270, 310
    see also water
hydrothermal vents, 168–9, *168–9*,
    171, 310
Hyperion (tree), 128, 130

ice ages, 31
ice caps, 233, 287, 310
ice caves, *108*, *230–1*, *286*
ice crystals, 253, 299
    see also snowflakes
ice sheets, 140, 142, 231, 233, 287,
    310
    see also Antarctic Ice Sheet;
        Greenland Ice Sheet
ice shelves, 233, 287, 310
icebergs, 233, *233*, 287, 310
ice-climbing, *210*, 211, *211*
igneous rocks, 27, *27*, *98–9*, 310
Iguazú Falls, Argentina–Brazil
    border, *206*, 207
Ijen volcano, Java, Indonesia, *73*
Ik Kil Cenote, Yucatán, Mexico,
    80–1
Illinois, moraines and, 235
Inaccessible Island, 153–4
Incas, at Machu Picchu, 94, *94–5*
India
    abandoned coal mines burning
        in, 305
    cyclones and tornadoes, 267–8
    monsoon festival, 273, *273*
Indian Ocean
    coral islands in, 150, 152, *152*
    tropical cyclones in, 263
Indian Ocean Tsunami (2004)
    (Boxing Day earthquake,
    Sumatra–Andaman Earthquake
    and tsunami), *50*, 51, 172, 174
Indiana tornado (1925), *266*, 267
Indo-Australian Plate, 23, 25,
    39–40, 43
Indonesia
    coral reefs in, 189
    drought in, 293, 295
Indonesia fires (1997), 298
Indus Gorge, Pakistan, 103, 105,
    105, 195
industrial melanism, 34, *34*
Inga Falls, Democratic Republic of
    the Congo, 203
insects *see* invertebrates
Institute of Geological and Nuclear
    Sciences (GNS Science), 43,
    48, 53
inter-cloud lightning, 243
interference, in rainbows, 252–3

Intergovernmental Panel on
    Climate Change (IPCC), 295
International Association of
    Volcanology and Chemistry
    of the Earth's Interior, 61
International Scale of River
    Difficulty, 194
International Seabed Authority,
    171
inundations *see* floods
invertebrates
    Antarctic and Arctic regions,
        147
    at extreme altitudes, 97
    butterfly wing, *306*
    butterfly wing scales, *306*
    in caves, 116
    in deserts, 118
    in estuaries, 199
    in forests, 137, *137*
    in oceans and seas, 168, *168–9*
    in swamps and wetlands, 222
    on dunes, 123
    on glaciers, 236
    prehistoric, 35
    smallest, 34
    volcanoes and, 54, 61
Ionian Sea, *265*
ionosphere, 255
Iran, blizzards in, 279
Ireland, peat bogs in, *224*
islands, *148–53*, 149–54, *155–7*
    islands-on-an-island, 150
    lakes on, 212, *212–13*
    largest islands, 154
    phantom islands, 149
    volcanoes as, 58, *61*
isostatic depression, 231
Istanbul, Turkey, 40
Italian Tsunami (1908), 175, *176*
Itaipu Dam project, 211
Ivrea, Italy, 235–6
Izmit earthquake (1999), 40

Jacob Riis Park, New York City, 247
Jakobshavn Glacier (Sermeq
    Kujalleq), Greenland, 233,
    233
James Price Point, Western
    Australia, 34–5
Japanese macaques, bathing, 74,
    76–7
Japanese tsunamis (1707, 1896,
    1972), 172
    see also Tohoku Earthquake and
        tsunami (2011)
Java, Indonesia, 150, *150*, 175
Jewel Cave, South Dakota, 110
Jiaozhou Bay Bridge, East China
    Sea, 180
Jigokudani onsen, Japan, 74, *76–7*
Jordan Rift Valley, 43
Joshua Tree National Park,
    California, *296*
Juan de Fuca Ridge, Pacific Ocean,
    168
'Judas' stack, Twelve Apostles,
    Australia, 186, *187*
Jupiter, 19, *19*

K2 (mountain), 88, *88*
Kabar Taal, India, 218
Kabir Kuh mountain ridge, Iran, 85
Kaffeklubben Island (Qeqertaat),
    149–50
Kaifeng, China, 275
Kaiko (submersible), 168

Kakadu National Park, Northern
    Territory, 220, *220–1*, *272*
Kalahari Desert, southern Africa,
    120, *294*
Kalaupapa Sea Cliffs, Molokai,
    Hawaii, 182
Kali Gandaki Gorge, Nepal, 103
Kamchatka Peninsula, Russia, 54,
    67–8
Kansas tornado (2007), *266*
Kanton Island, western Pacific, 152
Karakoram mountain range, 25,
    88, *105*
Kariba Gorge, *219*
Karst landscapes, 80–1
katabatic winds, 259, *259*, 310
Kati Thanda–Lake Eyre, Australia,
    218, *219*
Kawio Barat, Sulawesi, 58
kayaking, *194–5*, 195
Kaynasli, Turkey, *41*
Kazumura Cave, Kilauea, Big
    Island, Hawaii, 62
Kenyan drought (2011), *292–3*
Kerepakupai Merú (Angel Falls,
    Salto Ángel), Venezuela, 200,
    201
Kern family, carried by tornado,
    267
Khairpur Nathan Shah, Pakistan,
    274–5
khamsin (wind), 295
Khao Sam Roi Yot National Park,
    Thailand, *114–15*
Khatanga, Siberia, 131
Khmer Empire, 291
Khone Falls (Khone Phapheng
    Falls), Mekong River, Laos,
    200, 203
Kickapoo, Kansas, tornado at, 267
Kifuka, Democratic Republic of the
    Congo, 240
Kilauea, Big Island, Hawaii, 54,
    62, *63*
King Sound, Derby, 178
'king' tides *see* macro tides
Kinshasa, Democratic Republic of
    the Congo, 247
Kitum Cave, Kenya, 117, *117*
Kluane National Park and Reserve,
    Canada, *232*, 233
Kobe earthquake *see* Great
    Hanshin Earthquake, Kobe,
    Japan (1995)
Koelbjerg Woman, 226
Kola Superdeep Borehole, Russia,
    24
Kolihapeltis (trilobite), *30*
komodo dragons, 150, *151*
Krakatau, Indonesia, 59, 65, 174
Krubera-Voronja Cave, Georgia,
    112, 115
Kuiper Belt, 20
Kwajalein Atoll, Marshall Islands,
    152

La Brea Fire, California (2009), *304*
La Brea Tar Pits, Los Angeles, 226,
    227
La Niña
    drought and, 293
    monsoons and, 273–4
La Palma island, Canary Islands, 85
La Paz, Bolivia, 94
La Rinconada, Peru, 94
lahars (mudflows), 64, 83, *84–5*,
    85, 310

Lake Baikal, Siberia, 44, 212, *212–13, 309*
Lake District, England, 236
Lake Don Juan, McMurdo Dry Valleys, Antarctica, 214, *215*
Lake Eyre *see* Kati Thanda–Lake Eyre, Australia
Lake Geneva, tsunami on, 177
Lake Huron, waterfall beneath, 209
Lake Kariba, Zambia and Zimbabwe, 218, *219*
Lake Kivu, Great Lakes, Africa, 217–18
Lake Magadi, Kenya, 215, *216*, 217
Lake Malawi (Lake Nyasa), Great Lakes, Africa, 214
Lake Michigan, North America, 214
Lake Monoun, 'limnic eruptions', 217–18
Lake Natron, Tanzania, 215, 217
Lake Nyos, Cameroon (the 'Killer Lake'), 64, 217–18
Lake Ohau, New Zealand, 217
Lake Ontario, North America, 214
Lake Pukaki, New Zealand, 217
Lake Retba (Lac Rose), Senegal, *216*, 217
Lake Superior, North America, 214
Lake Tanganyika, Great Lakes, Africa, 214
Lake Taupo, New Zealand, 64
Lake Tekapo, New Zealand, 217
Lake Þingvallavatn, Iceland, *22*
Lake Toba, Sumatra, 64–5, 150
Lake Turkana (Lake Rudolf), Great Lakes, Africa, 214–15
Lake Victoria, Great Lakes, Africa, 214, *215*
Lake Volta, Ghana, 218
Lake Vostok, Antarctica, 218
'lake-effect' snow, 282
lakes, 212, *212–17, 214–15, 217–18, 219*
    faults and rifts and, *42–3*, 44
    hot pools, 69, 71
    in Antarctica, *126–7*
    in deserts, *122–3, 126–7*
    largest, 214
    lochs in Scotland, 43
    on islands, 212, *212–13*
    paternoster lakes, 236
    tsunamis and, 177
    see also reservoirs and dams
Laki volcano, Iceland, 62
Lambert, Bruce, 235
Lambert Glacier, Antarctica, 235–6, 287
lammergeier, 96, 97
Lanceola, 169
land use *see* human activities
landslides, *82*, 83, 85, 174
    under water, 85, 175, 177
Langjökull glacier, Iceland, *286*
Lanzhou, China, *195*
L'Aquila, Italy earthquake (2009), 52–3, *52*
larch trees, 130–1
Latin America, canyons in, 102
Laurentide Ice Sheet, 233, 235–6
lava, *36, 60*, 61–2, *63*
    see also volcanoes
lava tubes, 62
Leaena's Breath Cave, Nullarbor Plain, Australia, 116
lemurs, 153, *153*
leopard seals, 147
Lewis, Meriwether (Captain), 305

Lhotse (mountain), *89*
lichens, in Antarctica, 127
life on earth, origin of, 31
light *see* sunlight
lightning, 240, *240–8*, 243, 246–7, 249
    danger and damage from, 246–7, *247*
    fires caused by, 249, 298, 303
    nitrogen fixed by, 249
    staying safe in, 249
    volcanoes and, *242*
    see also cumulonimbus clouds (thunderclouds)
limestone *see* calcium deposits; sinkholes
limnic eruptions, 217–18, 311
Lindgren, Scott, 195
liquefaction, 48, 81, 83, *83*, 311
Little Ice Age, 291
livestock, drought and, *292–3, 294*
Livingstone, David, 203
Livingstone Falls, Democratic Republic of the Congo, 195
llamas, 95
Loch Ness, Scotland, 43
lochs *see* lakes
loess (clay-like soil), 193, 203
London fires (1212 and 1666), 301, 303
Lord Howe Island stick insects, 137, 154
Los Angeles earthquake (1857), 40, 186
Lucy (hominid), 44

Maasai Mara National Reserve, Kenya, *302*
Machu Picchu, 94, *94–5*
Mackinac Waterfall, beneath Lake Huron, 209
McMurdo Dry Valleys, Antarctica, 126, *126–7*, 214, *215*, 233
McMurdo Station, Antarctica, 140
macro tides ('king' tides), 178, *179*, 311
Madagasgar, 153, *153*
Magellanic clouds, *20–1*, 21
magma (molten rock), 27, 61, 65
    geothermal phenomena and, 54, 58, 67–77
magnetic poles, 142, 144–5
    auroral zones centered on, 255, 257
magnetosphere, 257
Malaspina glacier, Alaska, 235, *235*
Malay Archipelago, 150
Maldives, 152, *152*, 181–2, 189
maleo bird, nests in hot ground, 74
mammals *see* animals
Mammoth Cave system, Kentucky, 112, *112*
manganese nodules, 171
mangroves, 186, *187*, 189
Manikganj District, Bangladesh, *267*
mantle (Earth), 23–4, *23*, 311
Mariana Trench, 24–5, 39
    Challenger Deep, 167, *167*
marine lakes, *148*
marine waterfalls *see* submarine 'waterfalls'
Mars, 19, *19*
marshlands *see* swamps and wetlands
marsupial lion fossils, 116
Marysville, Victoria, *302*

Maujit Qaqarssuasia (the 'Thumbnail'), Greenland, 182
Mauna Kea volcano, Hawaii, 58, 92
Mauritius, 208, *208–9*
Mayans, 81, 291
Medieval Climate Anomaly, 291
megathrust earthquakes, 39, 47–8, 51, 174, 311
Mekong River, Laos, 203
Mer de Glace, French Alps, *93*
Mercury, 18–19, *18*
mesocyclones, 263–4, 300–1, 311
mesopelagic zone, *166*
Messina, Sicily, 175, *176*
Metallogenium, 171
metamorphic rocks, 27, 311
meteorites, 20
meteorologists, defined, 311
meteors, 20–1, *21*, 177
meteotsunami, 177, 311
methane, 225, 305
Mexican free-tailed bats, *116*, 117
microorganisms
    Atacama Desert, South America, 118
    cryophiles, 289
    early life on Earth, 31–2, 34
    fossilised in rocks, 90
    in Antarctica, 127, 203, 233
    in hydrothermal vents, 169
    in snowflakes, 280
    in swamps and wetlands, 222
    manganese nodules and, 171
    thermophiles, 72, 74, *75*, 311
Mid-Atlantic Ridge, 24–5, 44, 58, 94, 311
Mid-Oceanic Ridge, 94, 168–9, 170
Milky Way galaxy, 13, *18*, 20–1
Millennium Drought ('Big Dry') (1995–2009), 295
minerals *see* rocks and minerals
mining
    deep-sea mining prospects, 171
    earthquakes and, 53
    sinkholes and, 81
minor planets, 20
Miraflores Locks, Panama Canal, *197*
mires *see* bogs
Mississippi River, 199
mistral (wind), 259
mists, light scattering and, 250
Moderate Resolution Imaging Spectroradiometer (MODIS), 260
Modified Mercalli Intensity scale, 48
Mojave Desert, *296*
Mojave River, California, 199
Molokai, Hawaii, 182
Monaco, coastline of, 181
Mono Lake, California, *26*
monoliths, 97, *98–9, 244–5*, 311
monsoons, *269*, 274, 277, 291, 311
    monsoon festivals, 273, *273*
    monsoon forests, 135, 137
    origin of word, 268
Moon, 19, 177
moon haloes, 253
moraines, 235–6, 311
Morainic Amphitheatre of Ivrea, 236
Morecombe Bay, England, 186, *227*
Moreton Island, Queensland, 182, *183*
Moscow city fire (1812), 303

Mosi-oa-Tunya (Victoria Falls), Zambia–Zimbabwe border, *202, 203*
Mount Chimborazo, Ecuador, 94–5
Mount Cook *see* Aoraki/Mount Cook
Mount Etna, Sicily, Italy, *60*, 61–2
Mount Everest, 25, 58, 88, *89*
Mount Hasan, Turkey, 13
Mount Huascarán, Peru, 83, 287–8
Mount Kilimanjaro, Tanzania, 92, *93, 309*
Mount Merapi, Indonesia, 55
Mount Nyiragongo, Democratic Republic of the Congo, 61–2, *62*
Mount Pago, Papua New Guinea, 74
Mount Pelée, Martinique, Caribbean, 54
Mount Pinatubo, Philippines, 54, *56–7*, 65, *84*, 85
Mount Rainier, Washington State, 64, 282
Mount St Helens, Washington State, 65, 83
Mount Tambora, Sumbawa, Indonesia, 54
Mount Tarawera, New Zealand, 69, 71–2
Mount Tate, Toyama Prefecture, Japan, 282
Mount Taupo, New Zealand, 64
Mount Tempest, Moreton Island, Queensland, 182, *183*
Mount Unzen, Kyushu, Japan, 174
Mount Washington, Appalachian Mountains, 92
Mount Wingen (Burning Mountain), 298
mountain ash (swamp gum), 130, *131*
mountain climbing *see* climbing
Mountain River Cave, Vietnam, 113
mountains, 39, 88–99
    highest on land, 90
    submerged, 94
    see also canyons and gorges; valleys; volcanoes
mud pools, 68, *70*, 71–2, *72*, 74
mudflows *see* lahars (mudflows)
Multi-Angle Snowflake Camera, 282
mustelids, 131–2
Mykines, Faroe Islands archipelago, *156–7*

Nagano Mountains, Honshu, Japan, 74, *76–7*
Nagasaki Bay, Japan, 177
Naica Mine, Mexico, 114
Namib Desert, Africa, 122
Nanga Parbat, Pakistan, 97, 103, 105
Nanjing, China, 277
Nankoweap Canyon, Arizona, *101*
Napoleon I, 303
National Aeronautics and Space Administration (NASA), 13, 20
natural selection, 31, 34
Natural Trap Cave, Bighorn Mountains, Wyoming, 115
Navajo people, 97, *98–9, 107*
Nazca Plate, 47
Neptune (planet), 19, *19*
nerpa (freshwater seal), 212

The Netherlands, floods in, *276*, 277
Nettilling Lake, Baffin Island, Canada, 212
Nevado del Ruiz, Cordillera Central region, Colombia, 83, 85
New Caledonia, 154
New Orleans, Louisiana, 263
Newcastle Earthquake (1989), 53
Ngiri-Tumba-Maindombe wetland, 222
Ngorongoro Crater, 62
Niagara Falls, Canada–United States border, 200, *284–5*
Nightingale Island, 153–4
Nile river and delta, *190–1*, 191, 193, 199
  flooding, 268, *269*, 273
Ningxia, China, landslides in, 83
nitrogen fixation, by lightning, 249
Nohoch Nah Chich caves, Mexico, 117
Nordaustlandet, Norway, *237*
nor'easters, 279, *281*
North American Plate, 23, 25, 40, 44, 51
North Anatolian Fault, 40
North Carolina tornado (2011), *266*
North Carolina, treed bogs in, 227
North Celestial Pole, 142
North Geomagnetic Pole, 144
North Magnetic Pole, 144
North Pole Dome, Western Australia, 34
North Pole (North Geographic Pole), 140–7, *141*, *144–5*
North Water Polynia, 145
northern forest *see* boreal forest
northern lights (aurora borealis), *254*, 255, *256*
Nubian Plate, 43–4
Nullarbor Plain, Australia, 97, 115–16
nunataks (exposed peaks), 233
Nuptse (mountain), 89
Nuuk, Greenland, 149, *149*

Oahu, Hawaii, *158*
Oak Ridges Moraine, Ontario, 235
oasis, defined, 311
obliquely convergent boundaries, 43
ocean volcanoes *see* submarine volcanoes
'ocean-effect' snow, 282
oceans and seas, *160–71*, 161–71
  currents, 161, 163
  storm surges, 263
  trenches, 167–8
  waterfalls dropping into, 200
  waves, *158*, 163
  world's largest seas, 171
  see also coastlines and seashores; sea caves; sea cliffs; sea ice
ocelot, *223*
oil fields, 120, 305
oilbirds, 117
Okavango Delta, Botswana, *228–9*
Oklahoma, tornadoes in, 267
Old Faithful, Yellowstone National Park, *68–9*, 69
Olduvai Gorge, Tanzania, 105
Olkhon Island, Lake Baikal, Siberia, *212–13*
onsen (hot springs), 74, *76–7*, 120, 122, *122*, 311
Oort Cloud, 20

open canyons, 102, 169
open shafts *see* sinkholes
Orissa (Odisha), India, *260*
outlet glaciers, *230–1*
overhangs, world's highest, 97
Oviraptor, 124
oxbow lakes, 218
oxygen levels in atmosphere, 32–3, 305
ozone, 249

Pacific Ocean, 161
  coral reefs, 150, 152, 189
  seabed, 24
  tsunamis in, 172
  see also Ring of Fire
Pacific Plate, 23–5, 39–40, 43, 51, 65, 167
Pakistan Floods (2010), 274, *274–5*
palaeontologists, defined, 311
  see also fossils
palaeotsunamis, 177, 311
palm trees, 134
Pamukkale, Cokelez Mountains, Turkey, 71, *71*
Panama Canal, 196, *197*
Pando (clump of trees), 132, *133*
Pangaea, 24, 33, 311
Pantanal, South America, 221–2, *222–3*
paperbark trees, *221*
Papua New Guinea Tsunami (1998), *174–5*, 175
papyrus plants, *190–1*
Paraná River, Brazil–Paraguay border, 211
Paratethys Sea, 214
Parker Dam, Colorado River, Arizona, 218
Patagonian Ice Sheet, 233–4
paternoster lakes, 236
peaks *see* mountains; volcanoes
Pearl River delta, China, *198*, 199
peat bogs *see* bogs
penguins, 147, *147*, *255*, 288
peppered moth, 34, *34*
Perito Moreno glacier, Argentina, 234, *234–5*
permafrost, 144–5, 311
Persian Gulf, 163
Peru, 102–3, *102*, 273–4
Peshtigo fire, Wisconsin (1871), *300–1*
pesticide resistance, evolution of, 34
petrified forests, 128, *128*
phantom islands, 149
Philippine Sea Plate, 24, 51, 167
Philippines, typhoons in, 260, 263
photosynthesis, 311
  by thermophiles, 72, 74, *75*
  in deserts, 297
  in oceans and seas, 167
  in snow, 288
Piccard, Jacques, 167, *167*
Piccardi, Luigi, 43
Piddington, Henry, 259
piedmont glaciers, 235, 311
Pink and White Terraces, New Zealand, 71–2
piping pseudokarsts, 81, 311
pit caves (potholes), 109, *114–15*, 115–16
Pitch Lake, La Brea, Trinidad, 226
planets, 18–19
  see also Earth

plants
  Antarctic and Arctic regions, 147
  at extreme altitudes, *136*
  flowering plants, 33, 134
  in deserts and dunes, 120, *294*, *296*, 297
  in rivers and deltas, *190–1*
  in sinkholes, 80
  in snow, *278*, 288–9
  in swamps and wetlands, 221–2, *221*, 225, 270, 273
  in waterfalls and cascades, 207
  on coastlines and seashores, 186, *188*, 189
  on glaciers and sea ice, 236
  on islands, 154
  volcanoes and, 61, 92
  wildfires and, *302*, 303, 305
  see also biodiversity; trees
plate boundaries, 39, 58
plate tectonics, defined, 311
  see also continental drift (plate tectonics)
plates, defined, 311
  see also names of specific plates
platypuses, *12–13*
Plitvice Lakes, Croatia, *202*, 203
plugs, volcanic, 97, *98–9*
Pluto, 20
pocosins (forested bog habitat), 226
Pokili Wildlife Management Area, Papua New Guinea, 74
polar bears, 145, *146*, 147, 236, *237*
'polar highs', 259
polar year, 142, *143*, 147
Polaris, 142
poles on Earth, number of, 140
Polo, Marco, 122
polymetallic nodules, 171
polynias, 145, 311
polyps, in coral reefs, 189
Pompeii worms, 169, *169*
pororoca (tidal bore), 178
Port-au-Prince, Haiti, *52–3*, 53
potholes *see* pit caves (potholes); sinkholes
Powder River Basin, United States, 305
powder snow, 287
Praia do Cassino, Brazil, 182
prairie fires *see* wildfires
precipitation *see* rainfall
prehistoric creatures *see* dinosaurs; fossils
prehistoric permafrost, 144
primordial, defined, 311
Prince Edward Island, Canada, *181*
Protoceratops, 124, *124*
Pseudomonas syringae, 280
Puerto Princesa Subterranean River National Park, Philippines, *196*
puffins, *156–7*
Puu Oo, Big Island, Hawaii, *63*
P-waves (earthquakes), 47
pyramids of Giza, flooding near, *269*
pyrocumulus (pyrocumulonimbus) clouds, 300–1, *301*

Qiantang River, China, 178, *179*
'quake rate', 53
quaking aspen trees, 132, *133*
quartz (rock crystal), 114
Quebec, Canada, 257
Queen Mary's Peak, Tristan da Cunha, 153–4, *155*
quicksand, 226–7, *227*
quiver tree, *294*

rainbows, 250, *251–3*, 252–3
rainfall
  climate fluctuation, 291–2
  cyclones and, 263
  ENSO events and, 273–4
  fires and, 298
  from monsoons, 268
  in deserts, 120
  landslides and, 83, 85
  raindrop shape and size, 268, 270
  road safety and, *271*
  see also drought
rainforests, 137, *138–9*, 193, 203, 298
Rajasthan, India, *297*
Ramsar Convention, 220, 222
rapids, 194–5
  backward-flowing, 209
Rechnitzer, Andreas, *167*
Red Sea, 39, 163, *188*
reefs *see* coral reefs
reflection of light, 252
refraction (bending) of light, 250, 252
reg (desert pavement), 120
reindeer (caribou) migration, *144–5*, 145
renewable energy, 178
  see also hydroelectric projects
reptiles, 150, *151*, 221
  fossils, *30*, 35
  on dunes, 123
  volcanic eruptions and, 54
Reservoir-Induced Seismicity, 218
reservoirs and dams, 218, *219*, 291
  earthquakes and, 53
  see also hydroelectric projects; lakes
Réunion Island, 270, *270*
Reversing Falls, St John River, New Brunswick (Canada), 209
rhodochrosite, 114
rice terraces, 150, *150*
Richter scale, 48
Ridge A, East Antarctic Ice Sheet, 142, 259
rifts, 39, 43–4, 311
Rikoriko Cave, Poor Knights Islands, New Zealand, 184
Ring of Fire, 25, 47, 51, 311
  tsunamis in, 172
  volcano belt, 64–5
ringed seal, 145, *146*, 147
Rio Hamza, South America, 196
River Cave, New Britain, Papua New Guinea, *111*
riverine rainforest ecosystems, 203
rivers, 190–9, *190–9*
  dry, 196, *198*, 199
  longest, 193, 194
  subterranean, 195–6
  see also deltas
Rjukan, Norway, 211
roads through snow, *283*
rock archways, 184, 186
rock climbing *see* climbing
Rock Islands, Palau, *148*
rocks and minerals
  colour from, 71–2, 97, 113, 203
  Cueva de los Cristales, *24–5*, 114
  desert pavement, 120
  gemstones, 25, 27
  gold, 40, 94
  igneous, 27, *27*, *98–9*, 310
  in Japanese onsen, 74
  in lakes, 215

rocks and minerals *cont.*
  metamorphic, 27, 311
  rainbow rocks, *28–9*
  sedimentary, 27, 80, 97, 311
  see also calcium deposits; lava;
    magma (molten rock);
    mining
Rocky Mountains, North America,
  92, 101
Roe, Don, 215
Roscoe, John, 235
Ross Ice Shelf, 233, *234*, 287
Ross Sea, 163
Rotorua, New Zealand, 69, 71–2, *72*
Rub' al Khali (Empty Quarter),
  Arabia, 120, 122, 227
Russell Fjord, Alaska, *232*
RV *Polarstern*, *141*

Sac Actun (White Cave System),
  Mexico, *117*
Sahara Desert, *14*, 118, 120, *308*
  climate change in, 124, *124*
  dust storms, 124, 126, 295
  snow in, 279
Sahel region, 293, 298
Saidmarreh landslide, Iran, 85
salamanders, in caves, 116
Salar de Uyuni, Bolivia, 120
salmon, *204–5*, 207
salt caves, 114–15
salt water
  brackish defined, 310
  lakes and reservoirs, 214, *216*,
    217
  sea water, 163
saltpans, 120, 218
Samosir Island, Sumatra, 150
San Andreas Fault, California, *38*,
  39–40
San Francisco earthquake (1906),
  40
San Francisco earthquake (1989),
  41
San Francisco–Oakland Bay Bridge,
  California, *41*
San Salvador, El Salvador, 257
sand dunes, 120, 122, 124, 182,
  183
sandstone *see* sedimentary rocks
sandstorms, *12*, 13, 124, 126
Santorini, Greece, 64, *64–5*
Sarawak Chamber, Borneo, 109
Sarisariñama tepui, Venezuela, 80
sastrugi (snow dunes), 140
Saturn, 19, *19*
savanna fires (grassland fires), *302*
Saya de Malha Banks, Indian
  Ocean, 189
scaleless black dragonfish, *166*
Scandinavian ice sheet, 150
scattering of light, 250
Scheveningen, The Netherlands,
  277
Schönbein, Christian Friedrich, 249
Schoolhouse Blizzard (1888), 280
Scott, Robert Falcon, 126–7
scrubfowls, nests in hot ground, 74
scuba diving, 92, *188*
sea caves, 182, 184
sea cliffs, *180*, 182, *234*
sea ice, 236, *237*
  Arctic Ocean, 140, *141*, 142, 145
Sea Lion Caves, Oregon, 184, *185*
sea water, 163
seabed mapping, 175
  see also abyssal plains

seabirds *see* birds
seagrass beds, *188*, 189
seals, 145, *146*, 147, 212, 236
seas *see* oceans and seas
seashores *see* coastlines and
  seashores
seasonal forests, 135, 137
secondary rainbows, 252–3, *253*
sedimentary rocks, 27, 80, 97, 311
seeds, 134
seismic, defined, 311
'seismic gaps', 40
seismic sea waves *see* tsunamis
seismographs, 48, 311
seismometers, 47–8, 54, 311
selenite crystals, 114
semidiurnal tides, 177–8, *177*
serotiny, 303
Severe Tropical Cyclone Olivia
  (1996), 260
Severe Tropical Cyclone Yasi
  (2011), 274
severe tropical cyclones, 260
  see also cyclones
Severny Island Ice Cap, 233
Shaanxi province earthquake
  (1556), China, 51
shafts *see* pit caves (potholes);
  sinkholes
Shark Bay, Western Australia, *32–3*
shelf clouds, 243
Shenzhen, Pearl River delta, China,
  198
shield volcanoes, 54, 311
Shiprock, New Mexico, 97, *98–9*
Shiveluch volcano, Russia, 54
Shoemaker Levy-9 comet, 20
shovel-nosed snakes, 123
Siberia, 144, 222, 224
Sichuan province, China, 53
Sicily, Italy, 175, *176*
Sigma Octantis, 142
'silent' or 'slow-slip' earthquake, 51
Silver Lake, Colorado, 282
silverswords (plants), 92
singing dunes, 122
sinkholes, *52*, 78–83, *78–82*, 109
  cenotes, *80–1*, 81, 310
  submarine, 186
Siq passageway, Petra, Jordan, *106*
Sistema Zacatón, Mexico, 80
slab avalanches, 287
'slap-down' effect (earthquakes), 48
slash-and-burn agriculture, 298, 305
sleet, 282
slot canyons, 105–6
sloths, *138–9*
snow, *278*, 279–80, *280–1*, 282,
  283–9
  avalanches, 287–8
  in Antarctica, 126
  in deserts, 120, 126
  'snow canyons', 282, *283*
  'snow dunes' (sastrugi), 140
  staying safe in, 288–9
snow algae, 236, *288–9*, 289
snow monkeys *see* Japanese
  macaques
snowflakes, 280, *280*, 282
snowstorms, 279
  see also blizzards
solar eclipses, 13, *13*
solar flares, 257
Solar System, 18–20
solar wind, 257
Somalia, 293
Somalian Plate, 43–4

Sótano de las Golondrinas, Mexico,
  114–15, 115
South America, ENSO events in,
  274, 293
South American Plate, 44, 47
South Asian monsoon, 268, *269*, 275
South Celestial Pole, 142
South Dakota, caves in, 110
South Geomagnetic Pole, 144
South Georgia Island, *259*
South Magnetic Pole, 144
South Pole (South Geographic Pole),
  126, 140–7, *143*
southern lights (aurora australis),
  254, 255, *255*
Southern Ocean, 147, 161, 163, 236
Southern Patagonian Ice Field, 234,
  234–5
space, 16–21
  see also Moon; Sun
Space Shuttle *Endeavour*, *11*
speleothems, 110, 112–14, *114–15*,
  311
spelunkers, *108*, 113, 311
sphagnum moss, 222
sprites (coloured lights), 249
St Elmo's Fire, 257
St Peter's Basilica, Vatican City,
  lightning and, 240
stacks, 184, 186
stalactites, 110, *112*, 113
stalagmites, 113
Stanley Falls, Democratic Republic
  of the Congo, 195
star dunes (giant dunes), 122
stars, 20–1, 142
  see also Sun
Steamboat Geyser, Yellowstone
  National Park, 68
stick insects, 137, 154, 186
stone *see* rocks and minerals
Storegga Slides, Norwegian Sea, 85
'Storm of the Century' (1993), 279,
  281
storm surges, 263, *273*
storms, 243, 260, 263
  see also cumulonimbus clouds
    (thunderclouds); cyclonic
    storms; floods; lightning;
    monsoons; thunder
strangler figs, 137
stratovolcanoes, 39, 54, *55*, 311
  lahars and, 83, 85
'strike-slip' ('transform') faults,
  39–40, 43, 311
stromatolites, 32, *32–3*, 311
Styx River, Australia, 195
subduction, 24, 39, 51, 65, 167,
  170, 311
submarine caves and canyons,
  169–70, *169*, 184
submarine landslides (submarine
  'slumps'), 85, 175, 177
submarine mountains, 94
  see also Mid-Oceanic Ridge
submarine sinkholes, 186
submarine volcanoes, 58, *58–9*
submarine 'waterfalls', 207–9,
  208–9
submarine waves, 172
subterranean fires, 298, 305
subterranean lakes, 218
subterranean rivers, 195–6, *196*,
  199
subtropical highs, 295
succulent plants, 297
Suez Canal, 196

Sulawesi, Indonesia, 74, *188*
sulfuric acid, 72
sulfurous gases, 64, 71–2, 222
Sullivan, Roy, 247
Sumatra, Indonesia, 175
Sumatra–Andaman Earthquake
  and tsunami (2004) *see* Indian
  Ocean Tsunami (2004)
Sun, 18–19, *19*
  auroras and, 257
  looking safely at, 250
  sunbeams, *238*
  temperature of, 19, 243, 257
  tides and, 177
sun dogs, haloes and pillars, *252*,
  253
Sundarbans, Bangladesh and India,
  186, *187*, 189
Sunland Baobab, Limpopo
  Province, South Africa, 135
sunlight, 167, 250
sunsets, *238*, 250
Super Typhoon Haiyan (2013), 260,
  261, 263
super typhoons and super cyclonic
  storms, 260, *260*
  see also cyclones
supercells, *262*, 263, 311
supercontinents, 23–4, 33
supernovas, 18, 27, 311
supernumerary bows, 252
supervolcanoes, 65, 311
surfing, in tidal bores, 178
Surtsey volcano, Iceland, 58, 61, *61*
Suter, Matt, 267
swamp gum *see* mountain ash
swamps and wetlands, 150, *220–9*,
  221–2, *225–7*
  clearing of, 221, 273
  floods and, 270, 273
S-waves (earthquakes), 47
Swiss cheese plant, 137
Sydney, Australia, dust storms, *125*

taiga, 131
Talbot Bay, Western Australia, *178*,
  208–9
talipot palm, 134
Tamu Massif, Pacific Ocean, 58
Tangshan, China earthquake
  (1976), 53
tar, 226, *227*
Taupo Volcanic Zone, 72
Taylor, Thomas Griffith, 203
tectonic plates, 23, *23*
  see also names of specific plates
'teletsunami', 174
temperatures
  coldest, 88, 142, 282
  hottest, 72, 114, 118, 169, 295
  of the sun, 19, 243, 257
terraces, from calcium deposits,
  71–2
Tethys Sea, 88
Texas floods (1998), 274, *274*
Tham Kaew (Jewel Cave), Thailand,
  114–15
The Fang, Vail, Colorado, ice-
  climbing, 211, *211*
The Netherlands, floods in, *276*, 277
The Wonder (Bridal Veil Falls,
  Colorado), ice-climbing, *210*,
  211
thermophiles, 72, 74, *75*, 311
Þingvellir (Thingvellir) National
  Park, Iceland, 44, *44*
Thistle, Utah, 83

three-toed sloth, *138–9*
thunder, 243
   see also lightning; storms
Tibetan plateau, 95
tidal bores, 178, *179*, 311
tidal forests, 186, 189
Tidal Generating Station, Nova
   Scotia, 178
'tidal waves', 177–8
tides, *177*, 209
   electricity from, 178
   tidal water/tidal range, 177–8,
    178, 186, 208–9, 227
tidewater glaciers, *232*, 233, 311
Tiger Leaping Gorge, China, 105
Tiktaalik roseae, 32
timber *see* wood
time zones, in polar regions, 142
Titanic (ship), 149, 233
Todd River, Alice Springs, *198*, 199
Tohoku Earthquake and tsunami
   (2011) (Japanese coast), 39,
   48, *50–1*, 51–2, 172, *173*
Tokyo, Japan
   fire and earthquake (1923), 303
   earthquake design in, 51
Tollund Man, *225*
Toowoomba, Queensland, *270*
Tornado Alley, 267, *267*
tornadoes, *258*, 263–4, *264*, *267*
   damage from, *266*
   fire tornadoes, 301
   hot spots, 264, 267
   origin of word, 263
   people and objects carried by,
    267
   staying safe in, 264
TORRO (T) scale, 264
Totable Tornado Observatory
   (TOTO), 264
towns and cities
   fires in, 301, 303
   floods and urban development,
    273
   in calderas, 64, *64–5*, 72
   in polar regions, 140
   on coastlines and seashores, 189
   world's highest habitations, 94
   see also human activities
'trampoline' effect (earthquakes), 48
Trango Towers, Pakistan, 97
transform boundaries, 39
'transform' ('strike-slip') faults *see*
   'strike-slip' ('transform') faults
transneptunian objects, 20
travertine, 71, 311
Tree of Ténéré, Niger, 120
trees, 128–37, *128–37*, *299*, 303
   broadleaved, 130, 134–5
   commercial use of, 134–5
   lightning strikes of, 247, 249
   tallest species, 130
   treed bogs, 226
   see also forests
The Trembling Giant (clump of
   trees), 132, *133*
tremors, 47, 51–2, 64–5
   see also earthquakes
trenches *see* oceans and seas
tributaries, 191, 193, 311
Trieste (submersible), 167, *167*
trilobites, *30*
Tristan da Cunha, 153–4, *155*
Tri-State Tornado (1925), *266*, 267
troglobites, 116, 311
'trona' mineral, 217
Tropical Cyclone Mahina (1899), 263

Tropical Cyclone Tasha (2010), 274
tropical cyclones, 260, 263, 274
tropical depressions or
   disturbances, 260
   see also cyclones; tornadoes
tropical fish, *171*
tropical rainforests, 137, *138–9*, 193
tropical storms, 260
   deadliest, 263
   see also cyclones
tsunamis, 172, *173–6*, 174–5, 177,
   311
   after earthquakes, 47, 51
   Easter Island statues and, *153*
   landslides and, 85
   staying safe in, 172, *172*
tube worms, *168*
tufa rock, *26*
tuff rock for statues, 153
tumbleweeds, 297
tundra, 128, 131, 144–5, *144–5*,
   311
Tunisia, barchan dunes in, 122
Turkmenistan, drilling rig collapse,
   305
Turpan Depression, Gobi Desert,
   124
Twelve Apostles, south-eastern
   Australia, 186, *187*
twisters *see* tornadoes
Typhoon John (Hurricane John)
   (1994), 260
Typhoon Tip (1979), 260
typhoons, 260, *261*
   see also cyclones

Uluru (Ayers Rock), 97, *244–5*, *309*
Undara lava tube system,
   Queensland, 62
underground *see* subterranean
underwater *see* submarine
Unionville, Maryland, 270
United Kingdom
   earthquakes in, 47
   landslides in, 78
   sinkholes in, 78
United States
   drought in, 292–3, 297
   Tornado Alley, 267
Universe, 17–18
Ural mountains, Russia, 92
Uranus, 19, *19*
US Geological Survey (USGS), 51, 53

Valdez, Alaska, 282
Valle de la Luna (Valley of the
   Moon), Chile, *118–19*
valleys, 236
   see also canyons and gorges
Vargas State, Venezuela, 83
vegetated wetlands *see* swamps
   and wetlands
vegetation *see* plants
Velociraptor, 124, *124*
Venice, canals in, 196, *197*
vents *see* fumaroles
Venus, 18–19, *18*
Venus flytraps, 222, *225*
Verneau cave system, France, *110*
vertical caves *see* pit caves
   (potholes)
Victoria Falls (Mosi-oa-Tunya),
   Zambia–Zimbabwe border,
   202, 203
Victoria Harbour, Hong Kong, *241*
Victoria Island, Nunavut, Canada,
   150

vicuñas, 95, *96*
Vietnam, typhoons in, *261*
violent weather *see* weather
virga (desert rain or snow), 120, 311
visual phenomena *see* auroras;
   rainbows
Volcanic Explosivity Index (VEI), 54,
   65, 83
volcanic plugs, 97, *98–9*, 311
volcanoes, 54–65, *56–61*
   as islands, 58, *61*
   colossal-scale eruptions, 65
   'Decade Volcanoes', 61
   dormancy, 54
   fertile soil from, 92
   lahars and, 83, 85
   lightning and, *242*
   monitoring, 54
   mountains from, 92
   noise from, 59
   on other planets, 18–19
   rifts and, 44
   tectonic plates and, 24–5
   unpredictability of, 54
   volcano belt, 64–5
   see also craters; lava;
    stratovolcanoes
Volcanoes of Kamchatka World
   Heritage Site, *66*
vorticity, *258*, 263–4, 300–1, 311
Vostok Station, Antarctica, 142
Vrtoglavica Cave, Slovenia, 115

wadis (dry riverbeds), 120, 311
   see also dry rivers
Waimangu Geyser, 69, *69*
walking fish, 34
Walsh, Donald, 167
water
   hydrologic cycle, 270, 310
   management of, 291
   moraines as filters of, 235
   storage of *see* reservoirs and
    dams
   wetlands as filters of, 221–2
waterbirds *see* birds
waterfalls and cascades, 200, *201–*
   11, 203, 207–9, 211, *270*, 310
   ascent of by fish, *204–5*, 207
   Cataracts of the Nile, 191
   Congo River, 195
   Denmark Strait Cataract, 208
   frozen, *210–11*, 211
   into ocean, 200
   remnants of, 209, 211
   tallest land-based, 207
   see also submarine 'waterfalls'
waterholes, 218
'watermelon snow', 236, *288–9*,
   289
waterspouts, 264, *265*
wattle trees (acacias), 135, *302*
wave trains, 172, 174
waves, *158*, 163
weather, 259
   clearing of wetlands and, 221
   tsunamis, 177
   world's worst, 92
   see also climate change
weather fronts, 243, *258*, 259, 311
Weddell Sea, 163
Wegener, Alfred, 24
Weichselian Ice Sheet, 233, 236
Wellington, New Zealand, 43, 259
West African monsoon, 268, 274
Westminster, Texas, *264*
wet snow, 282

Whakarewarewa *see* Rotorua
whales, 145, 147
White Mountains, California, *137*
White Nile (river), 191
'white smokers', 169, 311
white-outs (blizzards), *278*
Whymper summit, Ecuador, 94
wildfires, 298, *299–302*, 300–1,
   303, *304–5*, 305
   fire prevention policies, 300
   lightning as cause of, 249, 303
   regrowth after, *302*
   staying safe in, 303
   tree survival and, 132, 134
   treed bogs, 226
wildlife *see* animals; birds;
   invertebrates
winds, 259
   dust storms, 297
   firestorms, 300–1
   katabatic winds, 259, *259*
   measuring force of, 264
   wind speeds, 92, *143*, 260
   see also blizzards; cyclones;
    tornadoes
wolverines (skunk bears), 131–2,
   132
wolves, prehistoric, 115
The Wonder (Bridal Veil Falls,
   Colorado), ice-climbing, *210*,
   211
wood, 128
   for boat building, 134–5
World War II bombing campaigns,
   firestorms from, 303

Xiaozhai Tiankeng (Heavenly Pit),
   Chongqing province, China, 80

yaks, 95, *96*
Yangtze River, 105, 193, 277
Yarlung Tsangpo Grand Canyon,
   Tibet, 103, *103*, 195
Yarlung Tsangpo River, Tibet,
   194–5, 195
Yellow River (Huang He), 193, *195*,
   202, 203
   floods, 193–4, 277
Yellow Water Lagoon, Kakadu
   wetland, *221*
Yellowstone National Park,
   Wyoming, 65, 67–9, *67*, *308*
   Grand Prismatic Spring, 72,
    74, *75*
   Old Faithful, *68–9*, 69
York, Nebraska, *258*
Yosemite National Park, 97
Yucatán Peninsula, Mexico, *33*
   Medieval Climate Anomaly, 291
   sinkholes, *80–1*, 81
   subterranean river under, 196
Yuki-no-Otani roadway, Honshu,
   Japan, 282, *283*
Yungay, Chile, 118

Zambezi River, Zambia and
   Zimbabwe, 203, 218
zebras, *228–9*
Zhangye Danxia Landform
   Geological Park, China, *28–9*
Zhemchug Canyon, 169
Zipingpu Dam, Sichuan province,
   China, 53
zone of subduction *see* subduction
zoological, defined, 311

EXTREME EARTH

CONSULTANT Dr Robert Coenraads BA (Hons), MSc, PhD, FGAA, FAusIMM

AUTHORS David Burnie, Jack Challoner, Celia Coyne, Sari Harrar, Karen McGhee

PROJECT EDITOR Dannielle Viera

PROJECT DESIGNER Andrew Burns

SENIOR DESIGNER AND COVER DESIGN Joanne Buckley

PICTURE RESEARCH Amanda McKittrick, Natalie Zizic

ADDITIONAL PICTURE RESEARCH Andrew Burns, Dannielle Viera

PROOFREADER Kevin Diletti

INDEXER Glenda Browne

SENIOR PRODUCTION CONTROLLER Martin Milat

READER'S DIGEST GENERAL BOOKS

EDITORIAL DIRECTOR Lynn Lewis

MANAGING EDITOR Rosemary McDonald

DESIGN MANAGER Donna Heldon

Extreme Earth is published by Reader's Digest (Australia) Pty Limited
80 Bay Street, Ultimo, NSW, 2007
www.readersdigest.com.au; www.readersdigest.co.nz;
www.readersdigest.ca; www.rdasia.com

First published 2015
Copyright © Reader's Digest (Australia) Pty Limited 2015
Copyright © Reader's Digest Association Far East Limited 2015
Philippines Copyright © Reader's Digest Association Far East
Limited 2015

National Library of Australia Cataloguing-in-Publication entry
Title: Extreme earth: wildlife, wild places, wild weather
ISBN: 978-1-922085-27-6 (hardback)
Notes: Includes index.
Subjects: Curiosities and wonders. Earth (Planet)—Miscellanea.
Geography—Miscellanea. Disasters.
Other Authors/Contributors: Reader's Digest (Australia)
Dewey Number: 032.02

Prepress by Colourpedia, Sydney
Printed and bound by Leo Paper Products, China

We are interested in receiving your comments on the content of this book.
Write to: The Editor, General Books Editorial, Reader's Digest (Australia)
Pty Limited, GPO Box 4353, Sydney, NSW 2001, or email us at:
bookeditors.au@readersdigest.com

To order additional copies of *Extreme Earth* please contact us at:
www.readersdigest.com.au or phone 1300 300 030 (Australia)
www.readersdigest.co.nz or phone 0800 400 060 (New Zealand)
or email us at customerservice@readersdigest.com.au

IMAGE CREDITS